The Geography of Korea

8 — 11 — 10

The Geography of Korea

Date of Printing : May 2010
Date of Publication : May 2010

Publisher : Kyoung-Soo Kim
National Geographic Information Institute (NGII)
Ministry of Land, Transport and Maritime Affairs
587 World Cup-Gil, Yeongton-Gu, Suwon-Si, Gyeonggi-Do, 443-772
THE REPUBLIC OF KOREA

Phone : +82-31-210-2600
Fax : +82-31-210-2704
Homepage : http://www.ngii.go.kr/eng/index.do

94980

9 788993 841077
ISBN 978-89-93841-07-7

Preface

Korea, the homeland of the Korean people, has experienced a miraculous economic progress and major social changes over the past several decades.
Along with the acceleration of globalization, the transformation compels us to provide current and accurate geographical information on our country to both the Koreans and the global community.

In 2003, the National Geographic Information Institute launched a project entitled *The Compilation of The Geography of Korea* to examine changes and progress across Korea over the past 20 years.
The National Geographic Information Institute had previously published *Topography of Korea* in the 1980s.
The Compilation of The Geography of Korea, a seven-year project, resulted in the publication of *Geography of the Chungcheong Region (2003), Jeolla-Jeju Region (2004), Gyeongsang Region (2005), Gangwon Region (2006), Seoul National Capital Region (2007), The Geography of Korea (2008),* and finally, this English version of *The Geography of Korea.*

The Geography of Korea details the current conditions of the Korean society, economy, and relevant social phenomena, as well as recent geographical and environmental information of Korea. The economic development and social change during industrialization and urbanization of Korea are examined.
It also describes Korea's response to challenges regarding population, transportation, and the environment that have emerged along with socioeconomic progress. Finally, it presents suitable solutions to these problems, and provides detail on the nation's long-term strategic plan for a sustainable future.

I hope this book can help people throughout the world understand Korea and the relationship between its culture, geography, and various government policies better. I believe it could serve as a valuable reference for future research on many aspects of Korea. The National Geographic Information Institute will continue to provide accurate and up-to-date geographical information on Korea domestically and globally. I solicit your continued interest and support for the National Geographic Information Institute.

Finally, I would like to extend my sincere gratitude not only to the Korean Geographical Society, but also to all the people and institutes involved in the publication of The Geography of Korea, for their efforts, cooperation, and contribution.

May 2010

Kim, Kyoung-soo
President of the National Geographic Information Institute
Ministry of Land, Transport and Maritime Affairs
Republic of Korea

Editors

Chapter 6   Ju-Seong Han (Chungbuk National University)
             Changjoo Kim (University of Cincinnati)
Chapter 7   Mu-Yong Lee (Chonnam National University)
             Minsun Doh (Western Illinois University)
Chapter 8   Tae-Yeol Seo (Korea University)
             Byung-Doo Choi (Daegu University)
             Boyoung Park (Radford University)
Chapter 9   Tae-Hwan Kim (Korea Research Institute for Human Settlements)
             Woonsup Choi (University of Wisconsin at Milwaukee)
Chapter 10 Won Sup Lee (Korea Research Institute for Human Settlements)

Senior Reviewer

Amy Patrick (Western Illinois University)

Reviewers

Barbara F. Boyd (Radford University)
Chris Sutton (Western Illinois University)
Eric Ribbens (Western Illinois University)
Robert South (University of Cincinnati)

Project Chief

Chul-sue Hwang (Kyung Hee University)

Working Assistants

HyunJoo Chun (Kyung Hee University)
Hyun-Chul Kim (Kyung Hee University)
JoonYoung Lee (Kyung Hee University)

National Geographic Information Institute

Kyoung-Soo Kim (President)
Kyo-Yeong Lee (Director, National Land Information Survey Division)
Heon-Ryang Im (Deputy Director, National Land Information Survey Division)
Jin-Hee Kim (Manager, National Land Information Survey Division)

Contents

Chapter 3. Population

Chapter 4. Settlement

Contents

Contents

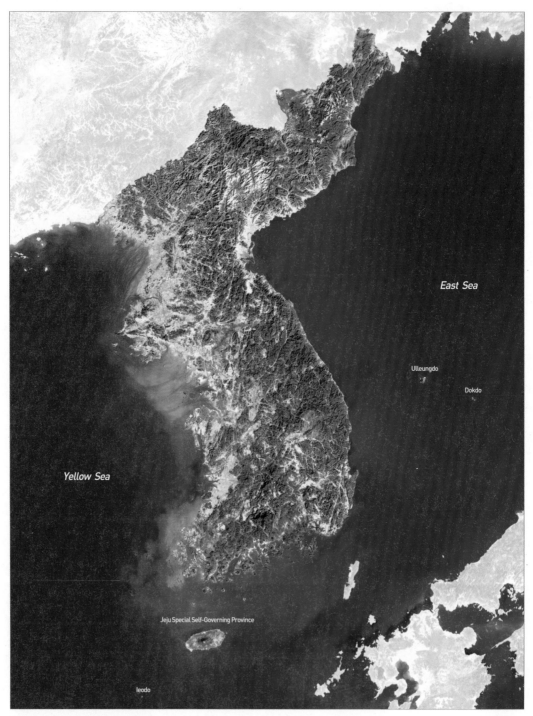

East Sea

Ulleungdo

Dokdo

Yellow Sea

Jeju Special Self-Governing Province

Ieodo

Satellite Image of Korea

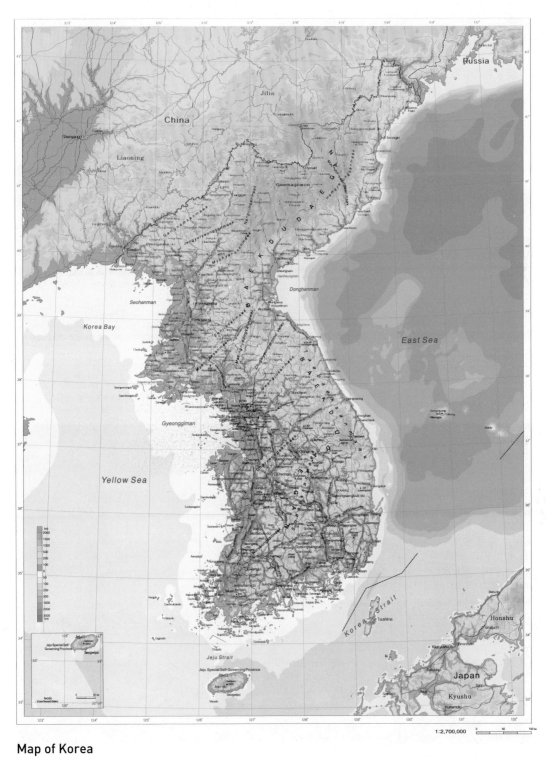

1:2,700,000

Map of Korea

Main Stadium of the 1988 Seoul Olympic Games

The 2002 Seoul Worldcup Main Stadium

Main Stadium of Busan Asiad

The 13th APEC House: Nurimaru(Busan)

Jongmyo Shrine
(UNESCO World Heritage, 1995)

Changdeokgung Palace Complex
(UNESCO World Heritage, 1997)

Gochang, Hwasun and Ganghwa Dolmen Sites (UNESCO World Heritage, 2000)

Haeinsa Temple Janggyeong Panjeon, the Depositories for the Tripitaka Koreana Woodblocks
(UNESCO World Heritage, 1995)

Hwaseong Fortress (UNESCO World Heritage, 1997)

Gyeongju Historic Areas (UNESCO World Heritage, 2000)

Seokguram Grotto and Bulguksa Temple (UNESCO World Heritage, 1995)

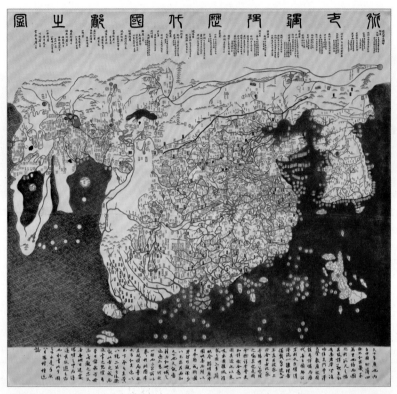

Honil kangni yokdae kukdo chido (混一疆理歷代國都之圖): Map of an Integrated Territory
of Historic Countries and Their Capitals, 1402, Kyujanggak Archives

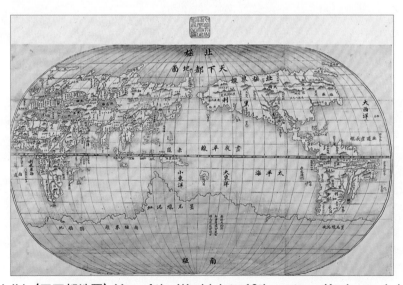

Chonha dojido (天下都地圖): Map of the World, late 18th century, Kyujanggak Archives.

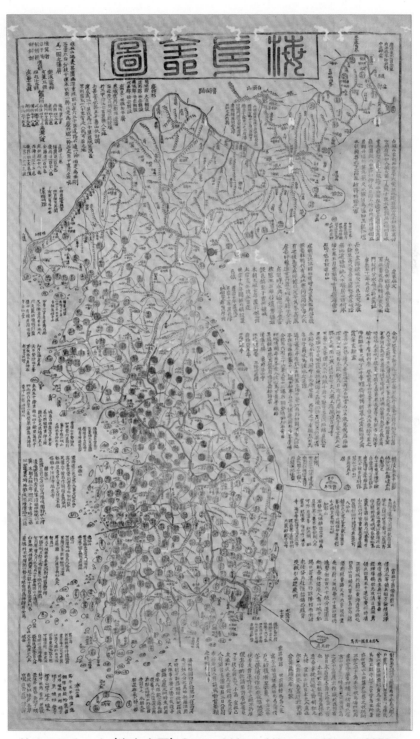

Haezwa chondo (海左全圖): General Map of Haezwa-Korea, 1850s.

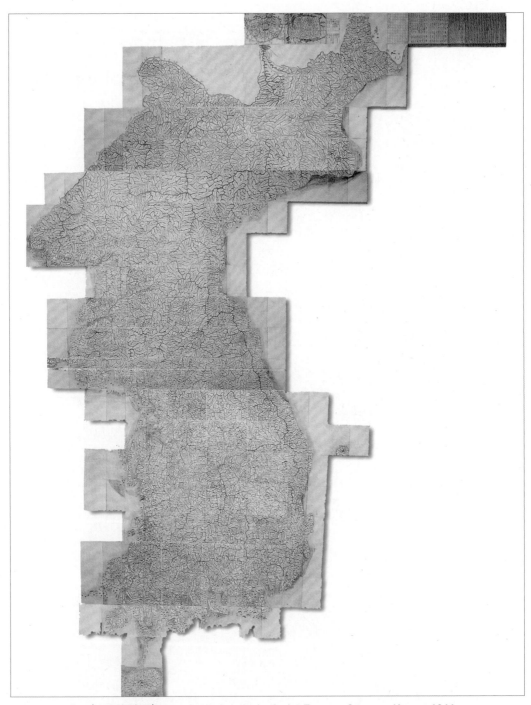

Taedong yojido (大東輿地圖) : Map fo the Land of a Great Eastern Country-Korea, 1861.

Chapter 1.
INTRODUCTION

Korea Bay

Soohanman

East Sea

Donghaeman

Gyeonggiman

Yellow Sea

Korea Strait

Jeju Strait

Chapter 1.1.

GENERAL GEOGRAPHY

1.1.1 Geography

1) Location

Korea lies adjacent to China and Japan. The northern border of Korea is formed by the Amnokgang (river) and Dumangang (river), which separate it from Manchuria. A 16-kilometer segment of the Dumangang to the east also serves as a natural border with Russia. The west coast of the Korean Peninsula is bounded by the Korean Bay to the north and the Yellow Sea to the south ; the east coast faces the East Sea.

Two hundred kilometers separate the peninsula from eastern China. The shortest distance between Korean and Chinese coasts is 200 kilometers and from the southeastern tip of the peninsula, the nearest point on the Japanese coast is also about 200 kilometers away.

Due to its unique geographical location, Chinese culture filtered into Japan through Korea ; a common cultural sphere of Buddhism and Confucianism was thus established between the three countries.

The Korean Peninsula extends about 1,000 kilometers southward from the northeast Asian continental landmass. Roughly 300 kilometers in width, climatic variations are more pronounced along the south-north axis. Differences in vegetation can be seen between the colder north and the warmer south.

The peninsula and all of its associated islands lie between 33°06′43″N and 43°00′42″N parallels and 124°11′04″E and 131°52′22″E meridians. The latitudinal location of Korea is similar to that of the Iberian Peninsula and Greece. The entire peninsula corresponds approximately to the north-south span of the state of California.

Longitudinally, Korea lies straight north of the Philippines and central Australia. The

Table 1.1 **The tips of Korean territory**

Extreme Points	Places	Coordinates
Northernmost	Yuwonjin, Hamgyeongbuk-*do*	43° 00′ 42″N
Southernmost	Marado, Jeju Special Self-Governing Province	33° 06′ 43″N
Easternmost	Dokdo, Gyeongsangbuk-*do*	131° 52′ 22″E
Westernmost	Maando, Pyeonganbuk-*do*	124° 11′ 04″ E

[Source : The National Atlas Of Korea]

meridian of 127°30′E passes through the middle of the Korean Peninsula. Korea shares the same standard meridian of 135°E with Japan. Seoul and Tokyo local time is nine hours earlier than Greenwich Mean Time (GMT).

2) Territory

The total area of the peninsula, including its islands, is 223,170 square kilometers of which about 45 percent (100,032 square kilometers) constitutes the territory of South Korea. The combined territories of South and North Korea are similar to the size of Britain (244,100 square kilometers) and Guyana (215,000 square kilometers). South Korea alone is about the size of Hungary (93,000 square kilometers) and Jordan (97,700 square kilometers).

There are about 3,000 islands belonging to Korea. The islands are located mostly off the west and south coasts ; only a handful of them lie off the East Sea. Ulleungdo, the largest island in the East Sea, serves as a major fishery base as does Dokdo. Bigger islands include Jeju Special Self-Governing Province - the largest, Geojedo, Ganghwado, and Namhaedo.

Until the 11th century, the territory of Korea encompassed most of Manchuria. By the 15th century, after repeated conflicts with China, Koreans retreated southward and the Amnokgang (river) and Dumangang (river) became the permanent Sino-Korean border.

At the end of World War II, the peninsula was divided into a northern zone occupied by Soviet forces and a southern zone occupied by U.S. forces. The 38th parallel served as the boundary between the two zones. In 1953, at the end of the Korean War, a new border was fixed at the Demilitarized Zone (DMZ), a 4 kilometer-wide strip of land that runs along the lines of ceasefire from the east to the west coast for a distance of about 241 kilometers.

3) Administrative Units

There are three administrative tiers in South Korea. The highest tier includes seven metropolitan cities and nine provinces (*do*). Designated metropolitan cities are those urban areas with a population of over one million. Seoul, the capital of South Korea, is the largest urban center, having 10 million residents. Busan is the second largest city, with a population of over four million. Daegu, Incheon, Gwangju, Daejeon and Ulsan, in descending order, are each home to more than one million people. At the second administrative tier, provinces (*do*) are subdivided into cities (*si*) and counties (*gun*). A city has a population of more than 50,000. A gun consists of one town (*eup*) and five to ten townships (*myeon*). Although they are administrative units, provinces (*do*) also play an important role in the regional identification of the people and many Koreans often identify themselves by the province in which they were born and raised. Metropolitan cities are subdivided into districts (*gu*). The lowest units are dong in cities and ri in provinces. In the last several decades, South Korea has witnessed the rapid growth of its urban centers. The population of these areas now constitutes over 85 percent of the national total. Urban growth has been particularly spectacular along the Seoul-Busan corridor, the Seoul metropolitan area and the Gyeongsang Province area. By contrast, the southwestern and northeastern regions have sustained a considerable loss in population.

4) Geographical Regions

Mountain ranges have traditionally served as natural boundary markers between regions. Because these natural boundaries inhibited contacts between peoples living on either side of the range, subtle, and sometimes substantial, regional differences developed in both the spoken language and customs of the people. These regional distinctions also correspond to the traditional administrative divisions set up during the Joseon Dynasty (1392-1910).

The Korean Peninsula is divided into three distinct regions : Central, South and North. These macro regions are divided into three separate geographical spheres, each of which shows particular economic, cultural and physical distinctiveness. In the Central region are the Seoul metropolitan area, Chungcheong and Gangwon provinces ; in the South, Gyeongsang, Jeolla and Jeju provinces; and in the North, Pyeongan, Hamgyeong and Hwanghae provinces. The term "northern area" traditionally referred to those regions of Pyeongan and Hamgyeong provinces prior to the division of the peninsula in 1945. The "North" now refers to all the areas north of the Demilitarized Zone, comprising Pyeongan, Hamgyeong, Hwanghae and the northern parts of the Gyeonggi and Gangwon provinces.

① The Central Region

This region consists of the Seoul metropolitan area which is part of Gyeonggi Province, Chungcheong Province to the south, and Gangwon province to the east.

The Capital (Seoul / Gyeonggi) Area

This includes Seoul and Incheon, which are encompassed by Gyeonggi-*do*. The capital area, as the name implies, is the center of all political, economic and cultural activity in South Korea. Clustered around Seoul are also a number of smaller cities, which form a continuous and sprawling urban area. The largest concentration of the nation's industries is in and around Seoul. The capital area is the hub of South Korea's transportation networks, with Gimpo International Airport located on the western outskirts of Seoul, the newly built Incheon International Airport, and railroad networks that connect to all parts of the country. The region serves as South Korea's gateway to the world. Given its strategic importance, the dialect spoken in Seoul is considered to be the nation's standard language.

Chungcheong Area

This region lies between the capital area and the South. Cheongju and Daejeon are the leading urban centers of the region, respectively. Lying just below the capital area, this region consisting of Chungcheongnam-*do* and Chungcheongbuk-*do* has been characterized as a southern extension of Seoul ; its proximity to the capital has been economically advantageous. New industries have recently mushroomed along the Asanman Bay on the west coast. The region has also profited from transportation and urban services available for Seoul and its vicinity. Chungcheong and Gyeonggi provinces specialize in horticulture and dairy farming to meet the huge demands of the nearby urban centers of the capital area.

Gangwon Area

This region lies to the east of the capital area. The Taebaeksan Mountain range, which runs north-south through the middle of the region, divides the province into eastern coastal and western inland areas. Gangneung, Chuncheon, and Wonju are its leading urban areas. Gangwon-*do* offers a variety of opportunities for tourism and sports, with its rugged terrain. Mining industries, once a major sector in the regional economy, have recently experienced a drastic decline due to competition from cheaper foreign-imported coal and minerals. The fall of mining industries, coupled with the national trend of rural-to-urban migration, are the major contributing factors for the recent migration out of the region. Gangwon-*do*, with less than 2 million residents, has now the smallest population of all the mainland provinces.

② The South Region

The region includes the Gyeongsang Province, located in the southeast, Jeolla Province in the southwest, and Jeju special self-governing province province which lies off the south coast.

Gyeongsang Area

This area includes metropolitan cities Busan, Daegu and Ulsan, being encompassed by Gyeongsangbuk-*do* and Gyeongsangnam-*do*. Busan and Daegu are the major urban centers of the province, being the second (4 million) and third (2.5 million) largest cities in South Korea.

This region is characterized by the vast basin of the Nakdonggang River and is surrounded by the Sobaeksan mountain ranges. Due to the rugged topography of the surrounding mountains, sub-areas within the region share common cultural traits such as dialect and custom, which are quite distinct from peoples of other regions. The fact that Gyeongsang Province also has another name, "Yeongnam," which literally means "south of the mountain pass," attests to the key role that the mountains have historically played in fostering regional differences between the Korean people.

Gyeongsang Province has one of the largest industrial agglomerations, second only to the capital area, due mainly to the heavy investments in the region by the South Korean government since the 1960s. These heavy industrial facilities of steel, shipbuilding, automobile and petrochemical factories are largely concentrated along the southeast stretch of Pohang, through Ulsan, Busan, Changwon, and Masan. The northern part also has two major clusters of industries around Daegu and Gumi, specializing in textile and electronics.

Jeolla Area

Jeolla Province is located southwest of the peninsula and comprises of Jeollabuk-*do* and Jeollanam-*do*. Gwangju, Jeonju, and Naju are their respective centers.

"Honam" is another name for Jeolla Province. The flat fertile lands of the Geumgang and Yeongsangang river basins, as well as the coastal lowlands, have made the region the major granary of the nation. The regional economy has lagged somewhat behind the capital and Gyeongsang regions due to sparse industrial investments made there during the past decades. However, this situation is changing and the region is now experiencing industrial growth in major urban centers like Gwangju and Jeonju, as well as along its western coast. Also, the tidal flats near Gunsan and Mokpo have recently been reclaimed, adding new land for industrial development.

The region is endowed with a very irregular coastline and countless large and small islands, and this unique landscape attracts tourists year-round.

Jeju special self-governing province Island Area

Jeju special self-governing province is the largest island in Korea located about 140 kilometers south of Mokpo in the South Sea. Its historic isolation from the mainland contributed to the Jeju special self-governing province peoples' distinct dialect and lifestyle. Of volcanic origin, the island has rugged topography of numerous hills, gorges, and waterfalls. Because of its subtropical climate and the unique lifestyles and customs of its people, tourism is the region's most important industry. The island is also famous for its subtropical fruits such as tangerines, pineapples and bananas. It is also known for its women divers.

③ The North Region

The northern part of the peninsula is divided into two geographic regions : Pyeongan Province in the northwest and Hamgyeong Province in the northeast. The former with its flatlands is also known as the Gwanseo region while the latter is often referred to as Gwanbuk. Pyeongan Province serves as the major agricultural area of the North. By contrast, Hamgyeong Province, due to its mountainous topography, boasts mining and forestry as its major economic activities. Pyeongyang, the leading urban center in the Pyeongan Province, is the capital of North Korea and Nampo serves as the gateway port to Pyeongyang. Hamheung and Cheongjin are the major cities of Hamgyeong Province.

The third geographical region of the North, Hwanghae Province lies to the south of Pyeongan Province. Once a part of the Central Region prior to the South-North division, Hwanghae Province shares a great many cultural similarities with other west-central regions of the peninsula. Gaeseong is the major city of the region.

5) Mountains and Hills

Between the Korean Peninsula and Manchuria flow, in opposite directions, lie the two largest rivers of the region, the Amnokgang (river) and Dumangang (river), both originating at Mt. Baekdusan (2,744m), the highest mountain in the region. The peninsula is surrounded by the Yellow Sea, the East Sea, and the South Sea.

Nearly 70 percent of the Korean Peninsula is covered by mountains and hills. Low hills in the southern and the western regions give way gradually to increasingly higher mountains toward the eastern and the northern areas. On the whole, the western and southern slopes of the peninsula are wide with some plains and basins along rivers, while the eastern slope is very steep as high mountains precipitate into the East Sea.

Most of the high mountains are located along the Taebaek mountain range which runs parallel to the east coast, roughly north-to-south. West of this range are the drainage basins of the Hangang and Geumgang rivers. This range extends to the Nangnim range in North Korea, forming the geological and geomorphological backbone of the peninsula and constituting the watershed between the western and eastern slopes of the peninsula. Mt. Nangnimsan (2,184m), Mt. Geumgangsan (1,638m), Mt. Seoraksan (1,708m), and Mt. Taebaeksan (1,567m) are some of the highest peaks along these ranges. Just southwest from the Taebaeksan range is the Sobaeksan range, which culminates in the massive Mt. Jirisan (1,915m). This range was historically a great barrier between the central and southern parts of the peninsula, and also between the eastern and western regions in the south. The Nakdong river basin is thus segregated in southeastern Korea. The Gaemagowon Plateau, the so-called "Roof of Korea," located in the northwestern corner of the peninsula, has an average elevation of about 1,500 meters above sea level.

The landmass of the peninsula is rather stable geologically in spite of its proximity to Japan ; it has neither active volcanoes nor strong earthquakes. There are, however, a few dead volcanoes that were formed during the Pleistocene era. Mt. Baekdusan is famous for a large caldera lake, "Cheonji," meaning heavenly tarn. Mt. Hallasan in Jeju special self-governing province island, the highest mountain in South Korea, was recorded to have had minor volcanic activity in the early 11th century. It has a small crater lake, "Baengnokdam," and there are about 400 parasitic cones in its piedmont.

About two-thirds of the Korean Peninsula is composed of pre-Cambrian metamorphic and granitic rock. Although the distribution of sedimentary rock is very limited, limestone is quite abundant in some regions and a number of limestone caves can be found, some of which are tourist attractions. Among the most famous caves are Gossigul, Gosugul and Seongnyugul, all of which are adorned with stalagmites and stalactites.

6) Rivers and Plains

Most of major rivers flow into the Yellow Sea and a few into the South Sea, draining the western and southern slopes of the peninsula. Considering its size, Korea has a relatively large number of long rivers, six of them exceeding 400 kilometers. The discharge of rivers fluctuates greatly due to the summer monsoon. In the summertime, rivers swell with heavy rainfall, flooding valley plains every once in a while. In drier seasons, the water level drops and often much of the river bed is exposed. Typhoons, which hit the southern part of the peninsula once every two or three years, also bring heavy rainfall in late summer and early autumn.

In the past, rivers were important for transportation. Historical capitals such as Pyeongyang and Buyeo are located adjacent to major rivers, as is Seoul. After the introduction of railroads and automobiles, however, the importance of rivers for transportation has decreased sharply, and rivers are now used mainly for the irrigation of rice fields and power generation. During the last two decades a number of huge dams have been constructed for flood control, electricity, and irrigation. But these dams have gradually begun to play a major role as reservoirs for piped water supply to large cities and industrial plants as a result of rapid urbanization and industrialization nationwide.

Most farming fields are narrow floodplains developed along rivers, especially in their lower reaches. These plains serve as the major rice-producing lands. Large tidal differences at the mouths of major rivers flowing into the Yellow Sea inhibited the development of deltaic plains, although rivers transport large amounts of sediment during floods. Only the Nakdonggang flowing into the South Sea has a small delta at its mouth. Erosional basins along rivers in areas of granitic rocks have also served as agricultural regions since ancient times. Many large cities such as Chuncheon, Cheongju, and Wonju are located in such basins.

7) Coasts

Korea has a long coastline divided into the east, west and south coasts. The east coast has small tidal differences, a third of one meter at the most, and a relatively smooth shoreline with few islands offshore. The Taebaek range runs closely along the East Sea. Where mountains protrude from the Taebaeksan range, coasts are rocky in general, but some beaches are found in places into which small streams carry sediment from the high mountains. In many instances, the beaches take the form of sand spits and bars enclosing lagoons, which are notable features of the east coast. Along the coast between Wonsan and Gangneung are located a series of lagoons, including Gyeongpo and Hwajinpo, two famous resorts. The highway connecting Gangneung and Seoul has been expanded recently, reducing the travel time between the central region and the east coast.

The shorelines of the south and west coasts are very irregular with innumerable small peninsulas and bays as well as a large number of islands. The west coast facing the Yellow Sea, which is very shallow, has large tidal ranges, which rise above 10 meters in places. Harbors have been difficult to develop since tidal flats are common coastal features, especially in bays into which rivers discharge sediment during floods. Tidal flats have been reclaimed from ancient times mainly for rice fields, but since the 1970s, the reclamation has grown in magnitude. The Saemangeum Project, the largest such project ever undertaken, seeks to reclaim a total of 40,100 hectares of the flats through the construction of huge dikes, but it faces strong opposition from environmental groups.

The south coast shows a typical ria shoreline, a coastal zone which has been submerged. The length of coastline is nearly eight times longer than its straight-line distance, and its indentation is far greater than that of the west coast. The tidal ranges are relatively small at two to five meters, and tidal flats are not as wide as along the west coast. Although mountains face the sea, there are few beaches and sea cliffs along the mainland coast, as innumerable islands prevent the penetration of waves from offshore. Narrow straits between the mainland and islands are associated with extremely rapid tidal currents. At Uldolmok toward the western end of the south coast, the tidal current reaches up to 13 knots.

1.1.2 People

Koreans are primarily one ethnic family and speak one language. Sharing distinct physical characteristics, they are believed to be descendants of several Mongol tribes that migrated onto the Korean Peninsula from Central Asia.

In the seventh century, the various states of the peninsula were unified for the first time under the Silla Kingdom (57 B.C.-A.D. 935). Homogeneity has enabled Koreans to be relatively free from ethnic conflicts and to maintain a firm solidarity with one another.

As of the end of 2005, Korea's total population was estimated at 48,294,000 with a density of 474 people per square kilometer. The population of North Korea is estimated to be 22,928,040.

Korea saw its population grow by an annual rate of 3 percent during the 1960s, but growth slowed to 2 percent over the next decade. In 2005, the rate stood at 0.44 percent and is expected to further decline to 0.01 percent by 2020.

A notable trend in Korea's demographics is that it is growing older with each passing year. Statistics show that 6.9 percent of the total population of Korea was 65 years or older in 1999, and 9.1 percent was in 2005.

In the 1960s, Korea's population distribution formed a pyramid shape, with a high birth rate and relatively short life expectancy. However, age-group distribution is now shaped more like a bell because of the low birth rate and extended life expectancy. Youths (15 and younger) will make up a decreasing portion of the total, while senior citizens (65 and older) will account for some 15.7 percent of the total by the year 2020.

The nation's rapid industrialization and urbanization in the 1960s and 1970s has been accompanied by continuing migration of rural residents into the cities, particularly Seoul, resulting in heavily populated metropolitan areas. However, in recent years, an increasing number of Seoulites have begun moving to suburban areas.

1) Population

The registered population of the Republic of Korea as of 2006 was 49,024,737. The population density of the country is 480 persons per square kilometer. As of 2005, the population of North Korea was 24,000,000. Fast population growth was once a serious social problem in the Republic, as in most other developing nations.

Due to successful family planning campaigns and changing attitudes, however, population growth has been curbed remarkably in recent years. The number of people aged 65 and older was up 0.5 percent from 2005 with about 4.56 million, which made up 9.3 percent of the entire population.

1.1.3 Language

Koreans speak and write the same language, which has been a decisive factor in forging their national identity. Koreans have developed several different dialects in addition to the standard used in Seoul. However, the dialects, except for that of Jeju-*do* Province, are similar enough for native speakers to understand without any major difficulties.

Linguistic and ethnological studies have classified the Korean language in the Altaic language family, which includes the Turkic, Mongolic and Tungus-Manchu languages.

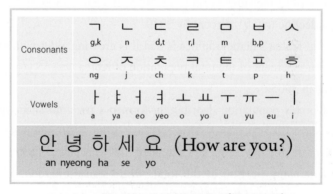

Figure 1.1 **The Korean Alphabet (Hangeul)**
(Source : The National Atlas Of Korea)

The Korean Alphabet, Hangeul, was created under the direction of King Sejong the Great during the 15th century. Before its creation, only a relatively small percentage of the population was literate ; few could master the difficult Chinese characters used by the upper class.

In attempting to invent a Korean writing system, King Sejong looked to several writing systems known at the time, such as old Chinese seal characters and Uighur and Mongolian scripts.

The system that Joseon scholars came up with, however, is predominantly based upon phonological studies. Above all, they developed and followed a theory of tripartite division of the syllable into initial, medial and final phonemes, as opposed to the bipartite division of traditional Chinese phonology.

Hangeul, which consists of 10 vowels and 14 consonants, can be combined to form numerous syllabic groupings. It is simple, yet systematic and comprehensive, and is considered one of the most scientific writing systems in the world. Hangeul is easy to learn and write, which has greatly contributed to Korea's high literacy rate and advanced publication industry.

THE REPUBLIC OF KOREA

Our country has cultivated a unique culture in its long history and has many time-honored traditions. Despite its territorial division in the 20th century, Korea has achieved remarkable economic and social developments, which have attracted the attention of the world. The nation has gained a central position in trade, and at the same time is growing into an East Asian economic hub.

Immediately following the Korean War, per capita income was a mere USD 67 but, as of 2007, it had reached a high of USD 20,045. The nation's exports also grew from USD 5.5 million in 1962 to USD 371.4 billion in 2006. Major exports consist of capital and technology-intensive products including electronic appliances, automobiles, ships, and semiconductors. Export markets have also diversified, and cover most of the world. Owing to its economic growth, Korea joined the OECD (Organization for Economic Cooperation and Development) in 1996.

Since the 1970s, Korea has participated in various projects in conjunction with international organizations. Private organizations have also engaged in activities of regional development, education, medical aid and refugee assistance in Central Asia, Africa, and other areas. Korea has dispatched UN Peacekeeping Forces to Georgia, India, Pakistan, Afghanistan, Lebanon, Liberia, and Sudan, contributing to the maintenance of world peace.

In 1991, the Republic of Korea (ROK) and the Democratic People's Republic of Korea (DPRK) joined the UN. Our country has also joined other various regional cooperative organizations and, in 2005, the APEC (Asian-Pacific Economic Cooperation) summit meeting was held in Busan.

1.2.1 Geographic Boundary

The territory of Korea consists of a land area with a north-south length of 1,100km. Korea has 3,960 islands, and its total area is 223,170km2. To the north, Korea is bordered by the Dumangang (Tumen River) and the Amnokgang (Yalu River), along with Russia and China. To the east, the nation is bordered by the East Sea, which is shared with Japan.

Korean territorial waters include the area 12 nautical miles from the mainland, or from the line connecting the islands that are farthest out from the mainland. In the case of Jeju special self-governing province, Ulleungdo, and Dokdo, territorial waters include the areas within 12 nautical miles from the coastlines. In the Strait of Korea, the territorial waters include only the area within 3 nautical miles from the straight base line. Territorial waters are under exclusive jurisdiction, but the northern waters of Jeju special self-governing province are an exception.

1.2.2 Territorial History

From the early days, our people lived in the vast areas including Manchuria and the Korean Peninsula. Major states included Gojoseon, Buyeo, Goguryeo, Baekje, and Silla. Our people introduced and conveyed continental cultures to maritime states. At the same time, our people were ceaselessly faced with pressures and challenges from the continental and maritime forces.

Following the unification of the three states by Silla in the 7th century, the displaced people of Goguryeo established Balhae, resulting in the Nambukguk Period (the era of the North and South States), represented by Silla in the south and Balhae in the north. In 926, Balhae was destroyed by Georan (Khitan) and our country lost Manchuria.

In the period of Goryeo, the efforts to recover the northern land continued, and by the end of the Goryeo period (14th century), the territory expanded up to Byeokdong, Ganggye, and Jangjin along the Amnokgang and up to Gapju and Gilju in Hamgyeong Province. In the early Joseon period (15th century), Sagun was established on the west side of the Amnokgang, and Yukjin was installed on the east side of the river.

In the Joseon period, our country was invaded by Japan (1492) and China (1636), but our people did not surrender, choosing instead to fight against the invaders and to defend our territory. In the latter Joseon period, our people began to move to Manchuria and our living area expanded.

In the 20th century, Japan expanded its imperial forces in East Asia and occupied our country for 36 years. Following the liberation from Japanese rule in 1945, our country was divided into North and South along the 38th parallel, leading to the Korean War. After the ceasefire was declared, the age of division began, and it has continued for over 50 years. North and South are coexisting on the Korean Peninsula under heterogeneous social systems, but both are making efforts to overcome the division through the building of mutual trust and the achievement of peaceful coexistence. Despite various difficulties, the two Koreas are expanding personnel and material exchanges through reunions of separated families and summit meetings.

Chapter 2.
PHYSICAL GEOGRAPHY

Korea Bay

East Sea

Gyeonggiman

Yellow Sea

Korea Strait

Jeju Strait

Chapter 2.1.

GEOLOGY AND LANDFORMS

CHAPTER 2

2.1.1 Geological Background

Generally speaking, most areas of the Korean Peninsula belong to an old land in terms of geology. Precambrian metamorphic rocks such as granite gneiss and crystalline schist are the most common rocks especially in an area of Massifs such as the Gyeonggi Massif and the Nangnim Massif (Figure 2.1).

A granite, the second most widely distributed rock, comprises the Triassic granite in the northern Korea and the Jurassic and the Cretaceous granite in the southern Korea. Among them, the Jurassic granite intruding into most precambrian rocks in the Gyeonggi Massif shows a pronounced zonal distribution with a specific orientation, northeast to southwest, which is possibly occurred in the Jurassic orogeny.

The Jurassic orogeny is known to the largest one in the geological history of the Korean Peninsula. During the orogenic earth crustal movement, numerous faulting with a specific orientation, northeast to southwest, occurred and these faults strongly influenced the landform development afterward.

Compared with these metamorphic and plutonic rocks, volcanic rocks such as basalt, andesite and rhyolite are much younger and their distribution is more restricted to the area of volcanic eruption in the Tertiary or Quaternary as in the case of Baekdusan and Jeju Special Self-Governing Province.

Sedimentary rocks including sandstone and limestone are mainly distributed in geological basins such as the Pyeongnam basin, the Taebaeksan basin and the Gyeongsang basin. The Pyeongnam basin and the Taebaeksan basin are well known as the area composed of the Paleozoic and the Mesozoic sedimentary rocks. The lower Paleozoic rocks include most limestone which has been used as a principal resource for the cement industry. And the upper

39

Paleozoic to lower Mesozoic rocks are composed of various kinds of sedimentary rocks including coals which have been used as one of the most important energy resources.

Most of the upper Mesozoic sedimentary rocks occur widely in the Gyeongsang basin located in the south eastern part of the Korean Peninsula. In some areas including Gyeongju, these sedimentary rocks are intruded by the Cretaceous granite which is often called as "Bulguksa granite". Compared with these rocks, the Tertiary rocks are distributed only in the limited area such as Aoji, Gilju-Myeongcheon, Pohang and Seogwipo. It means that most areas of the Korean Peninsula have been left as a terrestrial land since the Tertiary.

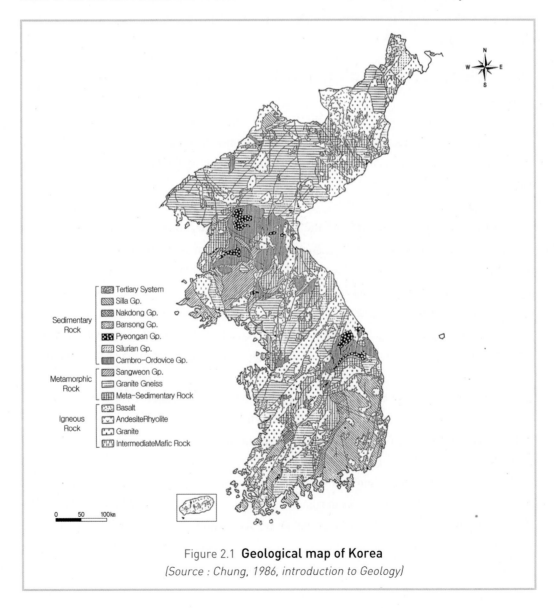

Figure 2.1 **Geological map of Korea**
(Source : Chung, 1986, introduction to Geology)

2.1.2 Landforms

1) Mountains

① Distribution of mountains

About 70% of the Korean Peninsula is covered by mountains and hills. High mountains are mainly located in the eastern and northern part of the peninsula. There are many high mountains with 2,000m above mean sea level (a.m.s.l.) in North Korea such as Baekdusan, Gwanmobong, Buksubaeksan, Nampotaesan and so on. Among them, Baekdusan is the highest mountain with 2,744m a.m.s.l.

Compared with mountains in North Korea, the mountains in South Korea are relatively lower. Even the highest mountains, Hallasan and Jirisan, are lower than 2,000m a.m.s.l. The high mountains over 1,000m a.m.s.l. in South Korea are mostly distributed along the Taebaeksanmaek and the Sobaeksanmaek. With the high Taebaeksanmaek located close to the East Coast, the general shape of the landmass in central Korea is tilting toward east. The tilting came from asymmetric upwarping of the landmass during the Cenozoic.

② Mountain ranges

Mountain ranges can be classified into three groups based upon the general direction of mountain chains : the Korean direction ranges, the Liaotung direction ranges, and the Chinese direction ranges. The Korean direction ranges, north to south, are strongly influenced by the Cenozoic uplift and constitute a backbone of landmass with their high mountains such as the Nangnimsanmaek and the Taebaeksanmaek.

The Liaotung and the China direction ranges are branching from these mountains and lowering toward west and southwest. Contrary to the Korean direction mountain ranges, the directions of these mountain ranges are strongly influenced by the movements of the Earth's crust during the Mesozoic era when faulting with specific direction occurred. During the Cenozoic uplifting, these faults led valley formation and orientation of mountains with Liaotung and China direction (Figure 2.2).

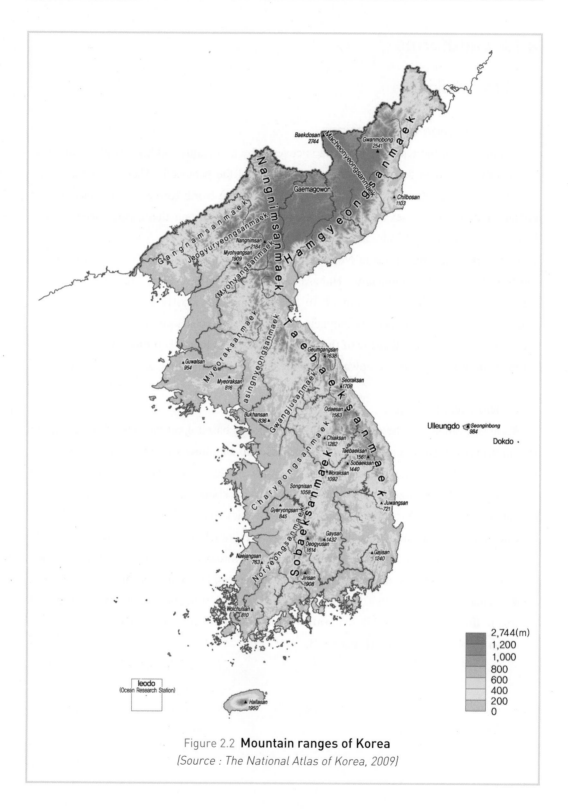

Figure 2.2 **Mountain ranges of Korea**
(Source : The National Atlas of Korea, 2009)

Table 2.1 **Planation surfaces of Korea**

Kobayashi (1931)	Tada (1941)	Yoshikawa (1947)		Kim, Sang Ho (1973)	
Yukbaeksan	Yukbaeksan	Yukbaeksan Odaesan		Yukbaeksan Odaesan	Yukbaeksan Odaesan
Yeoju	Yeoju	Yeoju	570m Daegwallyeong		Jecheon, Daehwa, Pyeongchang, Jeongseon, Hajinbu, Hoenggye etc.
			380m Hajinbu	Middle Surface	
			260m Jecheon		
			160m Chungju	Low Surface	Chungju Gimpo

(Source : Chung, 1989a, Korea Geography)

2) Planation surfaces and piedmont

In Korea, there are two kinds of planation surfaces in terms of landform characteristics including the geometric form and the elevation of surfaces : high and low planation surfaces (Table 2.1). The High planation surfaces have a wavelike mountain summit with high elevation and low local relief. They are interpreted as a relict landform with relatively flat surfaces left from the Cenozoic uplifting even though the original flatness has been partly destroyed. They are widely distributed especially along the summit of the Taebaeksanmaek and used for agricultural activities such as growing vegetables and raising cattle in some places. Maebongsan, Cheongoksan and Hwangbyeongsan are well known for agricultural use (Figure 2.3).

Contrary to the high planation surfaces, the low planation surfaces are widely distributed in areas near the West Coast and interpreted as a secondary planation surface formed by erosion reinforced by the Cenozoic uplifting. Kim (1973) suggested dividing them into two groups, middle and low planation surfaces, based upon the form and elevation level (Table 2.1).

The middle planation surfaces include a gentle hillslope and piedmont, stretching out from mountains to basin floors. Its elevation ranges from 300m-700m a.m.s.l. The piedmonts developed in basins of Jinbu, Hoenggye and Jecheon are good examples of the middle planation surfaces. Those in Hoenggye or Jinbu are often misunderstood as the high planation surfaces since the elevation is very close to the high planation surfaces on the Taebaeksanmaek. The low planation surfaces have been developed as a piedmont surrounding isolated mountains and hills. The elevation level is usually much lower than that of the middle

Figure 2.3 **High planation surface in Pyeongchang** *(Photo by Kim, J. W.)*

Figure 2.4 **Low planation surface in Namwon** *(Photo by Kim, J. W.)*

planation surfaces. The typical examples are found in many places of the West Coast region such as Chungju, Gimpo and Namyangju (Figure 2.4).

The landforming processes of piedmont are debatable. Most piedmonts show landform characteristics of a typical pediment with very thin slope deposits or alluvium (Chang, 1984 ; Kim, 1983). Some of them, however, have thick fluvial deposits like alluvial fan deposits (Chang, 1977 ; Yoon and Hwang, 2004). It means that the landforming processes of a piedmont are not the same, but influenced by various local conditions. Although the landforming processes are not the same, it is true that every piedmont has a very similar appearance. Piedmont provides places for human activities such as agriculture and industry.

3) Rivers

① General characteristics

Most of large rivers such as the Amnokgang and the Hangang flow westward into the Yellow Sea because of the high backbone mountains near the East Coast. These rivers with relatively low channel gradients transport sizable sediment loads from the large catchment areas and sometimes deposit them on the channel beds or low places near channels to make large alluvial plains and basin floors along the channels. However, the rivers on the steep east slope of the backbone mountains flow under quite different morphological conditions with small but steep drainage basin. These rivers have relatively short channel lengths, but flow fast with high velocity and transport more coarse channel bed materials than the rivers in the opposite gentle slope of the backbone mountains (Table 2.2).

The river discharge is very changeable seasonally since over the half of annual precipitation, mostly rainfall, occurs during summer rainy season lasting for about one month. Flooding caused by intensive rainfall often occurs over bank in the summer season. During the dry season from winter to spring, however, it is common to see little water even at the reaches of large channels. This flow regime influenced rivers to have morphological characteristics with wide and shallow channel in which various kinds of gravel or sand bars are developed.

Table 2.2 **Principal rivers in Korea**

Name	Drainage Area(km^2)	Main River Length(km)	Main River Gradient(‰)	Coefficient of River Regime	Note
Hangang	25,953	494	2.33	1:393	Entering Yellow Sea
Geumgang	9,912	398	1.25	1:298	
Yeongsangang	3,468	137	2.93	1:684	
Mangyeonggang	1,504	81	4.04	-	
Ansungcheon	1,656	76	1.40	-	
Sapgyocheon	1,649	59	1.80	-	
Nakdonggang	23,384	510	2.10	1:372	Entering South Sea
Seomjingang	4,912	224	3.87	1:715	
Hyeongsangang	1,133	63	8.06	-	Entering East Sea
Namdaecheon	475	55	23.53	-	
Osipcheon	394	56	19.23	-	

(Source : National Geographic Information Center, 1987)

② Fluvial landforms

• Stream channel pattern

Stream channel pattern which means the plan form is generally divided into three groups : straight channel, braided channel and meandering channel. Researchers are traditionally more interested in meandering channels with high sinuosity index. There are two kinds of meandering, free meandering and incised meandering. Free meandering channels are usually found on alluvial plain formed at places where streams flow into trunk streams and get into the sea or lake. Nowadays, most of the free meandering channels have been channelized to protect the land from flooding and drain away stream water more effectively. On old maps published 100 years ago, the typical free meandering channels are found in the lower reaches of tributary streams of the Hangang such as the Tancheon and the Seongnaecheon in Seoul.

Incised meandering channels are generally formed by bedrock uplift or downward sea level change and many valleys seem to be winding themselves. Based upon morphological characteristics, the incised meandering channels are divided into two groups : an ingrown meandering with symmetric valley side and an entrenched meandering with asymmetric valley side. In Korea, most incised channels are ingrown meanders. At rivers in high mountain areas such as the west side of the Taebaeksanmaek, it is not so rare to find this kind of meandering channels. The Pyeongchanggang, the Donggang and the Goljicheon are among

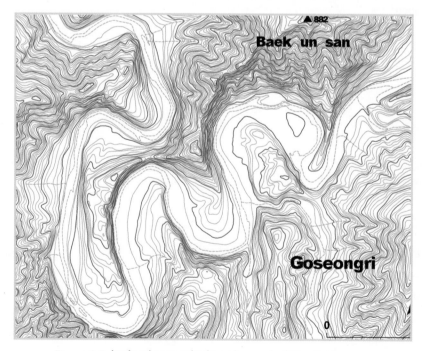

Figure 2.5 **Incised meandering channel of the Donggang**
(Source : 1:25,000 digital map of Mitan and Okdong, National Geographic Information Institute)

good examples (Figure 2.5). Small towns in this region are often located on the river terraces developed at the gentle slip off slope of the incised valley.

• Flood plans and river terraces

Rivers make various kinds of unique landforms in and near waterway by erosional and depositional processes. In terms of human activities, fluvial landforms such as flood plains and river terraces are more important since these comprise flat land surface with fine fluvial sediments. Most flood plains are made through lateral accretion occurred by channel migration and also vertical accretion by over bank inundating.

Flood plains can be divided into natural levee and back swamp in case of large plains. Natural levee is higher than back swamp and composed of more coarse materials such as sands while silt or clay size sediments are deposited in back swamp. Because of these landform characteristics, natural levees have been used for the location of towns and industrial activities for a long time.

Generally speaking, every river has its flood plain even though its size is different from place to place according to local morphological conditions. Especially, large rivers such as the Hangang, the Nakdonggang, the Geumgang and the Yeongsangang have sizeable flood plains at the place where two streams join together and at the lower reach of main stream. The flood

Figure 2.6 **Downstream of the Hangang in 1910s**
(Source : 1:50,000 topographic map in 1910s)

plain of the lower Hangang is one of the best examples. As the old map shows, people used natural levees like Ttukseom, Jamsil and Songpa as residential area at that time (Figure 2.6). However, the lower land behind levees was not used because of repeated inundating.

A river terrace, one of the most important fluvial landforms, is former flood plain and composed of flat terrace surface and scarp with more steep slope. River terraces are developed if channel erosion is activated by uplift and/or climatic change after wide flood plain formation. It is true that most rivers have terraces though their geometric forms are different each other since every stream has been influenced by Quaternary climatic change and intensive bedrock uplift in high mountain areas such as the west side of the Taebaeksanmaek.

Of many terraces in Korea, the river terraces at Yeoryang-Yongtan, Deokpori-Hasongri and Sapyeong-Sindanyang in the west side of the Taebaeksanmaek are well known because they show more pronounced terrace-like shapes (Figure 2.7). There are several terraces at different elevations. Generally, the lower terraces have not been disturbed much and so have kept the original forms while the higher terraces have had most of the original shapes transformed by long spanned slope processes. These river terraces in the west side of the Taebaeksanmaek are interpreted to have been developed through the activated channel erosion caused by increased rainfall since the beginning stage of Holocene after flood plain formation in the glacial period. In contrast, the flood plains located close to river mouths are transformed into terraces during eustatic sea level lowering in the glacial period. These terraces were covered by newly deposited sediments if sea level rose again after the glacial period. It is known that this kind of complicated terrace formation has occurred at lower reaches of rivers such as the Naengcheon in Pohang (Jo, 1987).

Figure 2.7 **River Terrace in Yeoryang** *(Photo by Kim, J. W.)*

- **Alluvial fan and delta**

An alluvial fan is a fan-or cone-shaped fluvial landform and often occurs at the boundary area between mountains and plains. Principal processes which form alluvial fans are fluvial deposition as well as mass movement like mudflow. If it rains under arid or semi arid climate, streams are usually flowing very quickly from the mountain valley toward the plain like a torrent. However, as the stream water is evaporated and infiltrated into the ground, streams with more water are changed gradually into mudflow or debris flow with relatively few water content. It has been suspected by many scientists for a long time if there is any typical alluvial fans in Korea as in Japan or elsewhere of the arid region since a fan-shaped gentle slope at the foothill area, piedmont, is more similar to a pediment in terms of sediment facies and the relationship to bedrock. Small size alluvial cones, however, can be found along the steep mountain valley.

Unlike alluvial fan, the delta is a fluvial landform occurred at the river mouth. If a river approaches to the base level of the coastal area, the flow velocity is reduced to near zero and its sediment load is deposited at the river mouth making a wide alluvial plain, delta. In Korea, the lower part of the Nakdonggang is known to have proper morphological conditions for delta formation since there is a negligible tidal range and so there is no strong marine process clearing out the sediments. The Nakdong delta is divided into two parts, upper delta and lower delta. The upper delta has been formed by fluvial depositional processes and composed of many islands with natural levee. The lower delta has been developed by marine processes which redeposited sediments transported to the sea by the Nakdonggang. The lower delta can be divided into beach ridges formed across the flow direction of river channel and tidal flats regularly inundated by sea water between beach ridges.

4) Seas and coasts

① Seas

The Korean Peninsula is surrounded by three seas under quite different geographic conditions : the Yellow Sea, the East Sea and the South Sea. The Yellow Sea located between the Korean Peninsula and China looks like a large bay and is sometimes called the Yellow Sea. Probably the name came from the yellow color of sea water caused by sediments continuously transported by streams. The Yellow Sea is a continental shelf with its shallow water under ca. 100m depth. The South Sea is more open to outside seas even though it is a shallow sea as well. It is gradually being narrowed toward east and becomes the Strait of Korea which is politically important as a gateway to the East Sea. The East Sea is surrounded by three countries : Korea, Japan and Russia. Contrary to the Yellow Sea, it is a kind of ocean with 4000m deep sea and several volcanic islands such as Ulleungdo and Dokdo.

Sea currents influencing the Korean seas are the Kuroshio Current and the Liman Current. The warm Kuroshio Current is coming from the south and flowing through the South Sea toward the East Sea. On the way, a tributary of the Kuroshio Current is stretching out into the Yellow Sea. At the East Sea, the cold Liman Current flowing north to south meets the Kuroshio Current coming from the opposite direction, south to north. The mixing zone at the boundary of two currents is a good place for a fishery. However, its location is moving toward south in winter and toward north in summer.

② Coasts

A coast is a boundary area between sea and terrestrial land. So, its morphology is influenced by the characteristics of both sea and land. The West Coast and the South Coast of the Korean Peninsula show a strongly indented coastline with headlands, bays and islands. Especially, the boundary zone of these coasts, so called Southwest Coast, is well known as a type of Ria Coast. Probably it came from sea water inundation by the postglacial marine transgression and also from the gradual land mass lowering toward seas.

Another important landforming factor is a tidal current with a sizable tidal range. The tidal range even reaches over 8m during spring tides in the West Coast such as the Gyeonggiman, the Asanman and the Cheonsuman. And the tidal range gradually reduces toward north or south from these bays. A wide tidal flat with shallow bays has been developed in intertidal areas under the macro-tidal condition. The morphology of the East Coast, however, is quite different from these coasts. Its coastline is not so indented and there are only a few bays and islands. In addition, the tidal range is negligible, so the tide has not been influential in the coastal landforming processes at the East coast.

③ Coastal landforms
• Beaches and coastal dunes

Beaches are formed by marine depositional processes and divided into sand beaches and shingle beaches with gravels. Generally speaking, lower energy waves make sand beaches and higher energy waves shingle beaches. The sizable sand beaches are found more often at the East Coast than any other places (Figure 2.8). The sand beach is one of the principal coastal landforms at the East Coast. The beaches between Gangneung and Jumunjin are well known for beautiful scenery and the beach materials are mostly coarse sand originated from granite weathering products (Figure 2.9). Beaches at the West Coast are generally small in size since

Figure 2.8 **East coast nearby Gangneung in 1910s**
(Source : 1:50,000 topographic map in 1910s)

Figure 2.9 **Sand beach at Gyeongpodae** *(Photo by Kim, J. W.)*

Figure 2.10 **Coast at Sinduri, Taean**
(Source : 1:50,000 topographic map in 1910s)

its coastline is strongly indented with small bays and headlands but many of them have been developed as recreation areas like beaches at the East Coast (Figure 2.10). Besides, the beach materials are usually finer since fine sand producing bedrocks are more widely distributed and rivers bring more fine sands than at the East Coast.

• Coastal dunes

A coastal dune is formed by eolian sand deposition. Commonly, its sands come from beach deposits. Sand dunes occur usually right behind a sizable beach by wind transportable sands and also where prevailing winds blow strongly as at the West Coast. The winter monsoon blowing from Siberia is known to contribute to the formation of sand dunes. Most big dunes at the West Coast have been seriously destroyed by digging out quartz sands to make glasses for a long time. Only a few dunes such as the Sinduri dunes and the Daecheongdo dunes keep less disturbed natural morphology (Figure 2.11). Recently, Korean government is trying to protect such dunes from human induced destruction since it is perceived among people that the role and function of dunes are very important in maintaining coastal ecosystems.

Figure 2.11 **Coastal dune at Sinduri, Taean***(Photo by Kim, J. W.)*

• Lagoons

A lagoon is a brackish lake or sea separated partly or completely from outside sea by coastal barriers. Lagoons are widely distributed at the area of the East Coast and the pronounced landform of the East Coast with sizable sand beaches and coastal terraces (Figure 2.8). Lagoons are known to have been developed by the Postglacial marine transgression. The size of lake has been reduced gradually by terrestrial processes including fluvial deposition soon after the formation. For this landform changing process, it is rare to find lagoons at the mouth of large rivers like the Namdaecheon in Gangneung. Among lagoons, the Yeongnangho, the Cheongchoho and the Gyeongpoho are famous as large and beautiful lakes.

• Intertidal flats

An intertidal flat is a land covered regularly by sea water during high tides. It is composed of various materials from gravel to clay. The intertidal flat is widely distributed at the West Coast and the South Coast along the coast of shallow bays with macro-tidal range such as the Gyeonggiman, the Asanman and the Cheonsuman. Most of the tidal flats have been reclaimed that nowadays it is hard to find the natural coastline at the West Coast and the South Coast. The reclamation of tidal flats gives serious negative effects against sound coastal ecosystem. At some areas like the Suncheonman, the tidal flat is used for ecotourism as an alternative to the reclamation.

• Coastal terraces

A coastal terrace is a landform developed by bedrock uplift and downward sea level

Figure 2.12 **Coastal terrace at Simgok, Gangneung** *(Photo by Kim, J. W.)*

change. It is mainly distributed at the East Coast from Gangneung to Ulsan (Figure 2.12). The coastal terraces at this area are found at different elevations, 10m-20m, 30m-40m a.m.s.l., for example. Among them, the coastal terraces with 10m-20m a.m.s.l show more pronounced terrace-like forms with a wide terrace surface since the formation is relatively recent compared to others. According to recent researches based upon OSL age dating method, the age of the 10m-20m high terraces is known to be ca. 80 thousand years BP and the age of the 30m-40m high terraces ca. 120 thousand years BP (Kim et al., 2007). It means that the 30m-40m high terraces at the East Coast are probably formed during the Last Glacial Maximum.

5) Volcanic landform

Volcanic landform is usually distributed at the place where volcanic eruption occurred in the past. Though most areas of the Korean territory belong to a stable land in terms of tectonics, there are volcanoes and wide lava plateaus in some places such as Jeju special self-governing province, Ulleungdo, Cheorwon-Pyeonggang and the Baekdusan.

Among them, Jeju special self-governing province, the largest island in Korea, is well known as its whole area is covered by various volcanic rocks erupted ca. 79 times since the Tertiary (Figure 2.13). It is suggested by volcanologists that a low level flat lava plateau was formed by fissure eruptions led by faults at the beginning stage of the formation of the island. The lava plateau has been gradually changed into the shape of a shield volcano and its ground elevation increased by repeated eruptions focused on the central place. This is why the island is a large shield volcano of which the summit, Hallasan, is a dome-like volcano, tholoid, and its surrounding slope is gentle like lava plateau. The 1,959m high Hallasan is the highest peak in South Korea with a crater lake, Baengnokdam, on the summit area.

Figure 2.13 **Volcanic dome of Sanbangsan, Jeju special self-governing province**
(Photo by Kim, J. W.)

Figure 2.14 **Dokdo, Ulleung-*gun***

On the gentle slope of Jeju special self-governing province, there are ca. 360 small adventive mono-genetic volcanoes most of which are scoria cones called as 'oreum' by residents. Besides, there are many lava caves in Jeju special self-governing province such as the Manjanggul, the Geumnyeonggul and the Hyeopjaegul. Some of them have interesting features like speleothem which is known to be formed by precipitation of calcite coming from cave outside through solutional processes of calcium bearing shells deposited on the ground surface.

Ulleungdo is another large volcanic island in the East Sea. Its general shape looks like a form of tholoid in which there are two calderas at different elevations surrounded by rim mountains including Seonginbong, the highest peak of the island. However, the volcano including its slope area under the sea level is known as a shield. Not far from this island, there

Figure 2.15 **Hantangang valley at Goseokjeong, Cheorwon** *(Photo by Kim, J. W.)*

is a small but beautiful volcanic island, Dokdo, which consist of two islands, named Dongdo (East Island) and Seodo (West Island), along with 89 other rocks(Figure 2.14).

The largest volcano in Korea is Baekdusan, the highest peak in the whole land of Korea. This volcano also shows shield-like general shape and its summit looks like a dome volcano, tholoid, with a large caldera lake, the Cheonji, in the central place. The huge lava plateau, the Baekdu Lava Plateau, at the surrounding area of the Baekdusan is composed of mainly lavas and pyroclastic materials such as tephra including white colored pumice erupted from acidic rhyolite magma.

The lava plateau located in the area of Cheorwon and Pyeonggang is another example of it although its size is smaller than the Baekdu Lava Plateau. It is known that the basaltic lava has been erupted at least 11 times from volcanoes in Pyeonggang formed on fault lines. The lave flew down ca. 95km distant along the Hantangang and covered its channels and nearby lowland to make lava plateau. After the formation of lava plateau, the newly developed the Hantangang eroded deeply the plateau and made a narrow valley with steep side slopes like a canyon (Figure 2.15).

6) Karst landform

A karst comprises various kinds of landforms such as doline, uvala and limestone cave which occurred through the solution of calcite in limestone, carbonation. The calcite bearing limestones are widely distributed in the areas of the Taebaeksan basin and the Pyeongnam basin, so most of karst landforms are found in these areas.

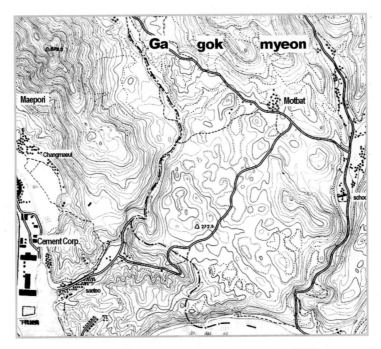

Figure 2.16 **Doline in Maepo, Danyang in 1980s**
(Source : 1:25,000 Maepo topographic map, National Geographic Information Institute)

A doline, a depression hollow, as one of the representative karst landforms is often used as a field for cultivation in many places since its flat floor can be easily cultivated. Motbat in Maepo is a typical case for it (Figure 2.16). The name, Motbat, is probably originated from the reason that the shape of doline cultivated into field looks like a small pond.

In terms of tourism, a limestone cave with speleothem is one of the most important resources. A speleothem, secondary sediments of calcite, includes stalactite, stalagmite and so on. The cave with speleothem is usually known to be developed by valley deepening and ground water level lowering followed by cave formation through underground solution. The Hwanseongul, the Gosudonggul and the Seongnyugul are more tourist attractive caves in Korea.

NATURAL ENVIRONMENT

2.2.1 Climate

One of the most distinct climatic features over the Korean Peninsula is the Asian monsoon system, which is caused by a large heat contrast between the Asian interior landmass and the Pacific Ocean. In winter, cold and dry conditions prevail because of the intrusion of local northwesterly (i.e., from the northwest) flow from the clockwise winds spiraling from the large, quasi-stationary, semi-permanent Siberian high pressure system to the west. In summer, a warm and moist climate exists owing to the influence of local southeasterly flow spiraling from the quasi-stationary, semi-permanent North Pacific high pressure system to the southeast. Therefore, most of Korea experiences cold and dry winters, but hot and humid summers. Figure 2.17 shows the location of weather stations and the climographs for selected stations in South Korea.

Because of the long north-south distance and the complicated topography, the Korean Peninsula has a wide diversity of local and regional climates. The adjacency of the northern region to the large Eurasian continent and the proximity of the southern region to the ocean demonstrate that the nation is strongly affected by both the continent and ocean, respectively. The many mountainous and hilly areas also influence local and regional climates, including the obvious impact of elevation changes on temperature and orographic effects on precipitation.

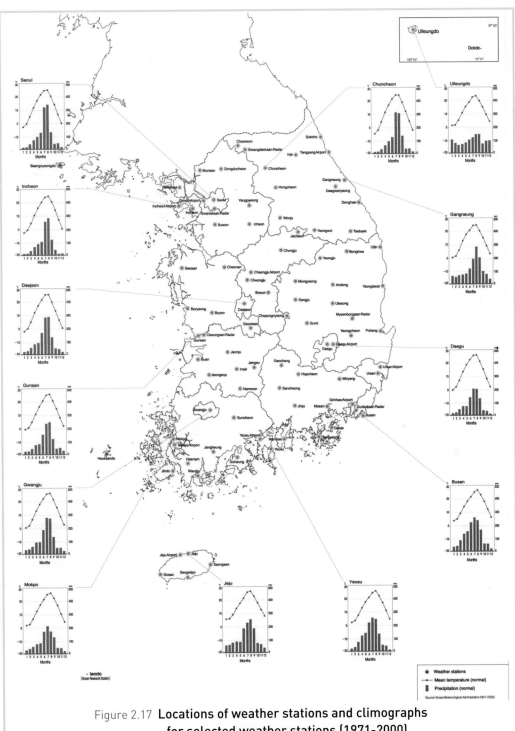

Figure 2.17 **Locations of weather stations and climographs
for selected weather stations (1971-2000)**

(Source : The National Atlas of Korea, 2007)

1) Temperature

The annual mean temperature generally increases from north to south and is higher in the coastal areas than in the inland areas (Figure 2.18). It ranges from about 6 to 16C°, responding to the effects of latitude, continentality, topography, and atmospheric and oceanic circulation features. Air temperature is lower in the Taebaek and Sobaek mountain ranges, and higher in regions nearer to the southern coast. Because of the effect of warm Pacific Ocean currents, the eastern coastal areas have higher mean temperatures than those on the west coast at the same latitude. For instance, the annual mean temperature in Gangneung near the eastern coast is 12.9C° while that in Incheon near the western coast is 11.7C°. Daegwallyeong (6.4C°) has the lowest annual mean temperature in South Korea because of higher elevations (842.5m) and latitude. Seogwipo has the highest annual mean temperature (16.2C°) largely because its extreme southern and insular location protects it from the cold dry air circulated by the Siberian high pressure system in winter.

Winter is the coldest season and January is the coldest month in Korea due to the influence

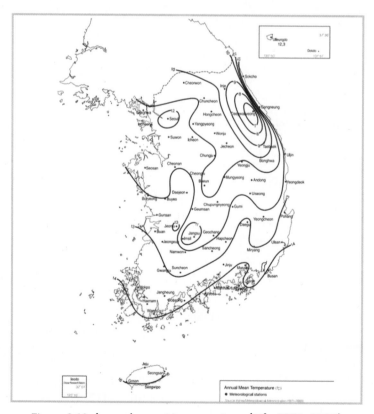

Figure 2.18 **Annual mean temperature (C°, 1971-2000)**
(Source : The National Atlas of Korea, 2007)

of the frigid Siberian air mass. Winter temperature increases from north to south in a similar spatial pattern to that of annual mean temperature (Figure 2.19, left panel). During winters, the temperature difference between the areas east and west of the Tabaek Mountain Range is more pronounced because the mountains limit the impact of the cold, northwesterly wind toward the east. Also, the warmer water temperature in the East Sea substantially increases the west-east temperature difference. At Gangneung on the east coast, January mean air temperature is 0.3C° while at Incheon on the west coast it is -2.4. Daegwallyeong has the lowest January mean temperature (-7.6C°) in South Korea. In the central areas of South Korea, the mean monthly temperature is below freezing only from December to February, but is from December to April at Daegwallyeong. Not surprisingly, January mean temperature is highest at Seogwipo (6.6C°) and is above 2C° in most of the southern coastal area.

In summer, the North Pacific high pressure and its associated circulation from the south dominate the climate in Korea. Summer is the hottest season and August is the month with the highest temperatures, except for the inland Gaema Plateau and surrounding areas in North Korea, which experience July maxima. August mean temperatures show less difference between northern and southern regions, and even less between eastern and western regions, in

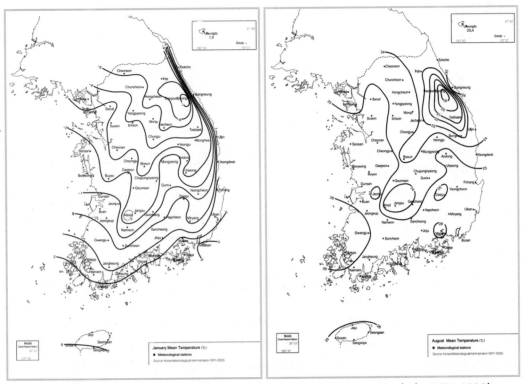

Figure 2.19 **January (left) and August (right) mean temperature (C°, 1971-2000)**
(Source : The National Atlas of Korea, 2007)

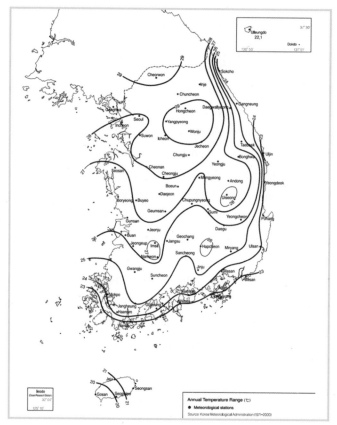

Figure 2.20 **Annual temperature range (C°, 1971-2000)**
(Source : The National Atlas of Korea, 2007)

comparison with winter (Figure 2.19, right panel). August mean temperature in most of the south surpasses 26C°, Daegwallyeong has the lowest August mean temperature (19.0C°) in South Korea.

The annual temperature range (i.e., the difference between the warmest and coldest month's temperature) decreases from north to south (Figure 2.20), but its spatial distribution differs slightly from that of annual mean temperature. The annual temperature range is affected less by altitude than annual mean temperature and more by other geographical features. For instance, annual temperature range is greater in the inland areas than in the coastal areas. The annual range at Hongcheon (29.6C°) is the largest in South Korea, while those of Yangpyeong (29.5C°), Wonju (29.3C°), and Cheorwon (29.3C°) are larger than most other areas. Notably, Uiseong (28.3C°) in the Yeongnam region has a much larger range than the surrounding regions. Locations with high annual ranges tend to have low winter temperatures and be located in inland basins. Gosan (19.8C°) in Jeju special self-governing province has the smallest annual temperature range.

2) Precipitation

Korea has relatively abundant precipitation with an annual mean of about 1,200mm, but regional differences are large because of the complicated topography. The major producers of precipitation include extratropical cyclones with their trailing fronts, Changma fronts, and typhoons. Any precipitation producing mechanism can produce increased to where topographically-enhanced atmospheric lifting occurs. Extratropical cyclones affect the entire peninsula, but the amount of precipitation from such cyclones varies spatially according to the speed and direction of storm movement, and local topographic effects. Precipitation from Changma fronts differs greatly across space because such fronts typically move back and forth in a south-north direction.

Annual mean precipitation generally increases southward, but its pattern is much more complicated than that of annual mean temperature (Figure 2.21). The southeastern coast of Jeju special self-governing province has the most precipitation in Korea, with Seogwipo reporting a mean annual total of 1,850.7mm. The areas along the southern coast, Jirisan, and the east coast of Gangwon-*do* also have higher annual precipitation than other regions. The

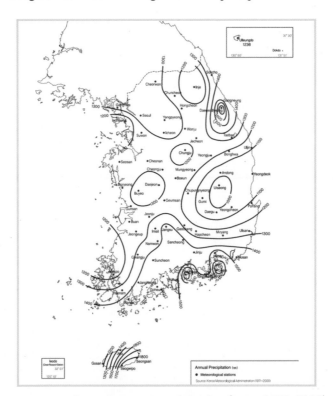

Figure 2.21 **Annual mean precipitation (mm, 1971-2000)**
(Source : The National Atlas of Korea, 2007)

annual precipitation in the southern coastal areas and Jeju special self-governing province is 1,400 to 1,800mm, while that in Daegwallyeong and the coast of Gangwon-*do* approaches 1,400mm. The Yeongnam inland areas, which are surrounded by mountains to the east, west, and south, have the lowest annual precipitation in South Korea, with about 1,000mm.

As in much of Asia, winter (December through February) in Korea is a dry season. Winter precipitation averages below 10 percent of the annual precipitation total except for some islands and coastal areas, but regional differences in the intensity of winter dryness do exist. Ulleungdo has the largest winter precipitation totals (296.1mm), which is about 25 percent of its annual precipitation. The coastal areas in Gangwon-*do* also experience relatively abundant winter precipitation due to snowfall caused by the combined effects of northeasterly airflow and the low temperatures of the Taebaek Mountains (Figure 2.22, left panel).

During summer, the southwesterly winds from the Asian summer monsoon circulation and the southeasterly winds from the western edge of the North Pacific high pressure area converge near Korea to create updrafts and zones of rainfall, particularly where mountains can enhance the updrafts. June through August precipitation represents about 50 to 60 percent of the annual precipitation total. These months are characterized by frequent heavy rainfall

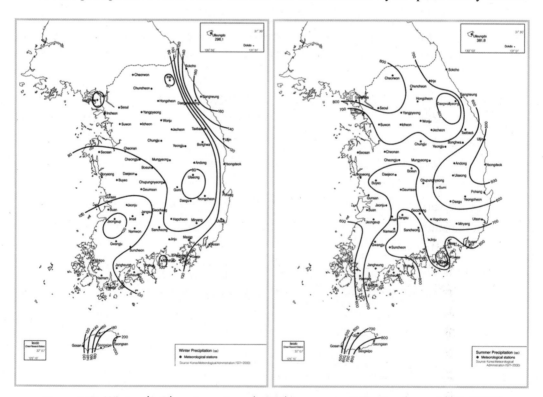

Figure 2.22 **Winter (left) and summer (right) mean precipitation (mm, 1971-2000)**
(Source : The National Atlas of Korea, 2007)

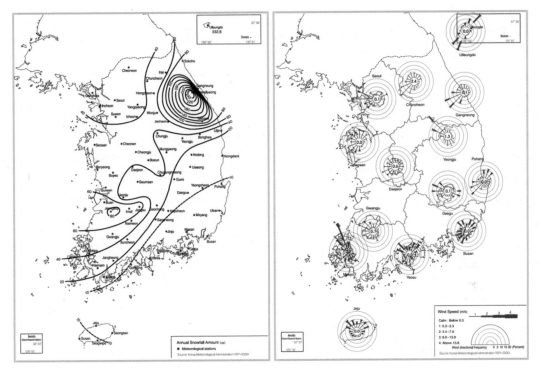

Figure 2.23 **Annual mean snowfall**
(cm, 1971-2000)
(Source : The National Atlas of Korea, 2007)

Figure 2.24 **Annual wind rose**
(1971-2000)
(Source : The National Atlas of Korea, 2007)

events in association with Changma fronts, typhoons, and extratropical cyclones. Summer precipitation generally decreases from the coast to the inland regions (Figure 2.22, right panel). The northwestern Yeongseo regions including Seoul, Ganghwa, Cheorwon, and the southern coasts have the most summer precipitation. On the other hand, the east coast and inland areas in Gyeongsangbuk-*do* have less summer precipitation.

Because the varying topography creates temperature differences and differing availability of oceanic moisture, snowfall totals differ among regions more widely than other climatic features. Snowfall in Korea is generally caused by three meteorological mechanisms : the passage of the extratropical cyclone, expansion of the semi-permanent and quasi-stationary Siberian high pressure system, and the passage of migratory high pressure systems which produce uplift at mountains. Daegwallyeong has the largest annual snowfall totals (243.1cm), with the snow generated by both cyclones and lifting associated with high pressure systems (Figure 2.23). Snowfall in Ulleungdo (232.8cm) is possible from all three mechanisms.

In winter, the prevailing northwesterly winds are caused by the clockwise flow around the eastern side of the quasi-stationary, semi-permanent Siberian high pressure zone over the

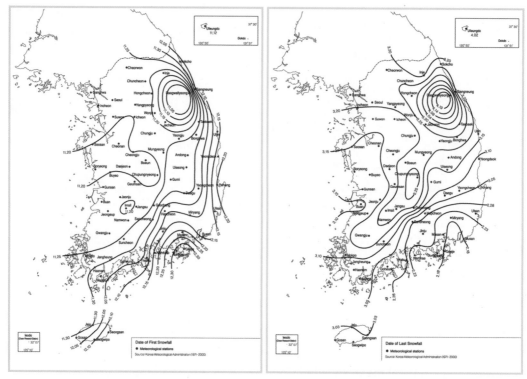

Figure 2.25 **Mean date of the first (left) and the last (right) snowfall (1971-2000)**
(Source : The National Atlas of Korea, 2007)

north-central Asia. In summer, southerly winds resulting from the North-Pacific quasi-stationary, semi-permanent high pressure system dominate Korea. However, local topographic effects make this monsoonal flow more complicated. For example, at Gangneung on the east coast southwesterly winds are dominant during summer and winter, while in Ulleungdo in the East Sea, southwesterly and northeasterly winds are dominant in all seasons (Figure 2.24).

Over the mountainous regions, lower temperatures cause the snow season to begin early and end late. Over the southern coastal region, the snow season begins later and ends earlier, owing to the higher air temperatures caused by longer summer days and higher angles of the sun in the sky, along with the slow release of energy accumulated during the summer throughout winter. The first snow of the season on average falls around November 5 at Daegwallyeong, but at Geoje on the southern coast it occurs near December 30 (Figure 2.25, left panel). The mean date of first snowfall in Seoul, Mokpo, and Busan is November 21, November 26, and December 20, respectively. The mean last snowfall occurs around February 19 in Geoje and Busan, March 11 in Mokpo, and March 21 in Seoul, but not until April 19 in Daegwallyeong (Figure 2.25, right panel).

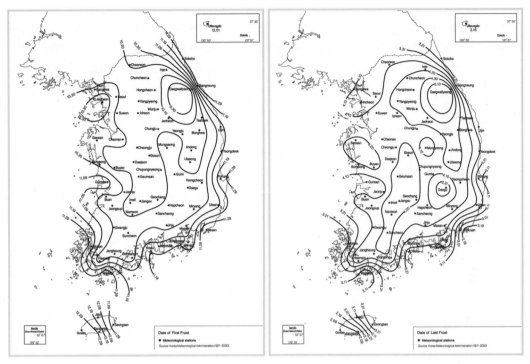

Figure 2.26 **Mean date of the first frost and the last frost (1971-2000)**
(Source : The National Atlas of Korea, 2007)

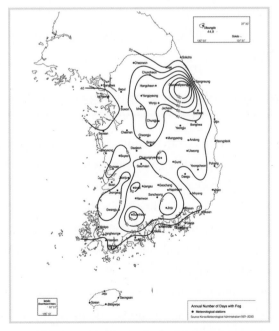

Figure 2.27 **Mean annual number of fog days (1971-2000)**
(Source : The National Atlas of Korea, 2007)

Predictably, the first frost occurs earlier over the northern parts of Korea than over the southern region, and earlier over inland locations than coastal regions (Figure 2.26, left panel). At Mokpo on the southwestern coast, the mean date of the first frost is November 26 while the mean date of the last frost is March 21. By contrast, the earliest mean date of the first frost occurs over the mountainous Gangwon-*do* region on September 7, with the mean date of the last frost on May 30. Over inland regions, the mean date of the first frost ranges from October 17 to 27, and the mean date of the last frost ranges from the first to the second ten days of April (Figure 2.26, right panel).

Because cooling factors are more prominent over mountainous regions than in the coastal region, the mean frequency of fog days increases from coastal to mountainous regions. The annual mean number of fog days at Daegwallyeong is about 120, while over eastern coastal regions only about 20 fog days per year occur (Figure 2.27).

2.2.2 Soil

Demands for soil resources in Korea are high, due to the high population density (about 490 people per km2) and the mountainous terrain. Rapid economic development and intensive land use changes during the last few decades have brought in many aversive impacts on soil distribution and quality. With the increase of awareness of environmental changes in recent years, soil' role as the regulator of water, material and energy over the land surface is becoming important in Korea.

1) The general characteristics of Korean soils

Soil is formed through complex interactions among various environmental factors, including human interventions. General soil characteristics can be best described by soil forming factors namely climate, parent materials, relief, organisms, and time. The majority of parent materials in Korea are acidic crystalline rocks that produce a coarse soil texture with loose structure. About 55% of the land area of Korea is granite and granitic gneiss, and about 10% is crystalline gneiss. Sedimentary and volcanic rocks cover 20% and 5% of the land area respectively. Fluvial and marine sediments that have been reclaimed for paddy fields cover about 5% of the land. Soils from igneous and metamorphic rocks are often more nutrient-rich than those from sedimentary rocks, even though their acidity is higher. In the Korean peninsula, granite that intruded during the Mesozoic Era makes up 33% of the total land area, producing unique undulating hilly terrains with coarse and well-drained soils on a deep weathering regolith.

Korea is located in the humid temperate climatic zone. The average annual rainfall is about 1,300 mm, ranging from approximately 980 mm (Daegu-*si*) to 1,440 mm (Jeju special self-governing province). About 50-60% of the annual rainfall occurs in the summer months July to September. During the summer, the precipitation far exceeds the potential evapotranspiration, leading to the active leaching of soil nutrients. As a result, the base saturation is low and soil acidity is high for the majority of soils. Temperatures in the winter months are often below the freezing point (monthly average temperature of -5 - 2C°). The freezing-thawing of surface soils during the winter hamper the formation of well-developed horizons. The strong seasonality also enhances the decomposition rate of organic materials and soil minerals. Under such climatic conditions, 2:1 layer or mixed layer clays (vermiculites and illites) are formed, while the formation of 1:1 layer clays (kaolinite) might also be possible due to the high temperature and leaching potential during the summer.

Mixed coniferous and deciduous forests are dominant vegetation types in Korea. Most forests in Korea are secondary after experiencing intensive destruction in the past. Forests were so heavily used for energy sources that the amount of organic materials added to soils was low. After electricity and fossil fuels became widely available in the '0s and '0s, bio mass in the forests is rapidly increasing. If this trend continues, vegetation in the forests may exert noticeable influence on soil formation in the future.

Korea is a mountainous country. Plains are only found along rivers and coastal areas. The typical landform of Korea can be described as the following : floodplains along river channels are connected to steep mountains via gently sloping pediment-like landforms. Along such a sequence, soil properties change continuously due to water and material flux over the land surface. Table 2.3 shows an example of catenary soil sequences at granite and granitic gneiss. Soil particles and nutrients eroded from steep sloping areas are accumulated downslope to form nutrient-rich soils. Soil water contents, pH, and cation exchange capacity (CEC) at downslope positions are higher than those at upslope positions. As a result, soil types change from Dystrudepts (typical Inceptisols) to Eutrudepts (nutrient-rich Inceptisols) and then to Endoaquepts (soils formed under the influence of ground water). The changes of soil properties and types along landscape positions are often associated with the changes in land use patterns : paddy fields on the flat plains, dry fields on the gently sloping pediments, and forests at the steep mountains.

The continuation of the same pedogenesis is an important factor for determining the formation of certain diagnostic horizons. The uplifted regions along the East Sea show rugged

Table 2.3 **Catenary soil development at granite and granitic gneiss**

Soil Series (tong)	Samgak →	Sanagju →	Eungok →	Sacheon →	Yecheon
Landforms	low relief hills and steep slope	base of hill, intermontane valley, alluvial fan	intermontane valley, alluvial fan	intermontane valley, alluvial fan, alluvium	intermontane valley, alluvium
Soil drainage	very well drained	well drained	slightly well drained	poorly drained	very poorly drained
Soil texture	sandy loam	sandy loam	sandy loam	sandy loam	sandy loam
Effective soil depth	30 - 50cm	30 - 50cm	50 - 60cm	50 - 60cm	10 - 30cm
pH	4.5 - 5.5		4.5 - 5.0	4.5 - 6.5	
CEC (cmolc/kg)	5	6	5	10 - 15	10
Base saturation (%)	30%	60%	45 - 70%	above 60%	above 60%
Land use	forests	dry fields (orchards)	paddy fields (dry fields)	paddy fields	paddy fields (flooded)
Soil types	Dystrudepts	Eutrudepts	Eutrudepts	Eutrudepts	Eutrudepts

[Source : Yeon Kyn Sonn(2007), Sun-Ho Yoo(2000)]

mountains with thin soil covers. On the other hand, the relatively flat areas at the western side of the peninsula experience relatively stable pedogenesis. Paleosoils are often found at these flat areas and also on narrow terraces formed along rivers and coastal areas. 'The 'ed soils'widely' distributed on these landforms are commonly believed to have been formed during subtropical climatic conditions in the past.

2) The spatial distribution of soil types

The soils of Korea show a complex spatial distribution due to heterogeneous parent materials and rugged landforms, in addition to a long history of human intervention. Two different soil classification systems are currently being used in Korea to describe soil distribution. The first is the Soil Taxonomy developed by USDA, and the other is a three-level hierarchical classification system developed for forest soils.

According to the Soil Taxonomy, 7 soil ordersare found in Korea among 12 orders designated. These are further divided into 14 suborders, 27 great groups, and 390 soil series (Table 2.4). 74.7 % of the land areas (about 6.7 million ha) are classified as Inceptisols, while

15.1 % (about 1.3 million ha) of them are Entisols. The dominance of these two soil types indicates that the overall pedogenic conditions of Korea hamper the formation of well-defined soil horizons. Ultisols and Alfisols that have clay accumulation at their B horizons occupy 4.99% and 3.67% of the land area respectively. Acidic Ultisols are commonly found on undulating hilly terrains and gently sloping areas at the base of mountains, while base-rich Alfisols are more common on flat areas near streams or on neural and alkaline rocks. Andisols developed on volcanic materials occupy less than 1.5 % of the land. These are dominant on volcanic islands such as Jeju special self-governing province and Ulleungdo, and show

Table 2.4 **Major soil types and their distribution area**

Order	Suborder	Great Group	Area(km^2)	Ratio(%)
Inceptisols	Aquepts	Endoaquepts	9,482.02	9.99
		Epiaquepts	245.29	0.26
	Udepts	Dystrudepts	44,984.30	47.41
		Eutrudepts	15,954.45	16.82
		Fragiudepts	219.49	0.23
Entisols	Aquents	Fluvaquents	112.45	0.12
		Endoaquents	581.52	0.61
		Hydraquents	37.91	0.04
		Psammaquents	178.24	0.19
	Fluvents	Udfluvents	1,067.51	1.13
	Orthents	Udorthents	10,478.79	11.04
	Psamments	Udipsamments	1,443.39	1.52
		Quartzipsamments	392.76	0.41
Ultisols	Udults	Hapludults	4,731.86	4.99
		Rhodudults	3.88	0.00
Alfisols	Aqualfs	Epiaqualfs	235.80	0.25
		Endoaqualfs	388.56	0.41
	Udalfs	Fragiudalfs	498.17	0.53
		Hapludalfs	2,352.10	2.48
Andisols	Udands	Hapludands	675.48	0.71
		Fulvudands	324.57	0.34
		Melanudands	380.56	0.40
		Durudands	13.68	0.01
	Vitrands	Udvitrands	6.25	0.01
Mollisols	Udolls	Hapludolls	82.24	0.09
Histosols	Saprists	Haplsaprists	0.44	0.00
	Hemists	Haplhemists	5.12	0.01
Total			94,876.84	100.00

(Source : Rural Development Agency, National Institute of Agricultural Science and Technology)

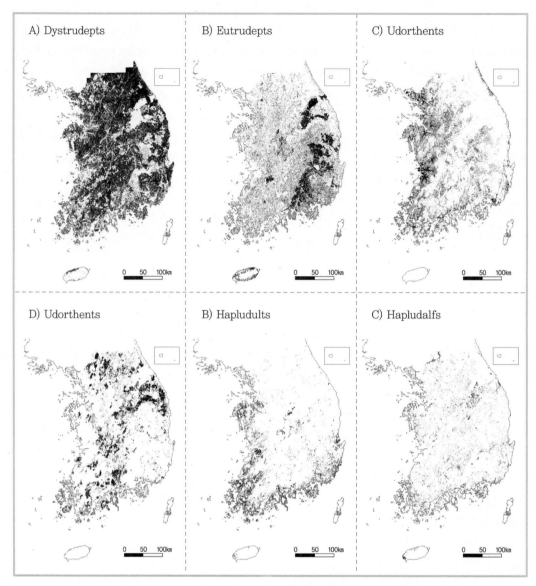

Figure 2.28 **The spatial distribution of great soil groups**
A) Dystrudepts (47.4%), B) Eutrudepts (16.8%), C) Endoaquents (10.0%),
D) Udorthents (11.0%), E) Hapludults (5.0%), F) Hapludalfs (2.5%)
(Source : National Institute of Agricultural Science and Technology, 2007)

scattered occurrence on tertiary volcanic rocks at Gyeonggi-*do*, northern Gangwon-*do*, and some parts of 'Taebaksanmaek and Sobaksanmaek'. Histosols are surveyed at Jeju special self-governing province and along the southern coast of Korea, covering less than 1% of the land. Mollidsols show a limited distribution at the southern part of Gangwon-*do*.

Figure 2.28 shows the distribution of six major great groups found in Korea. Among Inceptisols, the occurrence of Dystrudepts, Eutrudepts, and Endoaquepts are 47.4%, 16.8%, and 10.0%, respectively. These soils have altered soil horizons that have lost bases or iron-aluminum, but lacking illuvial features at subsurface soils. Examples of their soil characteristics and spatial associations can be found in Table 2.5.

Entisols do not have any soil horizons other than an A horizon. Because these soils have a weak capacity to retain moisture and nutrients, the utilization of these soils is limited. Udorthents that have no characteristic soil horizons cover about 11.0% of the land, and are mainly found at rugged mountains such as thd Taebaeksanmaek, Sobaeksanmaek and the Jirisanmaeks (mountain ranges). Psamments are found at coastal sand dunes and sand deposits. Fluvents developed at tidal flats and Aquents formed at floodplains make up less than 2% of the land.

3) Land and soil management

The nutrient status of Korean soils is considered to be infertile, due to the dominance of crystalline acid rocks and general climatic-terrain conditions. The result of soil analyses from over 400,000 soil samples show that the average organic contents is 2.3% for paddy soils and 2.2% for dry field soils. Average effective phosphorus content and cation exchange capacity are 100 ppm and 8.60 meq/100g respectively. The poor soil nutrient level requires intensive use of fertilizers that leads to the acidification and degradation of agricultural soils.

Intensive soil use has also caused soil compaction, which in turn accelerates topsoil erosion and the reduction of soil water content. The annual soil loss of Korea is estimated to be more than 50 million tons a year, mainly occurring from dry fields on sloping areas. The average soil loss from dry fields are 37.7 ton/ha, while soil loss from forests and paddy fields are 3.5 ton/ha and 1.0 ton/ha, respectively. Rainfed cultivated lands occupying less than 10% of the total land areas are responsible for more than half of the annual soil loss (about 27 million tons). Soil erosion is especially severe in the mountainous regions of Gangwon-*do* and southern parts of Korea. It is also serious in high rainfall regions, such as Namhae-*gun*,

Table 2.5 **Soil loss from rainfed agricultural lands in Korea**

Soil erosion class	weak	Slightly weak	Moderate	Slightly severe	severe	very severe
Annual soil loss (ton/ha)	0 ~ 6	6 ~ 11	11 ~ 22	22 ~ 33	33 ~ 50	50 <
rainfed agricultural land (thousand ha)	126	99	159	82	85	168

[*Source : National Geographic Information Institute, 2007, National Atlas of Korea*]

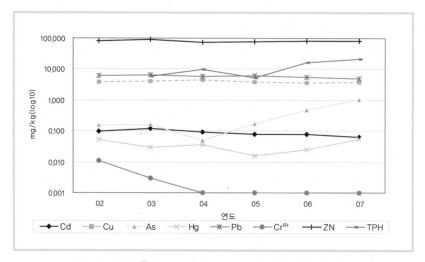

Figure 2.29 **Temporal changes of soil pollutants**
(Source : Ministry of Environment, 2007)

Geojae-*gun* and Gosung-*gun*. With the rapid increase of the demand for organically-grown seasonal vegetables, soil erosion has become an important environmental issue for mountainous regions in recent years.

Soil pollutions are not so severe, except for a few industrialized areas. The content of Cr6+ in soils has decreased and has not been detected since 2004 (Figure 2.29). Except As and Cd, overall content of soil pollutants remain low and steady since the soil pollutant monitoring started. In general, metropolitan areas such as Seoul, Pusan, and Inchon show a relatively high pollution level, while Jeju special self-governing province, Gangwon-*do*, and Chungchungbuk-*do* maintain a low pollution level. Comparing agricultural lands with other lands, the pollution level of paddy and dry fields are similar with the average, but orchard soils show a higher pollution level due to agricultural chemicals and fertilizers.

2.2.3 Vegetation

1) Flora and phytogeographic region

① Flora and floristic biodiversity

Korea has 8,271 plant species, including 4,662 vascular plant species (842 monocotyledon, 2,815 dicotyledon, and 314 fern and gymnosperm species). However, 0.1%, or 67square kilometers, of Korea' forests disappear each year due to human impacts and disturbances, and

Korea' floristic biodiversity is decreasing as a result. The Korean flora can be classified into five major elements, including circumpolar, East Asian, warm temperate, subtropical, and endemic. The circumpolar element is comprised of relict species that migrated from northern cold regions to the Korean Peninsula during the Pleistocene Epoch and survived in alpine areas. The East Asian element contains the common species of Northeast China and the Russian Far East, and the warm temperate element contains species common to the southern part of the Korean Peninsula, South China, and Japan. The subtropical element contains flora that originated in the subtropical regions of Asia, and the endemic element contains plants that only grow on the Korean Peninsula (Kyoyukdoseochulpansa, 1963).

The endemic vascular plants include those of the genera Pentactina, Echinosophora, Abeliophyllum, Hanabusaya, and Megaleranthis. Notably, Abeliophyllum is the only genera and species (Abeliophyllum distichum) that grows exclusively in Korea. Endemic species are generally found in the alpine and subalpine regions of the northern and southern parts of the nation, central mountainous regions, mountains in the west, and remote islands.

The abundance of plant species and the high proportion of endemic species on the Korean Peninsula reflect its flourishing biodiversity. Several unique conditions support the high biological diversity. First, the diverse climate zones, from subtropical climates on Jeju Special Self-Governing Province to the alpine climate in the north, because of the latitudinal range of the Peninsula (which stretches from 33° 4'to 42° 2'N), provide diverse habit at conditions. Second, 65% of Korea' land area consists of mountain ranges that are connected to each other and about 4,400 islands and wetlands nationwide, but mostly in the south and western coastal regions. Therefore, the Peninsula holds geomorphologically diverse environments. Third, old or relict species from the Tertiary Period survived in the region because earthquakes and volcanic activities were rare, and major glaciers did not advance during the glacial events of the Quaternary Period. Finally, species diversity grew during the Pleistocene when Japanese islands and the Eurasian continent were connected, providing wildlife species with ecological corridors and refuges (Kong, 2007).

② Phytogeographic region

The phytogeographic regions of the Korean Peninsula have been classified by several researchers. Korea was divided into 5 regions by Nakai (1935), 3 regions by Udvardy (1975), 7 regions by Oh (1977), and Lee and Yim (1978) and Kong (1989) both divided Korea into 8 regions. In all cases, these divisions were based on the geographic distribution of plant species.

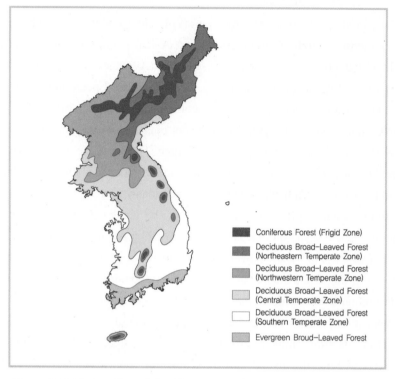

Figure 2.30 **Vegetation of the Korean peninsula** *(Source : Yim, 1970).*

2) Horizontal vegetation

Generally, vegetation zones have a horizontal transition by latitude and a vertical patterns by altitude. The distribution of vegetation on the Korean Peninsula is mainly-controlled by temperature, and it has latitudinal sequences in the north-south direction (Figure 2.30).

① Evergreen broad-leaved forest

Evergreen broad-leaved forests grow in a narrow zone between subtropical and temperate climates. They appear up to 35°N inland and 35.5°N in coastal areas, and they consist primarily of evergreen broad-leaved trees and deciduous broad-leaved trees on southern coasts and islands, where the annual mean temperature is 14C° higher. Currently, evergreen broad-leaved trees are being replaced by deciduous broadleaved trees, mixed forests, or human-induced secondary forests such as pine trees.

② Deciduous broad leaved forest

Deciduous broad-leaved forests are distributed between 35°N and 43°N, except in the alpine highlands. The annual mean temperature of the region ranges from 5C° to 14C°, and it is divided into south, central, and north zones depending on geographical location and plant composition.

The south zone is typically between 35° N and 36° N, but it moves up to 38° N in the east and 37.5° N in the west. The south zone consists primarily of simple forests of pine trees or Japanese black pine and mixed forests of oak, maple, and beech trees. The central zone stretches to 40° N in the east, 39° N in the west, and 38.5° N in the interior areas. Pine tree forests and mixed forests of oak and snowbell trees are common. The north zone extends from the northern part of the central zone to the China-Russia border, and is composed of linden, birch, oak, white pine, and fir trees.

③ Mixed forest

Mixed forests are a combination of conifers and deciduous trees. Natural forests in Korea are mostly mixed forests. The Hamgyeong, Taebaek, and Baekdu mountain ranges consist of 60% deciduous forests and 30% mixed forests. Mixed forests are advantageous for maintaining biodiversity and conservation, and they are resistant to wildfires, meteorological disasters, biological damage, and environmental pollution. Therefore, mixed forests are preferred to coniferous forests, which used to be commonly selected for reforestation.

④ Evergreen coniferous forest

Evergreen coniferous forests occur in the high alpine areas of the southern, central, and northern regions, where the annual mean temperature is below 5C° and the mean temperature of January is as low as -12C°. However, original coniferous forests were replaced by deciduous broad-leaved forests of birch, poplar, and elm trees or by mixed forests due to excessive development and frequent wild fires. Pine trees are a common conifer distributed in the plains and mountainous areas.

3) Vertical vegetation

The vertical distribution of plants on the Korean Peninsula is characterized by deciduous broad-leaved forests, evergreen coniferous forests, mixed forests, coniferous forests, shrubland, and grasses from the lower slopes to the alpine areas (Figure 2.31). It is expected that snowline and tree limit also existed during glacial events of the Pleistocene.

The forest limit or timberline occurs at the top of high mountains, and commercially valuable trees do not grow above this limit. The forest limit commonly exists where air

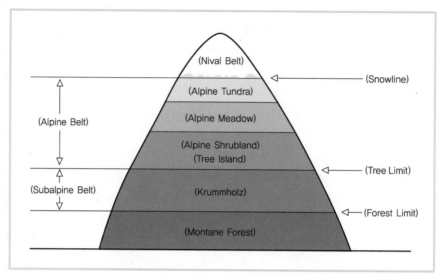

Figure 2.31 **Schematic diagram of forest ecotypes at various elevations**
(Source : Kong, 2002)

temperature is low, humidity is low, or soil and geomorphological conditions are poor.

In mountainous areas above the forest limit, where the growing season is short, habitat conditions are poor, and gusty winds are dominant, wind-shaped or flagshaped trees are observed. If growth conditions are extremely harsh, trees taller than 3 meters cannot grow above the tree limit. Small trees are scattered but occasionally are gathered like an island (called a tree island), and malformation of trees (krummholz) is also found near the forest limit.

Above the upper forest limit, shrubs and cassava trees create an alpine shrubland. At higher elevations, alpine meadows are formed by grass and for b species. The alpine tundra exists above the alpine meadows, and no woody plants are found in the tundra zone. An alpine belt is defined as the zone from the forest limit to the snow line.

4) Vegetation history

The oldest fossil vascular plant species growing on the Korean Peninsula were of the genus Neuropteris from the Carboniferous Period of the Palaeozoic Era. Coniferous trees, such as Elatocladus, Ullmannia, and Walchia, appeared during the Permian Period of the Palaeozoic Era, but they became extinct. Conifers or Pinaceae dominated from the Permian Period to the Jurassic Period of the Mesozoic Era, but they were reduced to 62% dominance throughout the Cretaceous Period of the Mesozoic Era.

Conifers were extensively replaced by dicotyledon species in the Cenozoic Era.

Particularly, dicotyledon plants were the dominant species during the Oligocene Epoch, and they comprised 65-81% of all plants during the Miocene Epoch. Evergreen broad-leaved trees, such as Myrica, Ficus, and Hedera, flourished above 37.5° N during the Oligocene. They moved north as much as 4° compared to the current distribution of the species, indicating that the climate of the Oligocene was much warmer than present. In the early-to-mid part of the Miocene, subtropical evergreen broad-leaved forests moved north as far as 42° N, and it is believed that the Miocene was one of the warmest times and significantly contributed to the formation of the current vegetation on earth.

Pinaceae, such as Taxus, Abies, and Thuja, became dominant during the mid Pleistocene because they were adapted to colder climates, but cold-loving northern conifers, including Pinus (haploxylon), Picea, Abies, and Larix, declined as the climate warmed. Dicotyledon plants dominated (50%-81% dominance) in the Pleistocene, and they continued to increase through the Holocene Epoch (91%). Dicotyledon plants were the dominant vegetation from the Oligocene to the Holocene on the Korean Peninsula. According to fossil records, the rate of plant extinction rapidly decreased for the period from the Oligocene to the Holocene : 17% of plant species became extinct during the Oligocene, 32%-44% became extinct during the Miocene, 16% became extinct during the Pleistocene (16%), and 6% became extinct during the Holocene. This finding indicates that climate change influenced the growths of plants, but it was not an abrupt environmental change that caused mass extinctions of plant species.

Conifers on the Korean Peninsula became prosperous during the Permian. Older genera such as Pinus, Abies, and Juniperus have shown more evolution and have wider geographic distribution patterns. Broad-leaved trees have continued to appear since the Cretaceous Period. However, tree species that require special ecological conditions, such as evergreen broad-leaved trees, have restricted distributions due to paleoclimatic and environmental changes of the Korean Peninsula.

ECOSYSTEMS

2.3.1 Fauna, Flora, and Forests

1) Current status of fauna and flora

The land area of Republic of Korea or South Korea, 99,000 square kilometers, consists of forests (65.7%), agricultural lands (21.9%), and others (10.0%). Significant amounts of forest (0.1%), agricultural land (0.9%), and wetland (1.6%) disappear each year as the demands of

Table 2.6 **Animals and plants in Korea**

Classification			Number of species
Animals (18,117 species)	vertebrates (1,528 species)	Mammals	123
		Birds	457
		Reptiles	25
		Amphibians	18
		Fishes	905
	invertebrates I (3,564 species)		3,564
	invertebrates II (13,025 species)	Insects	11,853
		Arachnids	1,172
Plants (8,271 species)	Higher plants (4,662 species)	Monocotyledons	842
		Dicotyledons	2,815
		Ferns, Gymnosperms	314
		Bryophytes	691
	Lower plants		3,609
Other (3,528 species)	Fungus		1,625
	Protozoan		736
	Prokaryote		1,167
Total	The total number of species of animals and plants is 26,388. If fungus, protozoan, and prokaryote species are included, it rises to 29,916 species.		

[Source : http://nre.me.go.kr]

urban development rapidly increase. The total number of animal and plant species is 26,388, including 1,528 vertebrate (842 mammal, 457 bird, 25 reptile, 18 amphibian, and 905 fish species) and 4,662 vascular plant species (832 monocotyledon, 2815 dicotyledon, and 314 gymnosperm and pteridophyte species) (Table 2.6).

Korea has 2,322 endemic animal and plant species, but biological diversity is declining due to land development, anthropogenic disturbances, and degradation of animal and plant habitats. The lack of facilities and personnel to conserve and systematically manage wildlife species makes it difficult to protect biodiversity.

2) Endangered wildlife

The first-grade (or grade I) endangered wildlife species are defined as those animal or plant species that are likely to become extinct because their populations have been declining significantly due to natural or human-induced threats. The second-grade (or grade II) endangered wildlife species include those species that experience significant population declines due to natural or human-induced threats and may become extinct in the near future unless current threats are reduced or removed.

Twelve species of mammals, 13 species of birds, 1 species of reptiles, 6 fishes, 5 insects, and 8 terrestrial plant species belong to the grade I endangered wildlife species. Examples include Naemorhedus caudatus Milne-Edwards or long-tailed goral (goat) (Figure 2.32), Platalea leucorodia Linnaeus or common spoonbill (Figure 2.33), Elaphe schrenckii Strauch or Korean rat snake, Pseudobagrus brevicorpus Bleeker or Korean stumpy bullhead (Figure 2.34), Callipogon relictus Semenow or long-horned beetle, and Diapensia lapponica var.

Figure 2.32 **Distribution of long-tailed goral (Naemorhedus caudatus)**
Figure 2.33 **Distribution of common spoonbill (Platalea leucorodia)**
Figure 2.34 **Distribution of Korean stumpy bullhead (Pseudobagrus brevicorpus)**
Figure 2.35 **Distribution of pincushion plant (Diapensia lapponica var. obovata)**
(Source : http://nre.me.go.kr).

obovata Schmidt or pincushion plant (Figure 2.35). The main factors responsible for the decline of these species include habitat loss, over-fishing or over-hunting, competition from invasive species, protective seizures of wildlife species for crops, and the effects of domesticated animals.

3) Harmful animals and plants

An exotic or non-native species refers to any species that came from a foreign country or distant environment in the same country. A naturalized species is a nonnative species that can survive and reproduce by itself after being introduced naturally or by humans to the habitat. Seventeen wildlife species have had adverse impacts on Korean ecosystems. These include 6 mammals (including Hydropotes inermis Swinhoe or water deer, Sus scrofa coreanus Heude or wild boar, Sciurus vulgaris coreae or Korean squirrel, Mogera wogura Temminck or Japanese mole, and rats) and 11 bird species (including Passer montanus L. or tree sparrow, Pica sericea Gould or Korean magpie, Garrulus glandarius L. or Eurasian jay, Microscelis amaurotis Temminck or brown-eared bulbul, Corvus corone orientalis L. or eastern carrion crow, Corvus monedula L. or jackdaw, Corvus frugilegus L. or rook, Phasianus colchicus karpowi L. or Korean ring-necked pheasant, and Streptopelia orientalis Latham or oriental turtle dove).

An invasive species is an exotic or non-native species now common even in preserved areas such as national parks. A significant number of exotic species are reported in protected areas, including the national parks of Byeonsan Bay (103 species), Mt. Jiri (75 species), Mt. Bukhan (70 species), Dadohaehaesang (64 species), Mt. Juwang (57 species), Mt. Wolchul (55 species), Mt. Worak (49 species), Mt. Gaya (45 species), Mt. Chiak (42 species), Taeanhaean (41 species), Mt. Songni (40 species), Mt. Gyeryong (38 species), Mt. Deogyu (38 species), Mt. Seorak (37 species), Hallyeohaesang (33 species), Mt. Odae (32 species), Mt. Sobaek (26 species), and Mt. Naejang (26 species). Invasive plant and animal species were introduced naturally or by humans from foreign countries and disturbed local ecosystems these species include all species of Trachemys scripta elegans Wied-Neuwied or red-eared slider, Rana catesbeiana Shaw or American bullfrog, Micropterus salmoides Lacepede or largemouth bass, Lepomis macrochirus Rafinesque or bluegill, Paspalum distichum L. or water finger-grass, Polyganum aviculare L. or common knotgrass, Solanum carolinense L or Carolina horsenettle, Ambrosia trifida L. or giant ragweed, Ambrosia artemisiifolia L. or common ragweed, and Ageratina altissima (L.) or white snakeroot.

The outflow of invaluable Korean natural resources, including animal and plant species, had maintained in 21th century. During the Japanese occupation period from 1910 to 1945 large number of biological resources have plundered to Japan. Extensive plant collecting activities under the auspices of a foreign governments or enterprises have continued by foreign scientists until 1980's, and outflow of more than 900 species have noticed. Reintroduction of improved breeds from abroad, such as beans, lilac, lily and others into Korea are reported.

4) Forests

The forested area of Korea decreased from 6,447,936 hectares in 1996 to 6,389,393 hectares in 2006. As of 2006, it consists of coniferous forests (42.2%), deciduous forests (26.0%), and mixed forests (29.3%). On average, each year 7,554 hectares of forests have been destroyed. These forests have been converted to roads (1,638 hectares), residential areas (1,140 hectares), industrial areas (948 hectares), cropland (931 hectares), golf courses (267 hectares), and grassland (249 hectares) each year. The list of deforested areas by province is headed by Gyeonggi-*do* (1,725.6 hectares), Jeollanam-*do* (782.6 hectares), Gangwon-*do* (776.6 hectares), Gyeongsangbuk-*do* (747.8 hectares), Chungcheongnam-*do* (709 hectares), Jeollabuk-*do* (671.8 hectares), Chungcheongbuk-*do* (550 hectares), and finally, Gyeongsangnam-*do* (451.6 hectares) (Yonhap News, 2003).

5) Global warming and ecosystems

As global warming becomes more severe, arctic and alpine plants that are distributed over alpine and subalpine regions are of great concern. These plants are relict species that survived on the Korean Peninsula, which was their primary refuge during the glacial events of the Pleistocene. As the climate became warmer about 10,000 years ago, they were redistributed on mountain summit areas of northern, central, and southern parts of the nation and Mt. Halla (Jeju Special Self-Governing Province). As temperature increases, temperate plants are moving to higher elevations, and arctic and alpine plants on mountain summit areas are threatened with extinction from competition by these invading plants. Numerous endemic species that are adapted to the alpine climates of Korea may not be able to resist temperature increases and will decline.

2.3.2 Ecological Potentials

1) Mountain areas

There are 79 high mountains taller than 2,000 meters at latitudes above 40° N in the Korean Peninsula, and they occupy 0.4% of the total national land area. In South and North Koreas, the number of mountains that are taller than 1,500 meters (but shorter than 2,000 meters) is 264, and their land area is 4.0% of the Korean land area. There are 788 mountain peaks between 1,000-1,500 meters in elevation, and the area of these mountains is 10% of the total land area. Smaller mountains (20% of the total land area) have their peaks between 500-1,000 meters, and other mountains (40% of the total land area) have their peaks between 200-500 meters in elevation. The current value of natural forests on these mountains amounts to USD 50 billion a year, including storage of water resources, improvement of water quality, absorption of carbon dioxide, generation of oxygen, preservation of natural ecosystems and biodiversity, support of human health, improvement of quality of life, and prevention of soil loss and landslides.

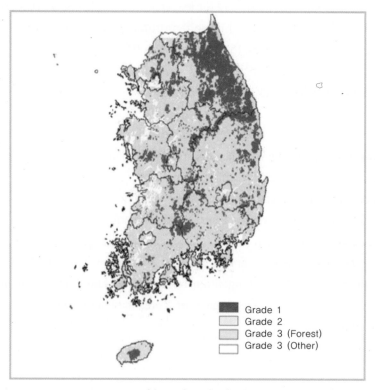

Figure 2.36 **Map of ecological status**
(Source : Ministry of Environment, 2005 ; National Geographic Information Institute, 2007).

2) Great Baekdu mountain range

Stretching from the Hyangno Peak in Goseong-*gun*, Gangwon-*do* to the Cheonwang Peak of Mt. Jiri, the Great Baekdu Mountain Range (Baekdudaegan) of R.O.K. or South Korea, the backbone of the Korean Peninsula, is 680 kilometers long and covers 3,567 square kilometers, which is close to the total land area of the national parks. The southern part of the Great Baekdu Mountain Range is currently being managed with the consideration of its ecological, historical, cultural, and geographical values and characteristics. This region consists primarily of the first- and second-grade areas (90%) in National Ecological Nature Status (Figure 2.36) and most of these areas (85%) are preserved by law as national or state parks and protected forests due to their ecological value. The conservation area is divided into three main zones. The core preservation zone is highly protected and preserved, and includes the main ridge of the mountain range. In the buffered area, which is adjacent to the core zone, development plans are restricted. The third zone is the transitional zone, where sustainable conservation and land use are selectively allowed (http:// www.konetic.or.kr).

3) Rivers

Among the six largest rivers of Korea, river systems which flow into the Yellow Sea or the Yellow Sea are strongly influenced by the tides because of the very large tidal range of the Yellow Sea. These rivers are the Amnok River, Han River, Daedong River, and Geum River. On the other hand, the Duman River and Nakdong River, which flow into the East Sea and South Sea, respectively, experience little tidal influence because of the small tidal range of those seas. Alluvial landforms are typical in the downstream areas of a river, and floodplains, which consist of natural levees and backswamps, are the most common example. Backswamps can be transformed into fertile cropland if they are protected by artificial levees and drainage systems are established. Traditionally, floodplains were commonly used as agricultural lands or built-up areas of a city due to a lack of plains in Korea. Most plains areas along a large river are coastal terraces and these areas are used as cropland in mountainous regions (National Geographic Information Institute, 2007).

4) Estuaries

An estuary is a transitional system where the river mouth flows into the sea and fresh water mixes with tidal sea water. This dynamic ecosystem is well known not only for its ecological value as a natural habitat, and a nursing and spawning place, but also for its economic value, protection from natural hazards like hurricanes, and aesthetic functions. However, Korean estuaries have been severely disturbed by embankment constructions and reclamation. Public attention is being paid to the ecological value of and conservation strategies for this sensitive environment.

Korea has at least 329 river mouths of various sizes. Thirteen major rivers (including the Han River, Nakdong River, Geum River, Yeongsan River, and Seomjin River, and 4 state-class major rivers) and 312 local rivers drain directly into the river mouths. The wetland area of these estuaries is 984.7 square kilometers, which is 41.2% of the total coastal wetland area in the nation.

5) Coastlines

The total length of the coastlines of Korea is 11,352 kilometers. Rock and sand coasts are 903 kilometers and 567 kilometers long, respectively, and human-made coastlines created by reclamation are 2,104 kilometers long, or 18.5% of the total coastline length. The East Coast stretches from the mouth of the Duman River to Song Island, Busan, with a direct distance of 809 kilometers, or actual distance of 1,727 kilometers, and its coastlines are monotonous. The South Coast is adjacent to mountainous regions and has significantly complex coastlines, which are known as rias coasts. The West Coast runs from the mouth of the Amnok River to Haenam, Jeollanam-*do*, and its direct and actual distances are 650 kilometers and 4,719 kilometers, respectively, with the characteristics of a rias coast.

6) Sand dunes

Sand dunes are sand hills that are created by the movement of sand. There are 131 locations with sand dunes in the nation, including Chungcheongnam-*do* (42 locations, 31%), Gangwon-*do* (32 locations, 24%), and Jeollanam-*do* (21 locations, 16%), where supplies of sand are sufficient and prevailing winds exist. There are 60 sand dunes on the West Coast, and major ones are Sindu, Mallipo, Woncheong, and Myongsasimni. Large sand dunes are also found on the East Coast, such as Osan and Dongho, and these sand dunes make up about 32% of all sand dunes in the nation. On the South Coast (including Jeju Special Self-Governing Province), 30 sand dunes (22.5%) exist, and these comprise a smaller portion compared to the other coastal areas. Sand dunes store coastal sand and ground water, are a natural levee system, and provide a habit at likely to hold rare species of plants and animals (Figure 2.37).

Figure 2.37 **Distribution and size of coastal dunes**
(Source : Ministry of Environment, 2005).

7) Lagoons

Lagoons are brackish water lakes that form when a river valley is submerged after a sea level rising and the mouth of that river valley is closed by the deposition of sand materials. Eleven lagoons on the East Coast are naturally created, and they are in a transitional zone between the land and ocean characterized by a brackish environment, where freshwater and sea waters are mixed. The three largest lagoons, in order by size, are Hwajinpo, Cheongchoho, and Yeoungnangho. By the size of drainage basin, Gyeongpoho has the largest drainage basin, followed by Cheongchoho and Hwajinpo. The water quality of these lagoons is poor, except for Cheongchoho and Songjiho, because the conservation plans for the lagoons are not properly developed.

8) Tidal flats

A tidal flat is a coastal area of low and high tides between coastlines, and is classified as a coastal wetland under the wetland conservation law. A tidal flat is a transitional area, where species from both land and ocean ecosystems coexist, and its biodiversity is so high that in

Korea 200 species of fish, 250 species of crustacean, 200 species of mollusk, 100 species of clam worm, and 120 species of seabird live on the tidal flats of the southwestern coasts. Clams, clam worms, microorganisms, and wetland plants filter out various pollutants from the land. A tidal flat is also a valuable tourism resource, providing areas for outdoor leisure and education. It also absorbs water during a flood and protects inland areas from typhoons and tidal waves by counteracting the energy these phenomena carry.

The total area of tidal flats is 2,393 square kilometers, and 80% of tidal flats are distributed on the western coast, including Jeollanam-*do* (1,054 square kilometers), Gyeonggi-*do* (839 square kilometers), Chungcheongnam-*do* (304 square kilometers), Jeollabuk-*do* (114 square kilometers), and Gyeongsangnam-*do* (83 square kilometers) (Ministry of Maritime Affairs and Fisheries, 1999). The tidal range of the western coast is between 4-9 meters, and it is one of the five major tidal flat areas in the world along with the coasts of the North Sea, Eastern Canada, Georgia in the United States, and the Amazon River. However, 25% of the tidal flats, or 810 square kilometers, was reclaimed between 1987 and 1998.

9) Islands

The total number of islands is 3,170 in 78 cities, provinces, and counties of Korea. Of these, 2,498 islands (78.8%) are on the south coast, 589 (18.6%) islands are on the west coast, and 83 islands (3.6%) are on the east coast. There are 491 inhabited islands and 2,679 islands are uninhabited. Jeju Special Self-Governing Province is the largest island in the nation (1,848.3 square kilometers), followed by Geoje Island (387.8 square kilometers), Jin Island (361.9 square kilometers), Ganghwa Island (302.4 square kilometers), Namhae Island (301.6 square kilometers), Anmyeon Island (113.5 square kilometers), Wan Island (90.2 square kilometers), Ulleung Island (73.2 square kilometers), Dolsan Island (70.6 square kilometers), and Geogeum Island (62.1 square kilometers). A recent study by the National Geographic Information Institute (NGII), however, claims that there are 4,400 islands throughout the nation (National Geographic Information Institute, 2007). The NGII discovered many islands previously unidentified using high resolution satellite and aerial images.

Uninhabited islands are rarely disturbed by humans, and their ecosystems remain healthy and stable. Unlike inland ecosystems, these islands maintain a number of regional endemic species and subtropical plant populations, which are important floristically. In addition, they provide critical habitat and sanctuaries for endangered or rare wildlife species, including endangered bird species. Therefore, their unique natural landscapes and resources are worth protecting.

2.3.3 Inventories, Maintenance and Conservation of Natural Resources

1) Inventories of natural resources

The ecological status of Korea, including the characteristics of landforms and landscapes, the classification and distribution of animals and plants, disturbances of vegetation, and values of conservation, is surveyed by the governmental inventory of natural resources (http://ecosystem.nier.go.kr). Environmental inventories consist of ecosystem surveys, such as the inland wetland survey, natural cave survey, uninhabited island survey, coastal dune survey, river basin survey, endangered and protected species survey, and special species (e.g., rare species) survey.

Maps of the current vegetation, natural green areas, and fauna were prepared by the first national environmental inventory project (1986-1990). During the second inventory project (1997-2003), general environmental geographic information systems and maps of eco-natural resources were produced and biological specimens were collected. Environmental inventories are used as a general database for various land evaluations, such as environmental impact assessment and land use transformation. They are also used as environmental conservation criteria when national land use systems need to be changed.

2) Eco-natural resource map

Environmental inventories that were completed in 2007 are summarized in the eco-natural resource map (794 pieces in 1:25,000 scale topographic maps). It shows that 7.5% of the total land area is comprised of first-grade endangered wildlife species areas, 39.2% is comprised of second-grade areas, 44.7% is comprised of third-grade areas, and 8.6% is classified as other protected area. The first-grade areas are designated as preservation areas under land use planning, and their natural value has to be maintained under protective conservation plans by law for any circumstances.

3) Natural reserves

① Status of natural reserves

Environmental reserve areas of Korea include 30 ecosystem reserves (294.5 square kilometers), 16 wetland reserves (247.3 square kilometers), 153 designated islands (10.0

square kilometers), and 76 natural parks (7,805 square kilometers). Natural parks consist of 20 national parks, 23 province parks, 33 county parks (441.4 square kilometers), and 544 wildlife reserves (1,397 square kilometers).

Wetlands play an important role as the feeding grounds of migratory birds and they are preserved under the Ramsar Convention. Korea was registered as a member of Ramsar in 1997, and Yong Swamp in Inje-*gun*, Gangwon-*do*, Upo Swamp in Changnyeong-*gun*, Gyeongsangnam-*do*, and Jangdo Swamp in Sinan-*gun*, Jeollanam-*do* are registered as Ramsar wetlands. The number of bird species that inhabit Korean wetlands is 337, with 170 species that inhabit tidal flats or coastal areas and 167 species in rivers or lakes.

Fifty-seven bird species are year-long residents in Korea, and 283 (over 70%) of all bird species are migratory birds. Migratory birds are grouped into four different types, including winter migratory, summer migratory, passage, and vagrant birds. Winter migratory birds (116 species) reproduce in northern areas, such as Manchu and Siberia, and visit Korea when it becomes cold. Summer migratory birds (64 species) come from the Philippines or Australia and visit Korea during the summer. Passage birds (103 species) stay in Korea for about a week on their way from Siberia to Australia or New Zealand. Finally, vagrant birds happen to come to Korea accidentally when they get lost.

The national parks consist of 16 mountain parks, 3 coastal parks, and 1 historical park, and their area amounts to 6,579 square kilometers (3,898 square kilometers in land and 2,680 square kilometers in water), or 6.6% of the total land area of the nation (http://ecosystem.nier.go.kr). There are 15,271 species that reside in national parks, including 7,334 insect, 3,559 plant, 1,265 benthic invertebrate, 1,170 higher fungus, 396 bird, 355 arachnid, 120 freshwater fish, and 64 mammal species.

② Ecosystem conservation areas

Ecosystem conservation areas are designated according to the following criteria : 1) areas classified as first-grade ecological areas, 2) pristine areas or areas with high biodiversity that deserve research or geomorphologically or geologically unique areas that need to be preserved for ecosystem stability and research, 3) important habitats of endangered or protected animal and plant species that need to be preserved, or 4) areas that are representative of various ecosystems. Special protective areas for wildlife animal and plant species, ecologically sensitive areas, and coastal ecosystem reserves are designated and maintained as specially protected reserves. Currently, 32 locations comprising 352.9 square kilometers are classified and managed as ecosystem conservation areas. These locations are administered by different governmental jurisdictions. Ten locations (242.7 square kilometers) are managed by the

Ministry of Environment, 4 locations (70.3 square kilometers) by the Ministry of Land, Transport, and Maritime Affairs, and 18 locations (39.84 square kilometers) by cities or provinces.

③ Conservation of ecological networks

There are 3 reasons for creating ecological networks. First, they connect ecologically high-rated areas to each other to secure ecological corridors, which make green areas ecologically healthy. Second, they transform ecosystem management strategies from individual habit protection to nationally structured conservation and management systems. Finally, they connect local ecosystems dynamically so that animal species can migrate from north to south on the Korean Peninsula.

Ecological networks consist of core areas, buffer areas, and corridors. Core areas are an ecologically important habit directly related to movement and reproduction of major animal and plant species. Buffer areas reduce the impacts of exterior threatening factors on core areas and corridors. Corridors connect core areas together. Among factors that threaten ecological networks are linear and areal factors. Linear factors are roads, railroads, access roads in forests, and electric transmission facilities. Areal factors include golf courses, ski resorts, residential development, and reclamation. These factors not only divide intact ecosystems but also jeopardize ecological functions, including species reproduction and ecological succession.

The Korean government designated the Great Baekdu Mountain Range, the DMZ, and island coasts as three core ecological axes. These ecological axes connect North and South Koreas, the east and west parts of the country, and terrestrial and oceanic ecosystems, respectively (Figure 2.38).

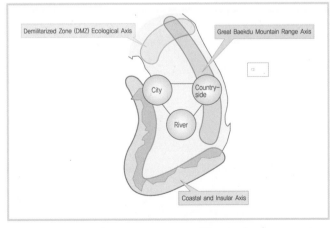

Figure 2.38 **Schematic diagram of ecological networks**
(Source : Ministry of Environment, 2002).

4) Environmental protection laws and government offices

Environmental protection laws and authorities vary depending on management areas and relevant legal jurisdictions. The Ministry of Environment, the Ministry of Culture, Sports, and Tourism, the Korea Forest Service, the Ministry of Land, Transport, and Marine Affairs, and the Ministry of Public Administration and Security are currently involved in environmental protection laws.

The Korean government designated environmental conservation areas (869 square kilometers of land and 2,203 square kilometers of ocean), natural ecosystem reserves (91.3 square kilometers), national, province, and county parks (7,714 square kilometers in total), and historic preservation areas (693.0 square kilometers) to protect the cultural values of the nation. In addition, hunting is prohibited in 507 bird sanctuaries (1,131 square kilometers), and development is restricted in 383 water resource conservation areas (1,202 square kilometers) to maintain high water quality.

Chapter 2.4.

NATURAL DISASTERS IN KOREA

CHAPTER 2

2.4.1 General Characteristics

Natural disasters include typhoons, floods, heavy rainfall events, strong winds, landslides, tsunami, heavy snowfalls, droughts, earthquakes, dust storms, and other disasters caused by natural phenomena (Article 2 of Counter-measures against Natural Disasters Act). Because of the abundant precipitation (about 1,200mm per year) and the hilly and mountainous terrain that covers more than 70 percent of Korea, streams flow rapidly. Therefore, most natural disasters in Korea are caused by hydrometeorological events such as heavy rainfall events and floods. The runoff often destabilizes the slopes, particularly those that have been devegetated, causing frequent landslides in addition to downstream floods. Such natural disasters are concentrated between June and September, when two-thirds of the average annual precipitation falls.

A total of 1,379 natural disaster events occurred during the 10-year period from 1997 to 2006. Of the 1,379 events, 555 were heavy rainfall events. During the same period, typhoons were responsible for 438 of the natural disasters, and heavy rainfall associated with typhoons caused 175 disaster events. These three types represented 84 percent of the natural disasters in South Korea. On the whole, relatively few areas are hit by heavy snowfall events compared to heavy rainfall events and typhoons. When considering property losses, typhoons were the most destructive disasters, with heavy rainfall events following (Figure 2.39).

Table 2.7 lists the top twenty natural disaster events based on property loss in South Korea. Typhoon 'Rusa' in 2002 and 'Maemi' in 2003 made landfall along the eastern and southern coasts of Korea, causing 246 deaths and property losses of 6.0 trillion won for 'Rusa' and 131 deaths and 4.8 trillion won for 'Maemi'. Of the 20 events, 19 occurred after 1980, 14 after 1990, and 7 after 2000. Other than two heavy snowfall events, all natural disasters were

93

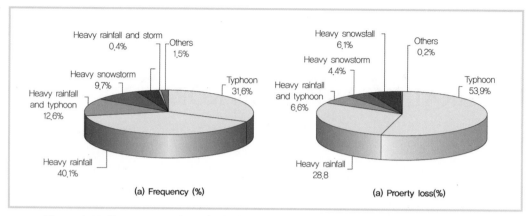

Figure 2.39 **Frequency of natural disasters and property damage by type, as a percentage of the total from all natural disasters, 1997-2006**

(Source : National Emergency Management Agency, 2007, Annual Report of Natural Disasters)

Table 2.7 **The twenty most destructive natural disasters, ranked by based on property loss in South Korea** *(Units : 1,000,000 won, people)*

Year	Type	Period	Property loss	Deaths
2002	Typhoon (RUSA)	08/30 - 09/01	5,988,605	246
2003	Typhoon (MAEMI)	09/12 - 09/13	4,805,472	131
2006	Heavy rainfall and Typhoon (EWINIAR)	07/09 - 07/29	1,883,389	62
1998	Heavy rainfall	07/31 - 08/18	1,438,542	324
1999	Heavy rainfall and Typhoon (OLGA)	07/23 - 08/04	1,235,300	67
2002	Heavy rainfall	08/04 - 08/11	1,068,068	23
1990	Heavy rainfall	09/09 - 09/12	843,314	163
2004	Heavy snowfall	03/04 - 03/05	722,240	0
1987	Typhoon (THELMA)	07/15 - 07/16	688,455	345
1995	Heavy rainfall and Typhoon (JANIS)	08/19 - 08/30	632,830	65
1987	Heavy rainfall	07/21 - 07/23	579,724	167
1996	Heavy rainfall	07/26 - 07/28	574,354	29
2005	Heavy snowfall	12/03 - 12/24	546,669	14
1989	Heavy rainfall	07/25 - 07/27	496,879	128
1991	Typhoon (GLADYS)	08/22 - 08/26	364,642	103
2005	Heavy rainfall	08/02 - 08/11	348,156	19
1998	Typhoon (YANNI)	09/29 - 10/01	316,885	57
2000	Heavy rainfall and Typhoon (PRAPIROON)	08/23 - 09/01	290,865	28
1984	Heavy rainfall	08/31 - 09/04	288,689	189
1959	Typhoon (SARAH)	09/15 - 09/17	283,395	849

(Source : National Emergency Management Agency, 2007, Annual Report of Natural Disasters)

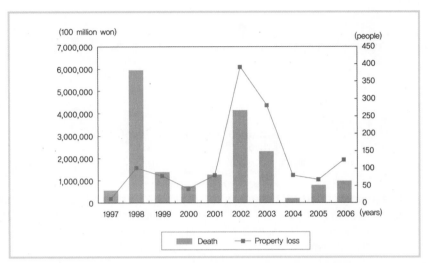

Figure 2.40 **Annual property loss and number of deaths caused by natural disasters, 1997-2006**

(Source : National Emergency Management Agency, 2007, Annual Report of Natural Disasters)

caused by heavy rainfall events and/or typhoons.

The number of deaths and amount of property loss are highly variable through time. For the 1997-2006 period, 1189 natural disaster-related deaths and total property damage of 19.6 trillion won occurred. Fortunately, the number of deaths caused by natural disasters has tended to decrease, but the property loss increases. The largest number of people killed by natural disasters in recent memory occurred in 1998, with 323 deaths caused by rainstorms, 57 by typhoons, and 1 by other natural disasters. Also notable was 2002, when 246 deaths were caused by typhoons (largely by 'Rusa') and 23 were caused by rainstorm. The smallest number of natural disaster-related deaths in recent years occurred in 2004, when nine people were killed by typhoon and five by rainstorms. The leading cause of property loss was typhoons in 2002 and 2003, heavy rainfall and typhoons in 2006, rainstorms in 1998, rainstorm/typhoon combinations in 1999, heavy snowfalls in 2004, and windstorms/snowfalls in 2001. Unfortunately, most natural disasters are unpredictable and enormous damage occurs repeatedly (Figure 2.40).

2.4.2 Types of Natural Disasters by Region

The most frequent events occurred in Gyeongsangbuk-*do* with 221 events over the 1997-2006 period, followed by Gyeongsangnam-*do* with 195 events and Gangwon-*do* with 172

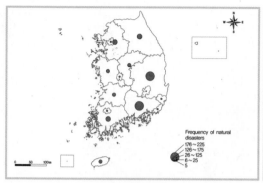

Figure 2.41 **Frequency of natural disasters by _si-do_, 1997-2006**
[Source : National Emergency Management Agency, 2007, Annual Report of Natural Disasters]

Figure 2.42 **Property loss due to natural disasters by _si-do_, 1997-2006**
[Source : National Emergency Management Agency, 2007, Annual Report of Natural Disasters]

events (Figure 2.41). The higher frequencies of natural disasters in Gyeongsangbuk-_do_ and Gyeongsangnam-_do_ are caused by heavy rainfalls and landfall of typhoons. Property loss was highest in Gangwon-_do_ (5.6 trillion won) followed by Gyeongsangnam-_do_ (3.7 trillion won) and Gyeongsangbuk-_do_ (2.6 trillion won). Gangwon-_do_ is frequently exposed to landfall of typhoons such as 'Rusa' in 2002, which was the most destructive typhoon recorded in South Korea (Figure 2.42).

1) Heavy rainfall

Natural disasters can be exacerbated by human activities. Concrete pavement increases surface runoff at the expense of infiltration and natural drainage. Large-scale deforestation also increases the proportion of precipitation that goes into surface runoff. A general lack of public awareness of the impacts of development on the flood and landslide hazard only increases the damage done by natural disasters. Some recent examples of such disasters were the devastating heavy rainfall events in Gyeonggi-_do_ in July '1996' and in Seoul and Gyeonggi-_do_ in August 1998.

During the 1997-2006 period, heavy rainfall events caused 1,041 deaths and 5.6 trillion won of property loss in South Korea. The largest number of deaths occurred in Gyeonggi-_do_ with 426 followed by 202 in Seoul (Figure 2.43). Together these comprise more than 50 percent of total deaths by heavy rainfall events. Property loss was greatest in Gangwon-_do_ (1.9 trillion won) followed by Gyeonggi-_do_ (Figure 2.44).

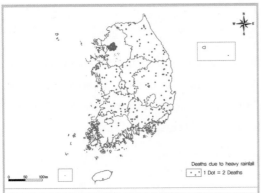

Figure 2.43 **Deaths due to heavy rainfall by** *si-do*, 1997-2006

(Source : National Emergency Management Agency, 2007, Annual Report of Natural Disasters)

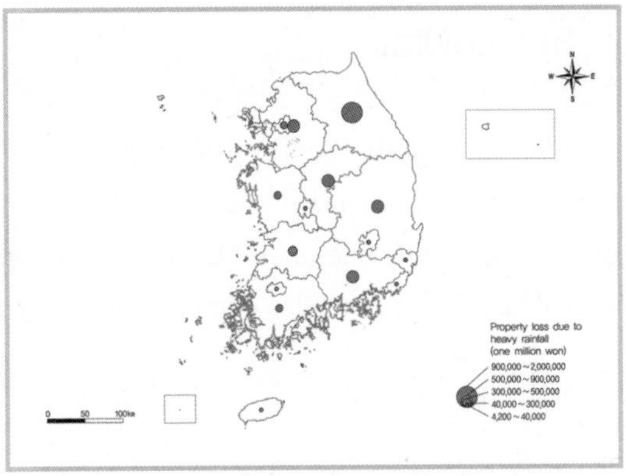

Figure 2.44 **Property loss due to heavy rainfall by** *si-do*, 1997-2006

(Source : National Emergency Management Agency, 2007, Annual Report of Natural Disasters)

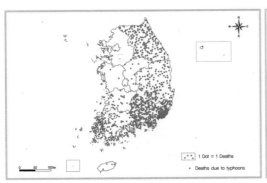

Figure 2.45 **Deaths due to typhoons by** *si-do*, 1997-2006

(Source : National Emergency Management Agency, 2007, Annual Report of Natural Disasters)

Figure 2.46 **Property loss due to typhoons by** *si-do*, 1997-2006

(Source : National Emergency Management Agency, 2007, Annual Report of Natural Disasters)

2) Typhoons

For the 1997-2006 period, 958 total deaths in South Korea were attributed to typhoons. The greatest number of deaths occurred in Gyeongsangnam-*do* with 298 people, followed by Gangwon-*do* (204), Busan (148), and Gyeongsangbuk-*do* (140) (Figure 2.45). These *si-do* are frequently in the path of northeastward-moving typhoons. Total property loss caused by typhoons was 10 trillion won, with the greatest in Gangwon-*do* (3.3 trillion won) followed by Gyeongsangnam-*do* (2.8 trillion won) and Gyeongsangbuk-*do* (1.8 trillion won) (Figure 2.46).

3) Snowfall

While snowfall poses occasional problems, heavy snow events occur only sporadically and are less destructive than other meteorologically-driven hazards described above. However, two recent events, one in 2004 and the other in 2005, each caused property loss of 1.2 trillion won. The greatest damages occurred in Chungcheongnam-*do* (Figure 2.47).

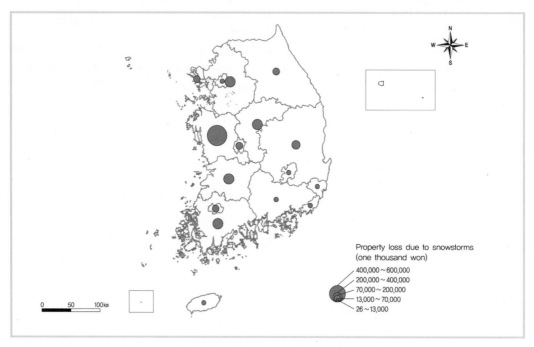

Figure 2.47 **Property loss due to snowstorms and heavy snowfall by** *si-do*, **1997-2006**
(Source : National Emergency Management Agency, 2007, Annual Report of Natural Disasters)

☐ Chapter 3.
POPULATION

Chapter 3.1.

POPULATION GROWTH AND DISTRIBUTION

3.1.1 Population Growth

Korea has experienced a dramatic demographic change over the last 40 years since the government launched an intensive birth control campaign via family planning while simultaneously kicking off an economic development plan in 1962. The annual population growth rate of 3% in the early 1960s fell to 1.5% in the 1ˢᵗ half of the 1980s, finally stabilizing below 1% in the 1990s. Such a rapid downward trend of annual growth rate was due not only to the strong population policy implementation, but also to the economic development followed by an increase in income and modernized lifestyle, which in turn have led to significant changes in cultural values, including favoring fewer children and the nuclear family. This slow-down in population growth became more evident after the mid 1990s because the birth rate rapidly dropped as the marital age went up. The rise in the marital age was a consequence of an increased ratio of women participating in the economy in Korean society as a result of improved educational achievement. For the period of 2000-2005, the annual population growth rate was 0.5%, which portends the issue of sluggish population growth in the near future in Korea. Figure 3.1 shows the population trend in Korea for the last 50 years. The population grew almost 2.2 times for the period of 1955-2005, reaching approximately 47.3 million in 2005. Of the global population in 2005 (6.465 billion), the Korean population made up 0.73%, making it the 26th most populous country in the world.

Taking a close look at the nationwide change in population based on the average annual growth rate for each metropolitan city and province level, it should be noted that a wide gap exists between the Seoul National Capital Area (the capital region or Sudogwon) and the rest

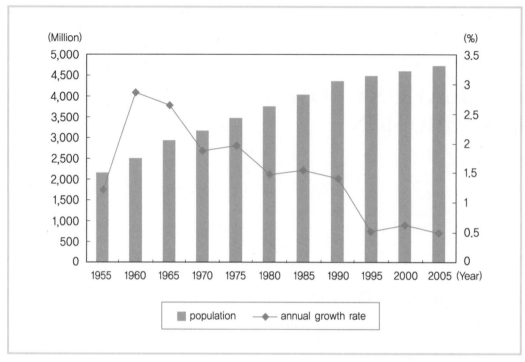

Figure 3.1 **Changes in population and annual growth rate, 1955-2005**
[Source : Statistics Korea, Population and Housing Census [each year]].

of the nation over the last 20 years (Table 3.1). The annual growth rate in the capital region continually has surpassed the national average growth rate, accelerating the population concentration in the capital region. However, within the capital region the annual growth rate in Seoul was negative after the mid 1990s, indicating an absolute population decrease. Thus, population growth in the capital region is mainly taking place in Incheon and Gyeonggi-*do*. Traffic congestion was getting worse and the cost of housing continued to rise until enough people decided to move out of Seoul and into new satellite cities in Gyeonggi-*do* ; as a result, in 1995, for the first time in history, the population of Seoul began to decline. Meanwhile, the flow of people into Gyeonggi-*do* increased so that during 1990-95 its average growth rate nearly hit the 5% mark, where the rest of the country showed only a modest 0.55%.

A comparison of the annual population growth rate maps at the *si* (city), *gun* (county) and *gu* (district/ward) levels for the last 20 years shows a very contrasting pattern of population growth. During 1985-1990, regions with increased population were located in the southwestern part of Gyeonggi-*do* and the 6 metropolitan cities of Seoul, Busan, Daegu, Incheon, Gwangju and Daejeon. In contrast, the regions with more than a 2% annual population decrease rate were located throughout most of the *guns* in Korea. In the case of the

Table 3.1 **Annual population growth rate by metropolitan city and *do* (province), 1985-2005**

Areal Units	Annual Population Growth Rate				
	1985 - 1990	1990 - 1995	1995 - 2000	2000 - 2005	1985 - 2005
Nation	1.4	0.5	0.7	0.5	0.8
The Capital Region*	3.3	1.7	1.1	1.3	1.8
Metropolitan Cities**	2.0	0.5	0.0	0.0	0.7
Seoul	1.9	- 0.7	- 0.7	- 0.2	0.1
Busan	1.5	- 0.2	- 0.8	- 0.8	- 0.1
Daegu	1.9	1.1	0.3	- 0.1	0.8
Incheon	4.9	3.7	1.4	0.4	2.6
Gwangju	1.8	2.0	1.5	0.9	1.5
Daejeon	2.2	3.9	1.5	1.1	2.1
Ulsan	3.8	3.7	1.0	0.7	2.3
Gyeonggi - *do*	5.3	4.8	3.3	3.0	4.1
Gangwon - *do*	- 1.7	- 1.5	0.3	- 0.3	- 0.8
Chungcheongbuk - *do*	0.0	0.1	1.0	- 0.1	0.2
Chungcheongnam - *do*	- 0.4	- 2.6	0.9	0.5	- 0.4
Jeollabuk - *do*	- 1.2	- 1.7	- 0.1	- 1.2	- 1.0
Jeollanam - *do*	- 1.5	- 3.8	- 0.7	- 1.8	- 2.0
Gyeongsangbuk - *do*	- 1.1	- 0.7	0.4	- 0.9	- 0.6
Gyeongsangnam - *do*	0.2	0.5	0.7	0.5	0.5
Jeju special self-governing province	1.0	- 0.4	0.3	0.7	0.4

* The Capital Region consists of Seoul, Incheon and Gyeonggi-do.
** Metropolitan cities include Seoul, Busan, Daegu, Incheon, Gwangju, Daejeon and Ulsan.
(Source : Statistics Korea, Population and Housing Census [each year]).

CHAPTER 3

population growth rate between 1995 and 2000, the annual growth rate of Seoul and Busan was negative, indicating a population decrease, whereas the population in the areas surrounding the 2 cities has shown a relatively high growth rate. In particular, there was a high population increase in the new satellite cities such as Goyang, Seongnam, Guri, Anyang, Uijeongbu, Siheung, Yongin, Namyangju and Gimpo in the capital region. As for the non-the capital region, Gyeongsan and Gimhae, which are adjacent to Daegu and Busan, showed high growth rates. As for the population growth rate during 2000-2005 in 234 regions including cities, *guns* and *gus*, 82 regions had a positive annual growth rate but 152 regions had a negative rate. Except for Gimhae, all the cities and *guns* with over 5% annual growth rates were in the capital region. The population in Yongin has increased at the fastest rate (12.3%) across the whole country and Gwangju, Hwaseong, Yangju, Paju, Gimpo, Osan and Siheung showed high annual growth rates. Moreover, the population decrease has slowed down in the regions close to the capital region, such as Gangwon-*do*, southern Chungcheongnam-*do* and some areas in Chungcheongbuk-*do*, where as the population decrease has escalated in both Jeollanam-*do* and Jeollabuk-*do* and most parts of Gyeongsangnam-*do* and Gyeongsangbuk-*do*.

As for the proportion of the population growth in the capital region to the total population growth of the whole country every 5 years, it was 93.4% between 1985 and 1990, but increased significantly to 133.7% between 1990 and 1995. This implies that the population increase in the capital region was 33.7% larger than the nationwide figure, meaning population decrease to the same extent took place in the non-the capital region (Table 3.2). The exodus of the non-the capital region population to the capital region in Korea that began to accelerate in the early 1990s resulted in significant regional discrepancies with respect to gain and loss of population. However, this proportion dropped to 76.3% from 1995 to 2000. But, the proportion increased to 123.6% during the period of 2000-2005, showing a re-intensification of the population concentration in the capital region. This provides evidence of a population inflow towards Gyeonggi-*do* from Seoul and the non-the capital region.

As described above, the population change in Korea for the last 20 years can be characterized by the accelerated concentration of population in the capital region, despite the significant population decrease in Seoul in the 1990s. By 1990 Seoul's share of the national population was 24.4%, showing that 1 out of every 4 Koreans resides in Seoul. However, in 1995 its share dipped slightly to 22.9% and down to 20.8% in 2005. The proportion of population in the capital region increased from 39.1% in 1985 to 48.2% in 2005, indicating that nearly a half of the nation's total population resides in the capital region (Table 3.3).

Table 3.2 **Population growth and its share in the capital region, 1985-2005**

(unit : 1,000 persons, %)

Areal units	1985 - 1990		1990 - 1995		1995 - 2000		2000 - 2005	
	No. of Growth	%	No. of Growth	%	No. of Growth	%	No. of Growth	%
Seoul	974	32.9	- 382	- 31.9	- 336	- 22	- 75	- 6.6
Incheon	431	14.5	490	40.9	167	10.9	56	4.9
Gyeonggi - *do*	1362	46.0	1494	124.7	1,334	87.4	1,431	125.2
The Capital Region	2,767	93.4	1602	133.7	1,165	76.3	1,413	123.6
Nation	2,963	100	1,198	100	1,527	100	1,143	100

(Source : Statistics Korea, Population and Housing Census [each year]).

Table 3.3 **Changes of the population share in the capital region, 1985-2005**

(unit : 1,000 persons, %)

Areal Units	1985		1990		1995		2000		2005	
	Population	%	Population	%	Population	%	Population	%	Population	%
Seoul	9,639	23.8	10,613	24.4	10,231	22.9	9,898	21.4	9,820	20.8
Incheon + Gyeonggi - *do*	6.181	15.3	7,974	18.4	9,958	22.3	11,459	24.9	12,946	27.4
The Capital Region	15,820	39.1	18,587	42.8	20,189	45.3	21,354	46.3	22,767	48.2
Nation	40,448	100	43,411	100	44,609	100	46,136	100	47,279	100

(Source : Statistics Korea, Population and Housing Census [each year]).

3.1.2 Population Distribution and Density

As shown above, the differential population growth rate among regions in Korea for the last 20 years has brought changes in the pattern of population distribution. In a broad context, the population distribution is the holistic sum of country's geographical, historical, sociocultural and economic situations. In order to examine how the population distribution of Korea has changed, the most common method used is to compare dot maps between two periods. To construct the dot map, the population for each *eup* (town), *myeon* (township) and *dong* (neighborhood) can be converted into dots based on the population number per dot. These maps enable easy checking of the population distribution patterns of either over- or under-population in each area.

By comparing the maps of 1985 and 2005, it is evident that the capital region, the Busan metropolitan area and other metropolitan cities have became densely populated, while most rural areas have depopulated (Figure 3.2). In particular, compared to the population distribution pattern in 1985, in 2005 it was noticeable that the southern part of Gyeonggi-*do* had become more densely populated, whereas the inland mountainous regions of Gyeongsangbuk-*do*, Jeollanam-*do* and Jeollabuk-*do* had become more depopulated.

Urbanization in Korea was a critical factor influencing the change of population distribution. The ratio of cities with a population over 50,000 to the total population in Korea was very low in 1949 (17.2%) and 1955 (24.5%). However, following the progression of industrialization and urbanization in the 1960s, the ratio of urbanization increased to 41.2% in the 1970s and to 74.4% in the 1990s. Until the 1980s, rapid urbanization in Korea was due to the population inflow from rural areas to the cities. In particular, from 1966-1970 when the

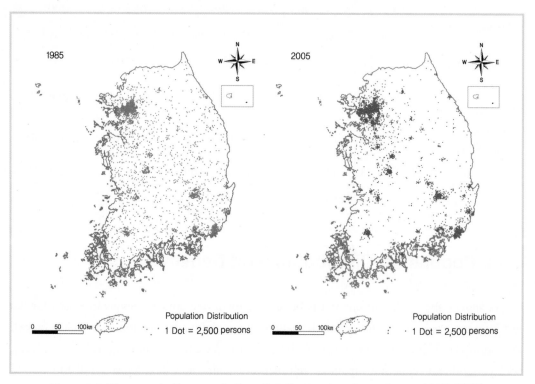

Figure 3.2 **Changes in the population distribution by city and *gun*, 1985-2005**
(Source : Statistics Korea, Population and Housing Census [each year]).

migration from rural areas to the cities most rapidly progressed, the population growth rate of the city greatly increased by an annual average of 7%, while that of rural areas decreased by an annual average of -1.5%. In general, the urbanization in Korea has been accomplished simultaneously with industrialization but the speed of urbanization sometimes exceeded that of industrialization. The cities had experienced population increases, with an annual average of over 4%, until the 1990s. Since the late 1990s, the urbanization has been influenced largely by the natural increase of population. During 2000-2005, the annual average population growth of cities was lowered to 0.9%, while the rural areas experienced an annual average population growth of -1.4%, showing a 2.3% difference in annual average growth rate between the cities and the rural areas. The ratio of the population residing in cities with over 50,000 was 81.5% in 2005, indicating that Korea has reached the final stage of the urbanization process just like other developed countries (Table 3.4).

As for the population distribution per metropolitan city and do (province), Gyeonggi-*do* ranked first with 10.4 million, followed by Seoul with 9.82 million, in 2005 (Table 3.5). Also, the total population of the 7 major metropolitan cities, 22.25 million (47.1%), is almost equal to the total population of the capital region, indicating that population growth in Korea has been concentrated in metropolitan cities for the last 20 years. The population size of other cities and provinces is as follows : over 3 million in Gyeonggi-*do*, Seoul, Busan and

Table 3.4 **Trend in urbanization rates, 1960-2005**

(unit : 1,000 persons, %)

Year	Total Population (A)	Urban Population (B)	Urbanization Rate (A/B) ◊ 100	No. of Cities	Annual Growth Rate (%) Urban	Rural
1960	24,989	6,997	28.0	27		
1966	29,193	9,805	33.6	32	6.98	1.51
1970	31,466	12,954	41.2	32	5.73	- 0.92
1975	34,707	16,793	48.4	35	5.33	- 0.65
1980	37,436	21,434	57.3	40	5.09	- 2.23
1985	40,448	26,443	65.4	50	4.29	- 2.63
1990	43,411	32,309	74.4	73	4.09	- 4,54
1995	44,609	35,036	78.5	73	1.63	- 2.92
2000	46,136	36,755	79.7	79	0.96	- 0.4
2005	47,279	38,515	81.5	84	0.94	- 1.35

(Source : Statistics Korea, Population and Housing Census [each year]).

Gyeongsangnam-*do* ; 2-2.5 million in Gyeongsangbuk-*do*, Incheon and Daegu ; 1.5-2 million in Chungcheongnam-*do*, Jeollanam-*do* and Jeollabuk-*do* ; 1-1.5 million for Gangwon-*do*, Chungcheongbuk-*do*, Daejeon, Gwangju and Ulsan ; and about 532 thousand, the smallest number, in Jeju special self-governing province.

The dot map of population distribution shows the population concentration in an absolute viewpoint. However, due to different sizes of administrative areas, an index most frequently used in comparing population distribution is population density (persons/km^2). Korea's population density increased from 408 persons/km^2 in 1985 to 474 persons/km^2 in 2005. Korea had already reached a high population density in the 1970s and is now ranked the 3rd most densely populated country, not including city states (e.g., Monaco, Hong-Kong) and small countries (e.g., Malta, Barbados, Bahrain), after Bangladesh (985 persons/km^2) and Taiwan (632 persons/km^2). However, the population density of metropolitan cities and the capital region in 2005 is only just above the national average and that of the non-metropolitan regions is far below the national average due to the continuously declining population in those regions. The population density of Seoul doubled during the 30-year period from 1960 (9,111 persons/km^2) to 1990 (17,532 persons/km^2). However, as the population of Seoul decentralized into satellite cities around Seoul after 1990, the population density of Seoul began to decrease. The population density of Seoul in 2005 still remained over 16,000 persons/km^2, indicating that Seoul is counted among the world's most densely populated cities.

Table 3.5 **Total population by metropolitan city and province in 2005**

(unit : 1,000 persons, %)

Areal Units	Population	Proportion	Areal Units	Population	Proportion
The Capital Region[*]	22,767	48.2	Gyeonggi - *do*	10.415	22.0
Metropolitan Cities[**]	22,249	47.1	Gangwon - *do*	1,465	3.1
Seoul	9,820	20.8	Chungcheongbuk - *do*	1,460	3.1
Busan	3,524	7.5	Chungcheongnam - *do*	1,889	4.0
Daegu	2,465	5.2	Jeollabuk - *do*	1,784	3.8
Incheon	2,531	5.4	Jeollanam - *do*	1,820	3.8
Gwangju	1,418	3.0	Gyeongsangbuk - *do*	2,608	5.5
Daejeon	1,443	3.1	Gyeongsangnam - *do*	3,056	6.5
Ulsan	1,049	2.2	Jeju special self-governing province	532	1.1

[*] : Seoul National Capital Area (the capital region)
[**] : Metropolitan Cities include Seoul, Busan, Daegu, Incheon, Gwangju, Daejeon and Ulsan.
(Source : Statistics Korea, Population and Housing Census, 2005).

Table 3.6 **Changes in population density by metropolitan city and province**

(Unit : persons/㎢)

Areal Units	1985	1990	1995	2000	2005 Statistical Density	2005 Physiological Density
Nation	408	437	449	464	474	2,579
Seoul	15,933	17,532	16,889	16,342	16,221	553,746
Busan	8,094	7,175	5,093	4,831	4,609	39,454
Daegu	4,462	4,892	2,766	2,801	2,786	21,841
Incheon	6,860	5,731	2,416	2,582	2,546	10,810
Gwangju	-	2,274	2,509	2,698	2,827	11,296
Daejeon	-	1,954	2,357	2,535	2,673	25,075
Ulsan	-	-	-	961	992	7,844
Gyeonggi - *do*	442	571	756	886	1,028	5,208
Gangwon - *do*	102	94	89	90	88	1,248
Chungcheongbuk - *do*	187	187	188	197	197	1,134
Chungcheongnam - *do*	340	242	207	215	220	753
Jeollabuk - *do*	274	257	236	235	221	837
Jeollanam - *do*	306	212	174	167	157	561
Gyeongsangbuk - *do*	155	147	141	143	137	902
Gyeongsangnam - *do*	297	312	332	283	291	1,771
Jeju special self-governing province	268	282	273	278	288	908

(Source : Statistics Korea, Population and Housing Census [each year]).

As the 3 metropolitan cities of Busan, Daegu and Incheon massively expanded their administrative districts, their population densities dropped because they absorbed nearby large, mostly rural areas. On the other hand, Gangwon-*do*, Jeollanam-*do*, Jeollabuk-*do* and Gyeongsangbuk-*do* have experienced population loss due to the outward migration. These regions have consistently experienced decreased population density. However, the population density of Gyeonggi-*do*, where many new towns and satellite cities were built around Seoul, has increased and reached 1,028 persons/㎢ in 2005 (Table 3.6).

For the purpose of comparing the population pressure and population capacity among regions in Korea, the physiological density (the total number of persons / agricultural land of land measured in square kilometers) is more useful than statistical population density because most of the population in Korea is concentrated on agricultural land, which occupies only 20% of the total national land. The government has cultivated and reclaimed land to expand

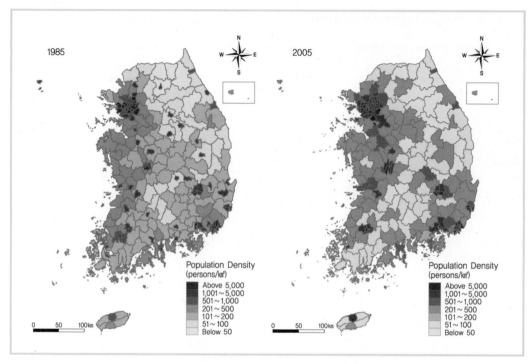

Figure 3.3 **Population density map in 1985 and 2005**
(Source : Statistics Korea, Population and Housing Census [each year]).

agricultural areas during the last 40 years. In spite of the government's effort, the agricultural land tends to decrease every year because of urbanization. The cultivated acreage, which was 1.985 million hectares in 1995, has decreased to 1.824 million hectares, bringing the total loss of the cultivated area to 0.16 million hectares (8%) for the last 10 years. As a result, the geographical population density has continuously increased, from 1,672 persons/km² in 1980 to 2,000 persons/km² in 1990 and then up to 2,579 persons/km² in 2005. In terms of physiological density, Korea is ranked 2nd in the world after Japan and its physiological density is 5.4 times higher than its statistical population density. As for the physiological density among regions, it is quite different from the statistical population density (Table 3.6). The physiological density of Gangwon-*do*, where the ratio of cultivated land is very low, surpasses that of Chungcheong-*do*, Jeollanam-*do*, Jeollabuk-*do* and Gyeongsangbuk-*do*. So the population pressure of Gangwon-*do* is much higher than of other regions. This suggests that regions with a low ratio of cultivated land have a correspondingly low capacity to support population.

Figure 3.3 shows the change in population density patterns among cities, *guns* and *gus* in Korea for the period of 1985-2005. As of 1985, regions showing high population density were the southwestern plain and coastal regions, while low density areas were those lying northeast of the Taebaeksanmaek and Sobaeksanmaek. In 2005 the number of *guns* with fewer than 50 persons/km² had increased to 20 and there were as many as 33 *guns* with 50-100 persons/km² due to rural-to-urban migration, a rapid decline in fertility and an aging population in rural areas. Mainly the mountainous regions of Gwangwon-*do*, Chungcheongbuk-*do* and Gyeongsangbuk-*do* have low population density. Inje-*gun* (19 persons/km²), close to the DMZ in Gangwon-*do*, has the lowest population density in the whole country, while Yangcheon-gu, which is located in Seoul, has the highest population density (27,256 persons/km²). Among sub-gus and *guns* (*dong* and *myeon* level), over 20 *dongs*, including Guro-4 *dong* (73,485 persons/km²) in Seoul, have the highest population density with 50,000 persons/km². In contrast, there are 105 *myeons* with less than 20 persons/km², revealing that there is huge difference between the highest and lowest population density numbers.

CHANGES IN POPULATION STRUCTURE

3.2.1 Changes in Sex and Age Structure of Population

1) Changes in sex structure

Looking at the nationwide trend in the sex ratio (the number of males per 100 females), Korea's sex ratio was somewhat high (101.5) in 1966 due to a tendency to prefer sons to daughters. But the sex ratio gradually dropped, becoming balanced in the 1980s. In 2005, the sex ratio had declined to 99.5, which was 1.3 less than the ratio of 100.8 in 2000. In general, the sex ratio at the time of birth is 103-107, with boys exceeding girls. However, especially in Korea, the at-birth sex ratio in 1994 peaked at 115.5, which in turn led to the highest ratio for the ages of 10 to 14 (112.2) in 2005. But recently, the sex ratio at the time of birth has been reduced, showing 110.2 in 2000 and 107.7 in 2005. The sex ratio is less than 50 for the over 80 age group. Because the death rate of males is much higher than that of females in the older age groups, the sex ratio drops as the age level goes up.

The national sex ratio follows a natural tendency, whereas the sex ratios in urban areas and rural areas show a big difference driven by social factors resulting primarily from inward and outward migration. The sex ratio for urban areas was balanced at 99 in 2005, whereas the ratio in rural areas, 96.5, shows that women outnumbered men. Figure 3.4 shows the huge difference in sex ratios between urban and rural areas, particularly in the marriageable age. The outward migration of young women from rural areas to urban areas causes the great difference in the sex ratio between the ages of 20 and 24. In 1985, the sex ratio of urban areas, 89.5, showed that women were dominant, while that of rural areas, 189.9, was more than twice as high as that of the urban areas. After that, the difference in the sex ratios between urban areas and rural areas in the age group of 20-24 declined. Nevertheless, in 2005 the sex ratio was still 105 in *dongs*, but 157.4 in *myeons*. This unbalanced sex ratio is likely to create some problems in the future and the eligible bachelors in the rural areas may find it difficult to marry due to the scarcity of women in rural areas, which implies that the rate of marriage to foreign brides would go up.

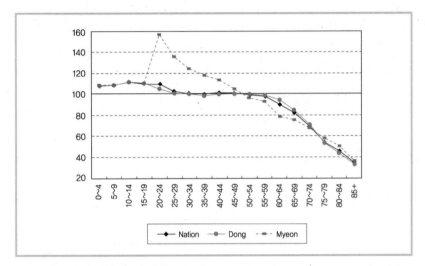

Figure 3.4 **Sex ratio between age groups in *dongs* (neighborhoods) and *myeons* (townships), 2005**
(*Source : Statistics Korea, Population and Housing Census, 2005*).

2) Changes in age structure

Since the socioeconomic behaviors in which human beings engage vary widely between age groups, the dynamics of change involving the different age groups are very important. Generally in order to grasp the characteristics of the population structure by age, the age distribution data are analyzed by 3 different methods as follows.

The median age method uses a single index to understand the age characteristics of a population and is often used rather than the mean age method because of an asymmetry in age distribution. All individuals gradually get older, but the median age in a certain society may become older or younger. When birth and death rates fall, the median age rises, while it falls when birth and death rates rise. Generally, a society with a 30-or-higher median age is called an "aging" society (Peters & Larkin, 2002). On the whole, as a society modernizes, the median age rises due to a declining birth rate. Hence, the median age is sometimes used as an index to indicate the level of modernization and the demographic transition stage of a population in a given society. As for Korea, the median age was 21.7 years in 1980, but it rose continuously to 27 years in 1990 and to 35 years in 2005, showing that the country has become an aging society. In regional terms, the median age is 34 years for *dongs*, 35.8 years for *eups* and 46.5 years for *myeons*. These figures show that more elderly people live in rural areas.

The age distribution in a certain society is divided into 3 age groups : the young age group (aged between 0-14), the working age group (aged 15-64) and the elderly age group (aged 65 and older). Each group's proportion to the total population is used to understand the age structure. Figure 3.5 shows the big change in the age structure over the last 45 years in Korea very well. In particular, the comparison between 1960, the year before the economic development began in Korea and 2005, nicely explains the process of population structural change. With economic development and modernization underway, the young age group began to shrink in number quite significantly while the elderly age group was growing in size. The ratio of those in the young age group (under 15), which was 42.9% in 1960, dropped more than half to 19.1% in 2005, whereas the ratio of those in the elderly population (over 65) tripled from 3.3% in 1960 to 9.3% in 2005. The decrease in the young age group population relative to the increase in the elderly population is mostly due to the increase in the average lifespan, a lower birth rate and a relatively lower death rate in accordance with national family planning, modernization and industrialization.

The population pyramid, which shows the age distribution of a specific year, is considered to be the most effective way to draw out general information about socioeconomic and

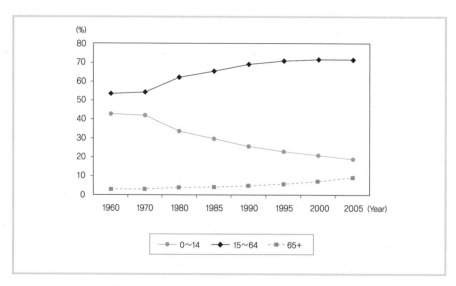

Figure 3.5 **Changes in age structure of population, 1960-2005**
(Source : Statistics Korea, Population and Housing Census [each year]).

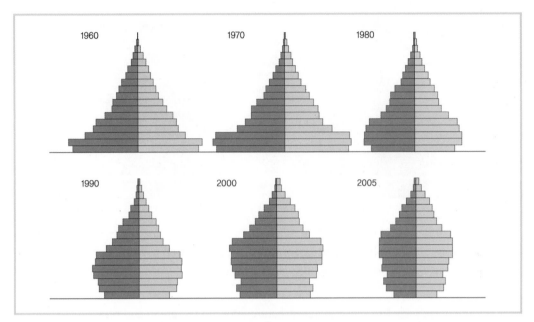

Figure 3.6 **Changes in the age structure pattern, 1960-2005**
(Source : Statistics Korea, Population and Housing Census [each year]).

demographical characteristics of a given society. The population pyramid is a special form of a horizontal bar graph, with age groups on the vertical axis and the number of males and females in these groups on the horizontal axis. Men are shown on the left side and women on the right from the center of the horizontal axis. From the population pyramid, historical changes in population during the last 100 years can be viewed all at once. That is, through the population pyramid the variations in population by age and sex can be observed. These variations are caused by war, migration and changes in the fertility and mortality rates. With economic development and modernization underway, the shapes of national population pyramids have changed due to the continuous decline in fertility rates. In 1960, the population pyramid showed a classical pyramid shape composed of high birth and death rates, but since the late 1980s it has shifted into a spindle type of structure marked by low birth and low death rates (Figure 3.6).

However, the shapes of population pyramids for each city and *gun* can be very different because of massive population movements from rural areas to cities and differences in labor force demands according to the economic base of each region. Especially when the population pyramids of urban and rural areas in 2005 are compared, the ratio of the child-age groups and youth/middle-age groups in urban areas is much higher than that in rural areas, while the ratio of older-age groups, especially over age 55, in rural areas is much higher than that in urban

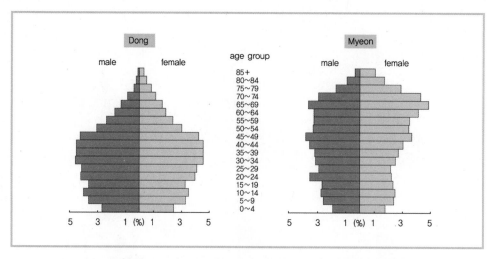

Figure 3.7 *Dong* (urban) and *myeon* (rural) population pyramids, 2005
(Source : Statistics Korea, Population and Housing Census [each year]).

areas (Figure 3.7). Such difference in age structure between the urban and rural areas seems to result from the migration of the younger age group populations from rural areas to urban areas. In rural areas, the ratio of older-age groups is high and the exodus of young women between age 20 and 24 is very conspicuous.

Aging in Korea is accelerating due to the increase in the elderly population along with the decline in the young population. In general, a country with a ratio of the elderly age group over 7% is classified as a country of an aged population, a category that can be subdivided into a super-aged society (over 20%), an aged society (14-20%) and an aging society (7-14%). The Korean seniors population increased from 175 thousand (4.3%) in 1985 to 436.5 thousand (9.3%) in 2005, so Korea has already joined the aging society. The biggest factors for entering the aging society category are a decline in fertility and an increase in life expectancy due to modernization and the development of medical science. In particular, a decrease in death rate as a result of longer life expectancy leads to an aging society.

The ratios of the elderly age group in each city, *gun* and *gu* level show very contrasting patterns. In 2005, the region with the highest ratio of the elderly population was Imsil-*gun* at 33.8% of its population. The elderly population in most areas of Jeollanam-*do*, Jeollabuk-*do* and Gyeongsangbuk-*do* comprise more than 25% of the total population. In contrast, the region with the lowest ratio of the elderly population is Yeongtong-*dong* in Suwon at 3.5%. The elderly population in Changwon, Ansan, Siheung and Osan cities comprises less than 5% of the total population. In addition, the elderly populations of Gumi, Suwon and Daejeon and Gangnam-*gu*, Songpa-*gu* and Gangdong-*gu* of Seoul comprise low percentages of their total populations.

Another way to determine the degree of aging in a society is the index of the aged-to-child ratio (ACR). The ACR is defined as the ratio of the young population (aged 14 and younger), to the elderly population (aged 65 and older). The figure of the ACR did not change much from 1960, with an index of 7.7, to 1970, with an index of 7.9. However, since the late 1970s, the ACR has increased in accordance with an increase in life expectancy generated by improvements in health care and nutrition, economic development and higher per capita income. It significantly increased from 11.4 in 1980, to 19.4 in 1990, to 35.0 in 2000 and to 48.6 in 2005. This can be interpreted as approximately 49 elderly people for every 100 young people.

3.2.2 Changes in Socioeconomic Structure of the Population

The relationship between the populations of the young age and elderly age groups and the population of the working age group is very important in economic terms. Therefore, the dependency ratio can be applied as an index of the economic structure of a population. The dependent population is largely divided into 2 groups. That is, one group consisting of those aged 0-14 and the other group consisting of those aged 65 and older, both of which are generally too young or too old to engage in productive economic activities. The population of the working age group (15-64) is defined simply by the age range, regardless of actual participation in economic activities.

The dependency ratio is often divided into 2 parts, called the youth dependency ratio and the elderly dependency ratio. Hence, the total dependency ratio is the proportion of the nonproductive population to the productive population and can also be calculated by adding the elderly dependency ratio and the youth dependency ratio. In 1960, the total dependency ratio was 86, with an elderly dependency ratio of 6 and a relatively high youth dependency ratio of 80. Since then, the total dependency ratio has gradually decreased as the birth rate has declined due to economic development and national family planning. The dependency ratio dropped considerably from 60.5 in 1980 to 52.1 in 1985 and steadily declined from 40.6in 1995 to 39.7 in 2005. In particular, the youth dependency ratio in 2005 was 26.7, which was much lower than in 1960, but the elderly dependency ratio increased gradually, reaching 13.0 in 2005 (Table 3.7). In the future, it can be anticipated that the dependency ratio of seniors will continuously increase and may reach 21 in 2020 if the ratio of the elderly population exceeds over 15% of the total population.

The transformation of household structure and the change of household characteristics are the representative indices that show the characteristics and change in social structure of a population. The fundamental unit of a modern society is the household. The household is usually defined as people "living together in a physical living environment" and is mainly based not only on primary relationships such as blood, marriage and adoption (called a "relative household"), but also on secondary relationships, mainly the sharing of a physical living space among non-related people ("non-relative household"). The most important and fundamental factor is the relative household, which can be categorized into one-, two-, three- and more generation types. The household's composition and characteristics reflect the basic structure of a society.

Since the 1980s, the total number of households rapidly increased from about 8 million in 1980, to 10 million in 1990 and to 16 million in 2005. During this period (1980-2005), the total number of households doubled and the proportion within the capital region rapidly increased from 36.6% in 1980 to 47.1% in 2005, which reflects the high concentration of households in the capital region. On the other hand, during the same period, the average number of people per household decreased from 4.55 in 1980, to 3.71 in 1990 and to 2.88 in 2005. If this trend continues, it can be anticipated that the average number of people per household will decrease to 2.6 in 2020. The main reason for this was the major shift to the

Table 3.7 **Changes in the dependency ratio in urban and rural areas, 1960-2005**

Classification	1960	1970	1980	1990	2000	2005
Total Dependency Ratio						
Nation	86.0	83.3	60.5	44.2	39.4	39.7
Urban	77.9	67.0	539.0	42.7	37.0	36.4
Rural	89.4	90.6	70.3	48.5	50.0	55.7
Youth Dependency Ratio						
Nation	79.9	77.2	54.3	37.0	29.2	26.7
Urban	74.0	63.1	49.9	37.6	29.5	26.7
Rural	82.4	85.9	60.8	35.1	28.0	26.7
Elderly Dependency Ratio						
Nation	6.0	6.1	6.2	7.2	10.2	13.0
Urban	3.9	3.9	3.9	5.1	7.5	9.8
Rural	7.1	7.7	9.6	13.4	22.0	28.9

[Source : Statistics Korea, Population and Housing Census [each year]].

two-generation household in Korean society and the significant increase in one-person households due to several social factors such as divorce, separation by death and an increasing number of people choosing to remain single.

The characteristics of the heads of households can be explored by the male-female ratio, marriage and one-person households. Traditionally, Korea had predominantly male-headed households. However, in recent years, with the radical change in social structure, the proportion of female-headed households has been rapidly increasing. The statistics show that in 1980, the number of male-headed households was 5.81 times larger than that of female-headed households, but that by 1995 that number had dropped to 5.04. By 2005 the male-to-female ratio of the heads of households was down to 3.56, a significant decrease in the male-female gap. In the spatial distribution of male/female heads of households, there is a higher proportion of male-headed households in metropolitan cities and the capital region than in rural areas, while there is a relatively small difference in the male/female heads of households ratio in rural areas, such as the Jeolla provinces and Gyeongsang provinces.

Overall, there has been a continued increase in one-person households both in number and proportion. The ratio of one-person households was 12.7% in 1995, but increased to 15.5% in 2000 and 20% in 2005, indicating that 1 in 5 households represents a one-person household (Figure 3.8). The increase in the ratio of one-person households was due to the increase in the number of singles over age 20, increase in divorce and the growth of one-person households among seniors over age 65. Also, the ratio of one-person households in rural areas appears to

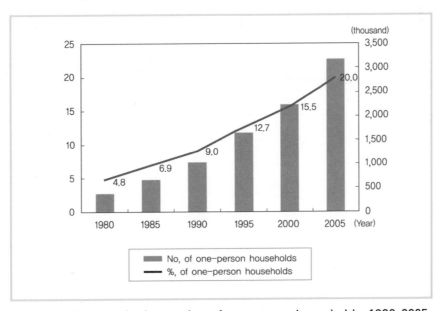

Figure 3.8 **Changes in the number of one-person households, 1980-2005**
[Source : Statistics Korea, Population and Housing Census [each year]].

be higher than that in the cities, showing that the ratio of the one-person elderly population is relatively high in rural areas. In general, the ratio of one-person households in the cities is high in the 30-40 age group and the ratio in rural areas is high in the age group over 70. The ratio of one-person households is relatively higher in rural areas, especially Gyeongsangnam-*do* and Gyeongsangbuk-*do* inland areas of Jeollanam-*do* and Jeollabuk-*do* and Gangwon-*do*, than in metropolitan cities and the capital region. In terms of the age structure of one-person households, the ratio of elderly one-person households is relatively higher and its spatial pattern is similar to that of all one-person households. The general tendency of the spatial pattern of one-person households indicates that the majority of the young people are in metropolitan cities and that the elderly people are in rural areas.

Chapter 3.3.

CHANGES IN FERTILITY AND MORTALITY

3.3.1 Fertility Rate : Its Characteristics and Changes

It is fertility that has the most significant effect on natural increase and thus population growth today. Crude Birth Rate (CBR) and Total Fertility Rate (TFR) are the most typically used indices to measure the fertility level. CBR is an index that simply shows the birth level of a society and represents how many people are born per 1000 persons a year. Figure 3.9 represents the change in fertility for Korea after the 1970s, showing a steep change in the level of fertility. The CBR, which was 31.2‰ in 1970, decreased to 15.4‰ in 1990 and 9.0 ‰ in

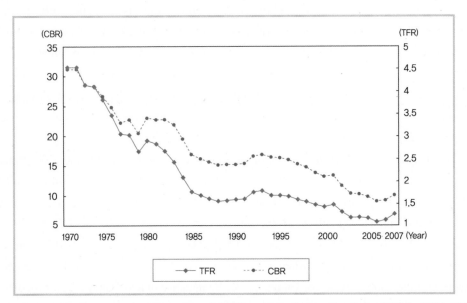

Figure 3.9 **Trends of Crude Birth Rate (CBR) and Total Fertility Rate (TFR), 1970-2005**
(Source : Statistics Korea, Vital Statistics [each year]).

2005. A closer look at CBR figures by metropolitan city and provinces in 2005 shows the big difference among regions associated with the migration flow as well as the population structure. The highest CBRs are found in Gyeonggi-*do* (10.3) and Jeju special self-governing province (10.2), while the lowest values are reported in Busan (7.0) and Jeollanam-*do* (8.0).

Since CBR indicates the rate of childbirth relative to the total population of a given country, a criterion being widely used to more precisely gauge the number of births is TFR. TFR is an index that shows the average number of children born to a mother over her fertility period (usually age 15-49). The TFR was as high as 6.3 during the period of 1955-1960, but dropped sharply to 4.6 during the period of 1965-1970 because of the spread of contraceptive use as one way of family planning. In the 1980s, the TFR had rapidly decreased to under 2 (1.76), which was the population replacement level. Such a drastic downturn in TFR may be explained by 2 main factors : (1) the national population control policy implemented via family planning with a host of educational programs to disseminate contraceptive devices ; (2) socioeconomic advancements leading to trends toward modernization and urbanization that have led to the preference for fewer children. From the mid 1980s to late 1990s, the TFR became relatively stable, between 1.4 and 1.8. But a sharp drop occurred again beginning in 2001 and in 2005 the TFR of Korea, at 1.08, was the lowest level in the world, showing an absolute decline of 0.39 within only 5 years. In 2008, the TFR of Korea is 1.2, still the lowest level in the world, indicating that a couple only has 1.2 children in a lifetime. Japan, the country known to have the lowest level of fertility in the world, has a higher TFR (1.32) than Korea. The TFRs of France (1.98), Germany (1.33), the United Kingdom (1.84) and the United States (2.1) are also higher than that of Korea. The more serious problem is that no country in the world has experienced a fertility level as low as Korea and the level of fertility in most developed countries has been gradually increasing recently. This low fertility trend will result in decreases in births in the short run and will cause various problems relating to a labor deficit and an aging population in the long run (Kwon, 2002).

As for the TFR of Korea by metropolitan city and province in 2005, the difference in fertility between regions is obvious. The TFRs of Busan (0.88), Seoul (0.92) and Daegu (0.99) are the lowest, scoring under 1.0, whereas Jeju special self-governing province (1.3), Jeollanam-*do* (1.28) and Chungcheongnam-*do* (1.26) show levels over 1.2. As for the TFR by each city, *gun* and *gu*, the TFRs of Jung-*gu* in Busan (0.69), Gangnam-*gu* in Seoul (0.71) and most metropolitan areas are under 1.0, whereas Hwacheon-*gun* has a TFR of 1.71 and Inje-*gun* and Yanggu-*gun* in the northern part of Gangwon-*do*, Yeongam-*gun* and Gangjin-*gun* in Jeollanam-*do*, Hwaseong-*gun* in Gyeonggi-*do*, Buk-gu in Ulsan city and Geoje city show TFRs of 1.5.

3.3.2 Mortality Rate : Its Characteristics and Changes

Rapid population increase is caused by a rising fertility rate and low mortality rate. The cause of death takes on various forms depending on the social and economic conditions of a given country, especially its health and sanitation levels, living standards and living environment. During the last 40 years, the mortality rate in Korea has dropped significantly and the cause of death has changed a lot. Mortality since 1960 has constantly and gradually decreased. The Crude Death Rate (CDR) was around 7‰ in the late 1970s, 6‰ in the 1980s, less than 5.5‰ in the 1990s and quite low at 5‰ in 2005 (Figure 3.10). Such a decrease in mortality rate results largely from the expansion of an improved healthcare and medical insurance system, which led to the creation of community health centers for all rural areas and access to advanced medical technology made possible by an increasing number of doctors, pharmacists and hospitals. A huge improvement in the standard of living, along with economic development, has played an important role in the decreased death rate in Korea. The spatial distribution of CDRs shows a critical urban-rural distinction because the CDR index is closely related to the age composition. Seoul (3.8) and Ulsan (3.8) reported the lowest rates, while Jeollanam-*do* (8.2) and Gyeongsangbuk-*do* (7.5) showed the highest rates.

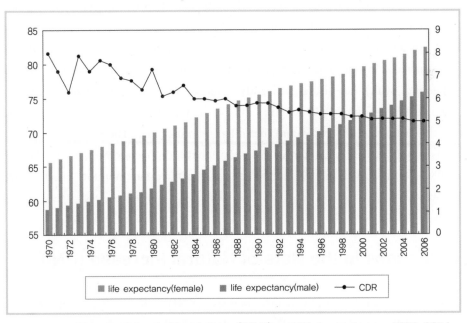

Figure 3.10 **Trend of Crude Death Rate (CDR) and life expectancy, 1970-2006**
(Source : Statistics Korea, Vital Statistics [each year]).

With declining mortality rates, the cause of death distribution pattern has also changed. In the 1960s, the cause of death was mainly digestive system problems followed by respiratory system problems and infectious and parasitic diseases. However, in the 1980s the major causes of death changed to malignant neoplasms (cancer) and hypertensive diseases. In the 1990s, cancer, cerebrovascular diseases, heart diseases and traffic accidents emerged as major causes of death. The change in causes of death distribution continued and in 2006, death from cancer represented 27% of total dead persons at the death rate of 134.8 deaths per 100,000 people, so cancer was the leading cause of death, followed by cerebrovascular disease, cardiac disorder, diabetes and suicide, respectively. Therefore, the percentages of deaths caused by digestive system problems, respiratory system problems and infectious and parasitic diseases have dropped, while those of circulatory diseases, cancer and injury from every kind of accident have increased.

Meanwhile, the continuous decline in mortality rate has resulted in an increased life expectancy in Korea. The life expectancy, which was around age 50 during 1955-1960, increased to age 62 in 1970 and over age 65 in 1979. This trend accelerated, bringing the life expectancy to over age 70 in 1988 and age 75 in 1999. In 2006, life expectancy in Korea was age 79.2, which was high compared to that of the world (Figure 3.10). In a span of 35 years, life expectancy had increased by 17 years. In particular, the life expectancy of women was very high (at age 82.4), as was that of men (at age 75.5). Such a difference in life expectancy between men and women has been gradually decreasing. A factor responsible for the significant increase in life expectancy has been the big drop in infant mortality rate due to family planning, which has also significantly reduced the death rate of women. Since 1960, the implementation of family planning has directly and indirectly played an important role in lowering the death rate of women and the infant mortality rate. The infant mortality rate in Korea was very high at 131.6‰ during 1946-1950, but it dropped to 60‰ in the 1960s, 34‰ during 1980-1985 and 10‰ in 1995. In the early 2000s, the infant mortality rate in Korea was very low at 8‰.

3.3.3 Changes in the Rate of Natural Increase (RNI)

It is noticeable that the rate of natural increase (RNI) in Korea based on the difference between the CBR and CDR has continuously decreased during the last 40 years. Since the decreasing trend has been sharper in the CBR than in the CDR, the gap between the 2 indices has been reduced. The RNI was somewhat high at 23.2% in 1970, but it dropped to below

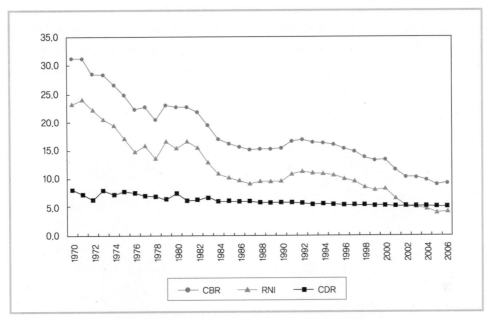

Figure 3.11 **Trend in RNI (CBR-CDR), 1970-2006**
(Source : Statistics Korea, Vital Statistics [each year])

10% (9.7%) in 1986. Although the RNI was over 10% in the early 1990s, it dropped rapidly again after 1997, reaching 4.0% in 2005 (Figure 3.11). This trend can be accounted for by the flattened CDR and the sharply decreasing CBR since the late 1990s. Korea's RNI of 4.0 is much lower than the world average (11.7), as estimated for 2005-2010 by the United Nations.

The spatial pattern of the RNI in Korea is reflective of those of the CBR and CDR and is directly related to population changes in each region. Gyeonggi-*do* reported the highest value (6.3) and Jeollanam-*do*, the lowest (-0.2). When the maps of CBR and CDR by city, *gun* and *gu* levels are compared together, an interactive effect can be seen between urban-rural areas and the age structure of the population (Figure 3.12). The CBR of rural areas is generally under 2, whereas that of Yeosu, Gumi, Anyang and Seongnam is over 20. Also, the difference in the CDR appears to be very significant. The CDR of big cities is under 3, while that of some rural areas is over 20. As a result, there is substantial spatial variation in the RNI among different regions. In most rural areas, the RNI is under -15, which indicates that the population decrease in those areas is very severe. The RNI in Cheongdo-*gun*, Uiseong-*gun* and Namhae-*gun* in the Gyeongsang provinces is as low as under -8, whereas that in Osan, Gwangsan-*gu* and Buk-*gu* in Ulsan and Gumi is as high as over 9. Such a contrast in the numbers becomes extreme at the sub-*gu* and *gun* level (*dong, eup, myeon*). The RNI in the nation's top 5 sub-*gus* and *guns*, including Seokjeok-*myeon* (26.4) in Chilgok-*gun* and Bokjeong-*dong* (25.9) in

Seongnam, is over 20, while that of the bottom 10 sub-*gus* and *guns*, including Jisu-*myeon* (20.6, the lowest) in Jinju, is under -18. The difference between the top and the bottom reaches 47, implying that the population increase, following the number of natural increase per 100 persons, differs by 47 persons.

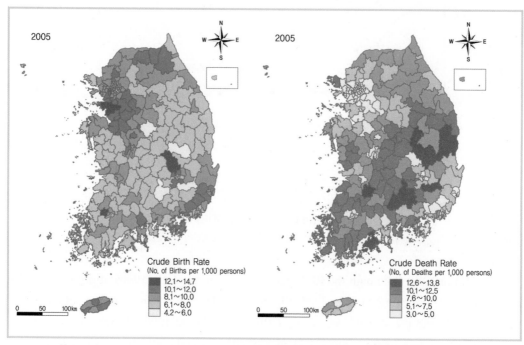

Figure 3.12 **Spatial distribution of CBR and CDR by city, *gun* and gu, 2005.**
(Source : Statistics Korea, Vital Statistics [each year])

Chapter 3.4.

POPULATION MOVEMENT

CHAPTER 3

3.4.1 Characteristics of Population Movement

Migration brings changes to the population distribution across regions, which in turn becomes a factor in subsequent population movements. The population movement of Korea for the last 40 years based on the population census data shows that extensive movement of the rural population towards the cities was initiated on a full scale in the late 1960s as rapid industrialization progressed. Using the census data, migration is defined as changes in residency across the *gu*, *si* and *gun* boundaries between the census data year and 5 years prior to the given census (Choi, 1997). The number of migrants reached up to 7.67 million during the late 1970s, representing 22.9% of the total population over age 5. This trend has continued and during 1995-2000 about 10 million people moved, resulting in a 25% migration rate, which was the highest on record. However, the population movement somewhat declined because of the IMF financial crisis, reducing the number of migrants to 8.97 million during 2000-2005, with a decreased movement rate of 20.4% (Table 3.8). The rate of population shift over the past 40 years has been around 20%, with 1 out of every 5 persons over age 5 changing residence. Compared to other developed countries, the rate of migration is still very high in Korea (Weeks, 2002).

Table 3.8 **Migration trend, 1960-2005**

Period	1960 - 1966	1966 - 1970	1970 - 1975	1975 - 1980	1980 - 1985	1985 - 1990	1990 - 1995	1995 - 2000	2000 - 2005
Migrants (1,000 persons)	3,018	4,394	5,209	7,658	8,402	9,831	10,087	9,577	8,968
Migration rate(%)	12.4	16.2	17.1	22.9	22.8	22	25	22.8	20.4

[Source : Statistics Korea, Population and Housing Census [each year]].

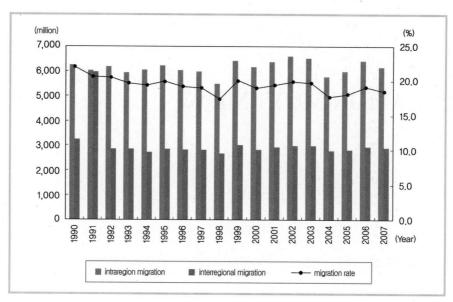

Figure 3.13 **Trend of inter/intraregional migration and migration rates, 1990-2007**
(Source : Statistics Korea, Vital Statistics [each year]).

As for the migration trend based on migration statistics of all resident address changes, the movement rate, which was 12.8% in 1967 when the resident registration was first applied, increased relatively to 22% in 1980. However, the migration rate gradually slowed down during the 1990s. Especially in 1998 under the IMF financial crisis, the rate greatly decreased to 17.4%. In the early 2000s, the migration rate was maintained around 19% but steadily decreased afterwards, showing the movement of 9.07 million people, which was about an 18.5% migration rate, in 2007 (Figure 3.13). When the total migration is compared to the interregional and intraregional migration numbers, it is observed that intraregional migration is occurring far more vigorously. The intraregional migration rate ranges 12-15%, while the interregional migration rate is only about 5-8%. This suggests that migration within cities and *guns* occurs more frequently than between cities and *guns*, implying that the neighborhood effect is a strong factor in the population movement.

As for migration, according to age group in 2007, among the total migration the age groups of the 20s and of the 30s are close at 21.8% and 22.9%, respectively, showing that 44.7% of the total migrants are from these age groups (Figure 3.14). Such a high rate of migration can be explained by graduation, enlistment in army service (or discharge from it), employment, marriage and housing. Moreover, the migration rate of the group age 0-4 appeared to be as high as 23.9%, which implies that the migration of young couples is accompanied by young babies and children.

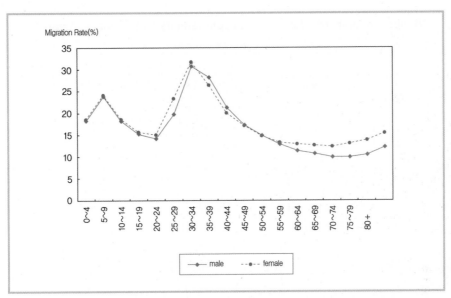

Figure 3.14 **Difference in migration rate by age group, 2007**
(Source : Statistics Korea, Vital Statistics, 2007).

Because of such a huge population movement, 45 out of 100 people in Korean appear to live away from their hometown. The percentage of those living away from their hometown was 21% in 1970 but rose sharply to 41.3% in 1990 and 44.4% in 2000. As for the cities and *guns*, the percentage of people born in a large city such as Seoul who reside in their birthplace is higher compared to those born in *guns* (except in Gyeonggi-*do* and Jeju special self-governing province). Jeju has the highest percentage (76.7%) of residents living in their birthplace. Ulsan, Gyeonggi-*do* and Incheon have percentages above 70%. The percentage for Seoul and other metropolitan cities is approximately 60%, whereas Jeollanam-*do* (38.3%) has the lowest. The *guns*, except in Gyeongsangnam-*do* (54.5%), show a percentage of 40%. This trend can be explained by the fact that in large cities, there are less move-out factors because of the relatively good environment in terms of economics, education and culture, whereas in rural areas people tend to move into big cities for employment and education.

Table 3.9 represents the number of net migrants in metropolitan cities and provinces from 1980 to 2007 in Korea. Metropolitan cities, except Seoul, Busan and Gyeonggi-*do*, have experienced net gain (in-migrants >out-migrants) for the last 28 years. On the other hand, Seoul and Busan experienced net losses of 0.98 million and 0.57 million, respectively and the rest of the provinces showed net losses, which indicates that there was more outward migration than inward migration. Gyeonggi-*do* has experienced the largest net gain (0.577 million) for the last 28 years ; approximately 55% of the current residents in Gyeonggi-*do* are

Table 3.9 **Changes in migration flow by metropolitan city and province, 1980-2007**

(Unit : persons)

Areal Units	Net Migrants			
	1980 - 1989	1990 - 1999	2000 - 2007	1980 - 2007
Seoul	1,126,863	- 1,578,473	- 523,922	- 975,532
Busan	212,211	- 460,672	- 317,553	- 566,014
Daegu	223,090	- 49,830	- 110,763	62,497
Incheon	351,406	413,543	40,310	805,259
Gwangju	75,294	113,456	- 22,821	165,929
Daejeon	26,179	226,686	36,890	289,755
Ulsan	-	- 3,630	11,670	8,040
Gyeonggi - *do*	1,792,698	2,394,572	1,580,257	5,767,527
Gangwon - *do*	- 381,129	- 166,619	- 85,012	- 632,760
Chungcheongbuk - *do*	- 367,000	- 12,152	- 30,298	- 409,450
Chungcheongnam - *do*	- 465,229	- 137,714	30,087	- 572,856
Jeollabuk - *do*	- 634,754	- 227,119	- 188,757	- 1,050,630
Jeollanam - *do*	- 835,182	- 466,062	- 245,734	- 1,546,978
Gyeongsangbuk - *do*	- 772,812	- 178,892	- 171,490	- 1,123,194
Gyeongsangnam - *do*	- 229,939	128,973	6,751	- 94,215
Jeju special self-governing province	- 23,853	3,933	- 9,615	- 29,535

(Source : Statistics Korea, Vital Statistics [each year]).

inward migrants from other regions. By contrast, the region with the highest net loss during the last 28 years is Jeollanam-*do* at 1.55 million, which represents approximately 85% of the current population in Jeollanam-*do*. Also, Gyeongsangbuk-*do* (-1.12 million) and Jeollabuk-*do* (-1.05 million) have more than 1 million in net loss due to the out-migration flow.

Among the important factors exerting influence on migrants who are the heads of households, based on the data from nationwide special surveys in 1997, are job, family, housing and education, in that order. A comparison of the reasons for migration between 1966 and 1997 indicates that economic reasons such as searching for a job or a transfer of workplace have declined considerably, while housing, family reunion and education have become important reasons to move. For instance, 71.6% of household heads moved for economic reasons in 1966, but in 1997, the proportion of migrants reporting economic reasons decreased to 36.4%. Such changes in migration reasons in the past 30 years reflect the industrialization and urbanization of Korean society. In the 1960s, both urbanization and industrialization began to proceed in full scale in Korea. Thus a majority of migrants moved from rural to urban areas mainly for economic reasons. However, in the 1990s the urbanization process had been almost terminated, while metropolitanization around large cities was widely observed. Consequently, most migration is between cities or from central cities to suburban areas within the same metropolitan region. For migrations in the 1990s, education or housing were more prevalent reasons than the economy (Choi and Chang, 2004). However, the economy was still the most important reason among men, whereas among women, marriage and dependence on the head of the household were important factors for moving.

3.4.2 Migration Flow into the Seoul National Capital Area

During the last 30 years or so, around 70% of migration occurring in Korea was inward or outward migration to or from the capital region. However, since the late 1990s, migration from the non-the capital region to the capital region has been relatively reduced, whereas the migration within the capital region has largely increased. In order to compare the flow and changes in migration between the non-the capital region and the capital region, the residential place from 5 years prior and the current one were compared based on data from 4 population censuses from 1975-1980, 1985-1990, 1995-2000 and 2000-2005. The inward migration from the non-the capital region to the capital region, which was 1.41 million during 1975-1980, increased to 1.55 million during 1985-1990. However, in the 2000s the inward migration from the non-the capital region toward the capital region decreased to 1.13 million (Table 3.10). Such a decline in inward migration from the non-the capital region to the capital region may be explained by the decrease in the potential population expected to migrate from the rural areas and the increase in the absorbing force of large cities in the non-the capital region.

Meanwhile, the destination for inward migration into the capital region has shown a significant change over the last 30 years. Of all inward migration into the capital region, 66.8% funneled into Seoul during 1975-1980, but this number gradually decreased to 42.3% during 2000-2005. In the same period of time, on the other hand, inward migration into Gyeonggi-*do* increased from 33.2% to 49.5%, indicating that almost half of the inward migration from the non-the capital region was into Gyeonggi-*do*. Consequently, until 1990 the volume of net-migration was larger in Seoul than in Gyeonggi-*do*. However, it reversed from 1995-2000 and 57.3% of total net-migrants to the capital region were in Gyeonggi-*do* in the period of 2000-2005, indicating that the destination of in-migrants into the capital region had shifted from Seoul to Gyeonggi-*do*.

Table 3.10 **In- and out-migrants to and from the capital region and non-the capital region by 5-year periods, 1975-2005**

(Unit : 1,000 persons, %)

Region	1975 - 1980	1985 - 1990	1995 - 2000	2000 - 2005
Inflow to The Capital Region	1,414(100)	1,547(100)	1,130(100)	1,139(100)
from the non - The Capital Regionto to Seoul	945(66.8)	829(53.6)	535(47.3)	482(42.3)
from the non - The Capital Region to Incheon	-	151(9.8)	96(8.5)	94(8.2)
from the non - The Capital Region to Gyeonggi-*do*	469(33.2)	567(36.6)	499(44.2)	563(49.5)
Outflow from The Capital Region	443(100)	622(100)	881(100)	722(100)
from Seoulto to the non - The Capital Region	317(71.6)	392(63.0)	432(49.0)	320(44.3)
from Incheon to the non - The Capital Region	-	45(7.2)	95(10.8)	78(10.7)
from Gyeonggi - *do* to the non - The Capital Region	126(28.4)	185(29.8)	354(40.2)	324(45.0)
Net Migration in The Capital Region	971(100)	925(100)	249(100)	417(100)
Seoul	628(64.7)	437(47.2)	103(41.4)	162(38.8)
Incheon	-	106(11.5)	1(0.04)	16(3.8)
Gyeonggi - *do*	343(35.3)	382(41.3)	145(58.2)	239(57.3)
Total Migrants of the Nation	3,739(100)	5,435(100)	5,386(100)	5,238(100)
Between The Capital Region and non - The Capital Region	1,857(49.7)	2,169(39.9)	2,011(37.3)	1,861(35.5)
Within The Capital Region	747(20.0)	1,656(30.5)	1,962(36.4)	1,953(37.3)
Within the non - The Capital Region	1,135(30.3)	1,610(29.6)	1,413(26.2)	1,424(27.1)

(Source : Statistics Korea, Vital Statistics [each year])

A close look at the interregional pattern of migration reveals that Seoul and other metropolitan cities have their own migration field close to provincial administrative boundaries as major destinations and origins. As expected, Seoul has the largest migration field when it comes to receiving hierarchical migration from other major destination cities and when sending migrants to nearby Gyeonggi-*do* and Gangwon-*do*, or farther to the northern part of Chungcheongnam-*do* and Chungcheongbuk-*do*. Other large cities have migration fields similar to their administrative boundaries. The regional distributions of migration flows for the metropolitan cities reveal established migration fields in contiguous areas similar to the above except for the capital region, which has the whole nation as a migration field and

Daejeon, which has inter-migration with the capital region. The higher regional concentration in terms of inward migration compared to that of outward migration indicates that metropolitan cities receive migrants from nearby and send them to more diverse areas.

Meanwhile, the number of in-migrants from the non-the capital region to the capital region in 2005 was about 575,000. As for the rate of regional share, the region with the most out-migrants to the capital region in 2005 was Chungcheongnam-*do*, having 7.8 thousand migrants (13.5%), with over 10% of the migrants from Gangwon-*do* and Jeollabuk-*do*. By contrast, the total out-migrants from the capital region to the non-the capital region in 2005 was 446,000. The region with the most migrants to the non-the capital region from the capital region was Chungcheongnam-*do*, reaching the highest number at around 77,000 (17.2%). 11.9% of the migrants were from Gangwon-*do* and 9.2% were from Jeollabuk-*do*. There was quite a similarity between the migration pattern of in-migrants from the non-the capital region to the capital region and the pattern of out-migrants from the capital region to the non-the capital region (Figure 3.15).

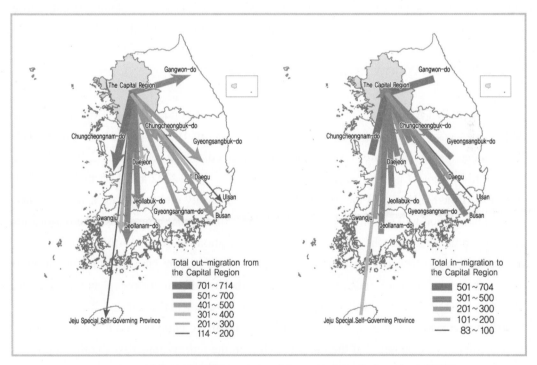

Figure 3.15 **Migration Flows to and from the capital region, 2005**
(Source : Statistics Korea, Vital Statistics, 2005).

POPULATION PROBLEMS AND PROSPECTS

3.5.1 Population Problems

For the last 40 years, Korea has experienced very rapid economic growth accompanied by unprecedented urbanization, which also generated side effects and problems. Among those problems, the most serious ones related to the population can be grouped into 3 parts.

1) Problem of low fertility

The decline of fertility in Korea was achieved radically within a short period of time. The TFR, which was 6.0 during the 1960s, decreased to 4.53 in 1970 and less than 2.0 in 1984. Since then, the fertility rate has continuously dropped, never recovering 2.0 at all. The downward movement is more dramatic : 1.30 in 2001, 1.17 in 2002 and 1.08 in 2005, which was at the time the lowest in the world. If such a low fertility rate continues, it is anticipated that the population will no longer grow in 2021 and will decrease afterwards. The reasons for such low fertility rates are the expansion of higher education and job opportunities for women, more attention to self-accomplishment, expansion of dual-income families, transformation to a nuclear family structure, increase in one-person households, more prevalence of divorce, increased cost of rearing children and insufficient governmental support and a patriarchal culture that considers women as fully responsible for raising children and household chores. In particular, it is supposed that the radical decline in the fertility rate after the IMF financial crisis was related to economic difficulties and the cost of private education is considered to induce low fertility (Kim, 2004).

The reason why low fertility is recognized as a serious social problem is because it is directly connected to the slowdown of economic development and loss of global competitiveness due to the population decline and aging. Particularly, in the case of Korea where the percentage of the elderly population is getting higher as a result of low fertility and a rapid transformation into an aging society, the cost of social welfare for the elderly population gets considerably heightened and this cost gets transferred to the younger working-age population. However, as the young labor force gets decreased according to the population decline, a severe imbalance between demand and supply in social welfare is inevitable throughout the society. The problem of low fertility in Korea is exacerbated as it correlates with the issues of a dwindling workforce and an aging population.

In order to solve the low fertility problem, local governments have proposed multilateral incentives to promote childbirth, but it is no easy task to resolve the problem of low fertility. Giving birth to a child significantly affects a woman's life ; therefore, the fertility rate cannot be increased without a fundamental strong alternative plan. Rather than direct intervention by the government in controlling the number of births, it is more important to provide a social environment and conditions that encourage having children as part of the process of planning and deciding one's personal life. It is necessary to build up a system that can accommodate the changes related to women's evolving roles at home and in society by positively acknowledging women's desires and values so that they can be compatible with marriage, childbirth and child rearing. Moreover, alternatives that support compatible management of working and housekeeping must be prepared in terms of family, the workplace and society and family-friendly working environments and child care facilities must be established (Sohn, 2005).

2) Problem of aging

The rapid decline in the fertility rate, the improvement of the infant mortality rate and the substantial increases in life expectancy have brought about the big issue of population aging. Aging, like low fertility, is rapidly spreading in Korea. Korea is known as "a country that has few children, lives long and gets older." Korea became an aging society in 2000, with more than 7% of its population over the age of 65. If this trend continues, it is anticipated that Korea will become an aged society with more than 14% of its population over 65 by 2018 and become a super-aged society in 2026 with an over-65 population exceeding 20% of the total population. It is projected that there will be 18 years between the transformation from an aging society to an aged society and only 6 years between an aged society to a super-aged society, indicating that the speed of aging in Korea is ranking top among the member nations of the OECD (OECD, 2004). Although population aging is a global phenomenon, the pace is much faster in Korea than in any other developed country.

In an aging society with low fertility, economic development will slow down due to the deterioration of labor productivity as the productive labor population decreases and the working force experiences aging. In particular, a radical decrease in the fertility rate combined with rapid aging impacts a broad range of serious economic, political and social problems that are unfamiliar to us. An ineffective welfare policy and gender and age barriers to the labor market in Korea add serious social strains. Unlike the other developed countries, Korea is not fully equipped with various kinds of social security systems, so rapid aging of the population will bring significantly negative effects to the whole society and economy as well. A large increase in the expense of supporting the elderly population will seriously burden social welfare systems like pensions and medical insurance (Mun and Hah, 2007 ; Shim and Chai, 2004). Also, there will be a workforce shortage in the labor market due to the lack of a young labor force, hindering the economic growth of Korean society. Moreover, it is anticipated that the disproportionate ratio of women to men over age 65 will pose a severe problem because women in this age group tend to have less experience with economic activities and less income activities than men in this age group. Besides, since women over age 65 have not amassed a fortune for supporting their children, they will experience great financial difficulties as well as other serious issues such as health problem and loneliness (Lee, 2003).

3) Excessive concentration of population in the Seoul national capital area

The main feature of the population distribution in Korea in the past 4 decades is an excessive concentration of the population in the capital region. Rapid industrialization and urbanization have brought about unprecedented economic growth and they have also caused the excessive population concentration in the capital region. Even though the extent of net migration flow into the capital region has been mitigated slightly in recent years, the population concentration in the capital region has been intensified and the social cost caused by the over concentration has become huge. Despite the multilateral experiments and diverse policies conducted by governments in order to solve this problem, such efforts have not been effective or satisfactory yet.

The most prominent characteristics appearing after 1990 within the capital region are suburbanization and metropolitanization of the surrounding areas of Seoul. The destination of the in-migrants into the capital region has gradually changed from Seoul to Gyeonggi-*do*. In addition, there is more vigorous migration within the capital region than between the capital region and the non-the capital region. As a result of this migration pattern, the population in

Gyeonggi-*do* is rapidly increasing. Consequently, the capital region has come to occupy about half of the total population of Korea. In other words, the centralization of Seoul was transformed into the centralization of the capital region, indicating that the "one-pole-concentration in Seoul" has been reproduced in the form of the "one-pole-concentration in the capital region" (Choi and Chang, 2004). the capital region has been transformed into a megalopolis that embraces its surrounding areas. The main cause of continuous population concentration in Gyeonggi-*do* is the supply of new housing, which began with the first 5 new towns built in the capital region. The population concentration is expected to intensify because of the second and third development of new towns within the capital region.

Such an excessive concentration of population in the capital region has caused a serious problem of regional inequality. The population concentration has changed from Seoul to the capital region, bringing more intense conflict between the capital region and the non-the capital region. The construction of new towns as a resolution for the housing problem in the capital region intensifies the regional inequality by accelerating out-migration from the non-the capital region, inducing population increase in the capital region (Chang, 2002). Since the capital region has a far better environment for jobs, education and cultural facilities along with the concentration of political, economical, cultural and social power, new town development in the capital region contributes to promoting potential population inflow from the non-the capital region.

Meanwhile, the population concentration is accompanied by a traffic congestion driven by massive commuting flows within the capital region, thus resulting in environmental problems such as excessive energy consumption and air pollution. In order to alleviate the housing shortage in the capital region, attention has been given only to the quantitative supply of housing rather than to the quality of life, traffic issues and environmental problems.

3.5.2 Population Prospects and Policy Implications

When anticipating the population of Korea in the near future, the most noticeable phenomena would be the decline of the young population due to a fertility rate way below the replacement level, problems of very rapid population aging and the intensification of a population concentration in the capital region. Based on projected population estimates, the Korean population will continue to change dramatically in terms of its size, structure and distribution. Korea will have a smaller but older population as a consequence of very low fertility rates and increased longevity. The prospects for population can be reviewed through 3 aspects.

First, the transition of the TFR, which has the greatest effect on population growth in Korea, is expected to steadily decrease until 2020 and then slightly increase to 1.26 in 2030. Accordingly, the annual population growth rate will continuously decline, reaching less than 0.2 after 2010 and even reaching a negative rate of population growth by 2020. This low fertility trend not only means a decrease in newborn babies, but also leads to an insufficient workforce when these newborns reach the working age group, combined with an increase in the elderly population because of a longer life expectancy. In addition, the population growth rate will reach a negative value because of sustained low fertility rates until 2030 and accordingly the workforce population will decline, resulting in a higher percentage of aged workers. This trend suggests that a serious problem will appear in Korea in terms of social welfare and global competitiveness. Evidence from the many developed countries who tried to resolve low fertility problems earlier than Korea suggests that it is highly unlikely that fertility will rebound and reach the replacement level in the near future. It means that it is remarkably difficult to raise the fertility rates already lowered once by implementing political measures. In particular, social values such as deferred marriage, celibacy and fewer children that permeate our society hinder the implementation of policies promoting childbirth or controlling the low fertility rate. The anticipated trend of low fertility is expected to contribute to the population decline. The total population of Korea, which was 48.14 million in 2005, is estimated to be 49.34 million in 2018 and then decrease to 48.64 million in 2030. In the

Table 3.11 **Population projections in Korea, 2005-2030**

Item		2000 - 2005	2005 - 2010	2010 - 2015	2015 - 2020	2020 - 2025	2025 - 2030
Total Fertility Rate		1.26	1.13	1.16	1.18	1.22	1.26
Annual growth rate (%)		0.48	0.3	0.16	0.02	- 0.09	- 0.19
Population (million)		48.14	48.88	49.28	49.33	49.11	48.64
Population density (persons/km^2)		483	490	495	495	493	488
Life Expectancy	Male	73.4	75.6	76.6	77.6	78.5	79.4
	Female	80.5	82.4	83.3	84.2	85.1	85.9
% of population 65+		9.1	11	12.9	15.6	19.9	24.3
% of population 0 - 14		19.2	16.2	13.7	12.4	11.8	11.4
Median age		34.8	38	41	43.8	46.4	49

[Source : Statistics Korea, Population Projections for Korea, 2006].

meantime, population density in Korea, which was 483/km² in 2005, will maintain at a similar level at 488/km² in 2030 due to the population decrease (Table 3.11).

Second, the population structure will also change on a large scale. The most prominent change, because of fertility decline, will be a gradual decrease in the percentage of the young age group from 19.2% in 2005 to 11.4% in 2030. The main cause of the lower percentage for the young age group is low fertility ; however, it is also the result of an interplay between other factors such as fewer children born due to socioeconomic changes, increases in the costs of rearing children due to the increased cost of private education, a rise in the average marital age due to women's expanded participation in economic activity and avoidance of childbirth. Meanwhile, the age group over 65, which comprised 9.1% of the population in 2005, is anticipated to increase to 24.3% in 2030 due to the longer life expectancy. Consequently, the total ratio of population dependency, which was 39.4 in 2005, will decrease to the lowest point of 36.3 in 2016 and then increase again because of the increasing elderly age group and decreasing productive population, reaching 55.4 in 2030, indicating that every 2 persons from the productive population must support at least 1 person from the non-productive population. The life expectancy in Korea will continuously increase. Men's life expectancy, which was 73.4 in 2005, is expected to reach 79.4 in 2030 and women's life expectancy is expected to increase from 80.5 to 85.9 during the same period. The difference in life expectancy between men and women is expected to become slightly smaller, but there will still be more than 6 years of difference. Korea will head toward becoming an aged society due to its longer life expectancy and the decrease in newborns caused by the low fertility rate.

The effects of population aging are tremendous and profound. When it comes to a super-aged society, the burden of dependents on the productive age group will bring critical financial problems to the social security systems including national pension, healthcare insurance and basic social services. In particular, there will be a great pressure on the finances of healthcare insurance because of increased expenditure on public medical treatment due to the increased population in the age group over 65. In the face of population aging and the financial instability of the public pension and healthcare insurance systems, institutional restructuring must be undertaken seriously. For solving the problem of a declining workforce in an aging society, the most urgent matter is to revitalize the labor market. In order to revitalize the labor market, it is necessary to establish strategies for utilizing the female workforce, promoting labor activity in the youth group and increasing the participation rate of the elderly age group in the labor market. It is necessary to construct a comprehensive program, including strengthening of systematic devices to accelerate the participation of women in the labor market and life-long education, to stabilize and improve the quality of the elderly age group labor force as well as to raise the labor productivity of those newly entering the labor market.

Third, it is projected that the population concentration in the capital region will worsen, since migration flows are highly selective in terms of age and education. In-migrants into the capital region are expected to improve the competitiveness of the capital region. This is mainly because most in-migrants are younger and have a higher education level. Given that an excellent labor force should reside in the non-the capital region in order to have balanced regional development in Korea, selective migration toward the capital region by a high-level labor force will pose a serious problem. Specifically, in the era of a globalized and knowledge-based society, competitiveness between regions and cities is considered very important. Thus there will be more conflicts and difficulties. The main reason for such anticipation is that the comparative advantage possessed by the capital region will be strengthened, followed by improved competitiveness, which will accelerate population inflow from the non-the capital region to the capital region. In particular, as we are now entering into the creative economy, a group of the creative, high-level labor force will become the originator of competitiveness and creativity in regional economic development. Considering such a context, the imbalance of regional economic development may intensify. This suggests that policies attempting to lessen regional inequality should enhance the capacity of the non-the capital region to produce and attract excellent human resources as well as the necessary infrastructure. In order to alleviate the concentration of population in the capital region, a policy that can fortify competitiveness of large cities in the non-the capital region will be attractive.

Chapter 4.

SETTLEMENT

THE FORMATION AND CHANGES OF THE KOREAN SETTLEMENT SYSTEM

4.1.1 The Formation of the Korean Settlement System

Throughout their long history, Koreans have occupied the northeastern part of the Asian continent. With a good understanding of their natural environment, they have established their ecological life realm. In Paldo Chongdo (Map of the Eight Provinces) published in the 15th century of the early Joseon Dynasty, the accurate shape of the Korean Peninsula was depicted, revealing the settlement space of Koreans at that time as being the entire Korean Peninsula. It is interesting to note that the places in the central part of the Peninsula were shown in larger while the ones in the far north were smaller-a representation of Korea as seen from the capital city. Major mountains and rivers were drawn with their names indicated, as were the major cities of the eight provinces. In actuality, this was the mental map of Korea in the minds of Koreans including the map maker, who lived in the capital city, Seoul. They viewed places in Korea that were far away from Seoul as small and less important. Figure 4.1 indicates that the importance of Seoul in the Korean geographic identity was established early in the minds of Koreans and the Seoul area was established as the symbolic center of Korea.

The history of early Korean settlements can be traced as far back as the Paleolithic civilization, when settlements were scattered both in and outside of the Korean Peninsula. However, the history of the contemporary Korean settlement system started in the Neolithic civilization, when more extensive settlements were established. Often settlement systems were established when the center of the settlement space became more of a space and such spaces gradually evolved into villages, towns and larger cities and eventually into an administrative state.

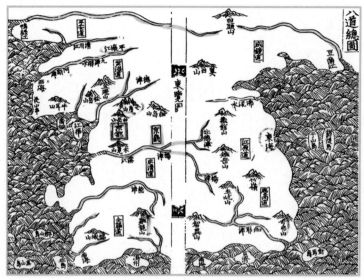

Figure 4.1 **Geographic extent of the settlement space in the Early Joseon Dynasty ; Paldo Chongdo (Donglamdo) implies a mental map envisioned by Koreans.**
(Source : Sinjeung Donggukyeojiseungram(King Chung-jong,1530))

4.1.2 The Evolution of the Settlement System and Its Characteristics

Located on the far-eastern side of the Asian continent, Korea has a mid-latitude, temperate monsoon climate. Early Korean settlements evolved from Manchuria and gradually moved into the Korean Peninsula. The various dynasties have affected where the capital city has been located. During the Three Kingdom Period (57 B.C.-935 A.D.), the capital city of the Goguryeo Kingdom in Manchuria was first in Jolbonseong, and then moved later to Guknaeseong. Following that, the capital moved south to Pyeongyang. In the southeastern Korean Peninsula, Gyeongju evolved as the capital of the Silla Dynasty, while the capital of the Baekje Kingdom was in Uiraesung, secondly Gongju and later moved to Buyeo. Following that, during the Goryeo Kingdom (918 A.D.-1392 A.D.), the capital was in Gaeseong, more centrally located in the Peninsula. The last kingdom, Joseon (1392 A.D.-1910 A.D.), established its capital in Hanyang (or Hanseong) at the location of today's Seoul (see detailed locations of previous capitals in Figure 4.2). Seoul has been the capital of Korea since 1392, which has made it an administrative presence for over 600 years. In fact, the word "Seoul" means "capital city" in the Korean language. Seoul continued to be the capital of South Korea after the partitioning of Korea in 1945, while Pyeongyang became the capital of North Korea.

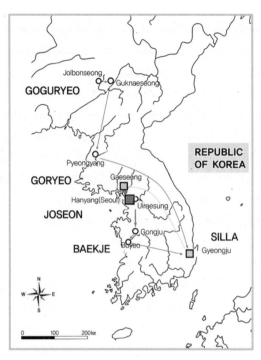

Figure 4.2 **Centralization process of the Korean settlement system.**

1) X-shaped structure of the Korea settlement system

Historically, settlement space in Korea has always been centered around the respective capital cities of the dynasties and other settlements grew outward from these centers. The capital city has been the nodal point where people, resources and information were circulated. It has been the focal point of human activities, the control point of national power and the core of national settlement networking. Seoul has been the ultimate node, usually at the territorial center, as well as the center of national authority, with the power to unite the nation. It has also been the symbolic center and a convenient location for defense and has excellent connectivity throughout the country.

Hanyang (Seoul), the hub of the transportation network, was connected to everywhere in Korea during the Joseon Dynasty. Road networks, a torch communication network and water transportation systems were located along the X-shaped network structure so that the Korean settlement system was solidified. The X-shaped structure includes 2 main transportation axes : the Gyeongbu Axis and the Honam Axis. The Gyeongbu Axis (Seoul-Busan Axis), a primary transportation network, connects the northwestern corner of Korea (Seoul) and southeastern corner (Busan), while the Honam Axis (Daejeon-Mokpo Axis), a secondary transportation

145

network, connects the mid-point of Korea (Daejeon) and the southwestern corner (Mokpo). From their daily lives to international relationships, Koreans' main activities have always been reflected along the X-shaped developmental axes. The expressways, KTX rails, broadband cable networks and other innovative technological infrastructures were all established along the X-shaped developmental axis and reinforced the basic framework. Consequently, the settlement systems along the Gyeongbu Axis that connected the capital region (Seoul National Capital Area) with the Busan metropolitan area, as well as the southeastern coastal industrial complex, grew much faster than other regions (Table 4.1).

Today, more than half of the country's population is concentrated along both axes in the X-shaped structure. The proportion of the population located in the axes increased drastically from 37.1% in 1965 to 60.5% in 1995. Since 1995, the proportion declined a little because of the population concentration in other metropolitan areas and the relative population decline along the Honam Axis. Yet the population along the X-shaped structure still dominates the country by comprising over two-thirds of the total population when all the cities in the capital region are included. This structure reinforces an already strong Seoul-Busan and southeastern coastal axis, creates a regional disparity between the X-shaped structure regions and those outside the X and expands the disparity in depth and width.

Table 4.1 **Change in spheres of Korea's main settlement axes.**

Year Population Administration Boundary		1966		1975		1985		1995		2005	
		Number	Ratio	Number	Ratio	Number	Ratio	Number	Ratio	Number	Ratio
Nation		29,159,640	100.0	34,678,972	100.0	40,419,652	100.0	44,553,710	100.0	47,041,434	100.0
SEOUL BUSAN AXIS	Seoul	3,793,280	13.2	6,879,464	19.8	9,625,755	23.8	10,217,177	22.9	9,762,546	20.8
	Incheon	525,827	1.8	797,143	2.3	1,384,916	3.4	2,304,176	5.2	2,517,680	5.4
	Anyang	52,287	0.2	134,746	0.4	361,503	0.9	590,545	1.3	609,886	1.3
	Suwon	127,733	0.4	223,718	0.6	430,487	1.1	754,670	1.7	1,039,233	2.2
	Osan	20,815	0.1	31,115	0.1	47,838	0.1	70,330	0.2	131,792	0.3
	Pyeongtaek	188,863	0.6	224,925	0.6	180,357	0.4	311,940	0.7	374,262	0.8
	Cheonan	71,182	0.2	96,663	0.3	170,085	0.4	329,622	0.7	518,171	1.1
	Yeongi-*gun*	108,945	0.4	105,223	0.3	92,604	0.2	80,763	0.2	80,389	0.2
	Daejeon	314,991	1.1	506,223	1.5	865,687	2.1	1,270,873	2.9	1,438,551	3.1
	Okcheon-*gun*	111,991	0.4	103,028	0.3	83,462	0.2	61,441	0.1	51,690	0.1
	Yeongdong-*gun*	123,564	0.4	108,939	0.3	84,725	0.2	61,973	0.1	49,338	0.1
	Gimcheon	56,850	0.2	67,031	0.2	77,190	0.2	146,923	0.3	135,166	0.3
	Gumi	21,231	0.1	41,949	0.1	142,052	0.4	309,968	0.7	381,583	0.8
	Daegu	845,189	2.9	1,309,131	3.8	2,028,370	5.0	2,445,288	5.5	2,456,016	5.2
	Cheongdo-*gun*	121,985	0.4	103,938	0.3	72,783	0.2	50,256	0.1	39,435	0.1
	Miryang	206,115	0.7	179,224	0.5	151,705	0.4	121,409	0.3	105,651	0.2
	Ulsan	112,848	0.4	252,281	0.7	550,207	1.4	966,628	2.2	1,044,934	2.2
	Busan	1,426,019	4.9	2,450,125	7.1	3,512,113	8.7	3,809,618	8.6	3,512,547	7.5
Subtotal		8,257,222	28.3	13,645,872	39.3	19,889,977	49.2	23,932,959	53.7	24,276,715	51.6
HONAM AXIS	Nonsan	259,540	0.9	226,253	0.7	191,864	0.5	146,471	0.3	124,779	0.3
	Iksan	289,706	1.0	292,335	0.8	319,921	0.8	322,134	0.7	306,974	0.7
	Gimje	254,999	0.9	221,302	0.6	170,940	0.4	115,407	0.3	90,376	0.2
	Jeonju	220,432	0.8	311,237	0.9	426,382	1.1	562,832	1.3	622,092	1.3
	Jeongeup	277,506	1.0	248,080	0.7	199,691	0.5	138,984	0.3	115,416	0.2
	Jangseong-*gun*	129,934	0.4	115,794	0.3	81,599	0.2	52,140	0.1	41,682	0.1
	Gwangju	403,495	1.4	606,468	1.7	905,673	2.2	1,257,063	2.8	1,413,644	3.0
	Naju	245,162	0.8	212,121	0.6	166,885	0.4	107,762	0.2	86,823	0.2
	Muan-*gun*	317,742	1.1	128,058	0.4	102,688	0.3	67,747	0.2	54,257	0.1
	Mokpo	162,166	0.6	192,888	0.6	236,038	0.6	247,362	0.6	244,543	0.5
Subtotal		2,560,682	8.8	2,554,536	7.4	2,801,681	6.9	3,017,902	6.8	3,100,586	6.6
Sphere Total		10,817,904	37.1	16,200,408	46.7	22,691,658	56.1	26,950,861	60.5	27,377,301	58.2

[Source : Statistics Korea, Population and Housing Census [each year]]

2) The centralization process of the Korean settlement system

The historical evolution through which the capital cities of Korea have progressively moved from the periphery areas of the Korean Peninsula toward Seoul was a part of the centralization process (Figure 4.2). It may reflect the fact that Koreans have considered Seoul as the best location in terms of landform, transportation, communication networks and other socioeconomic characteristics. Having the capital in the center of the Peninsula has provided the best accessibility to the capital from the periphery areas of Korea for the last 600 years. In that sense, solidifying the capital in the central location of Korea has created a good balance within the Korean settlement system.

3) Industrialization and changes in the settlement system

① Central tendency of population shift in South Korea

A study indicating how the population center has shifted since World War II reveals the changes in the settlement pattern in South Korea. Figure 4.3 indicates that the population center of South Korea was in the Chungcheong region and has been shifting gradually from the southeast to the northwest as Korean society has become more industrialized and the population has migrated more toward the capital region.

As shown in Figure 4.3, the population center of Korea has been Cheongwon-*gun* since 1975. However, it has shifted gradually to the northwest toward Cheongju-*si* during the last 3 decades. Currently the center of the population is in Cheongju-*si* in Chungcheongbuk-*do*. The Korean industrial structure also shifted, from manufacturing in the 1980s to information and service industries in 2005.

The shift in the population center is another indicator of changes in settlement patterns in the spatial organization of Korea. In a pre-industrial, traditional Korean society, the choice of locations was decided by Pungsu principles (Feng Shui in Chinese) that symbolized the most auspicious location. As Korean society has become industrialized and more urbanized, functional efficiency has replaced the traditional Pungsu principles in locational decision making, particularly for the high-rise apartment buildings constructed everywhere.

② Land use changes and urbanization

The changes in the settlement system triggered by urbanization can also be examined through the land use patterns. As shown in Table 4.2, there has been a major decline in agricultural and forestry land use while industrial, residential and transportation land uses have increased drastically. Consequently, the urbanized areas with surrounding residential and industrial areas have grown dramatically and most of them have been concentrated in the southeast and the capital region.

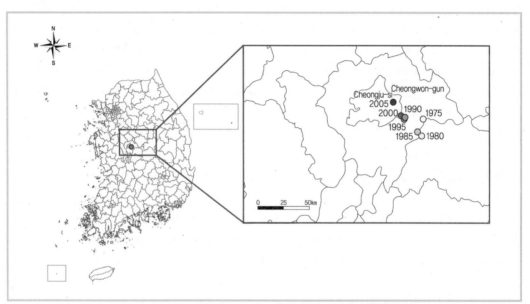

Figure 4.3 **Central tendency of the main settlement system :**
Weighted mean center of the urban population

(Source : Statistics Korea, Population and Housing Census [each year])

Table 4.2 **Changes in land use structure through the urbanization process** *(Unit : km²)*

	Total	Paddy/ Ordinary	Forest	Farm	Residence / Building Site	Factory Site	Road, Rail Site
1990	99,274	21,484	65,571	817	1,937	246	1,922
(Ratio)	(100.0)	(21.6)	(66.1)	(0.8)	(2.0)	(0.2)	(1.9)
1995	99,268	21,039	65,506	931	2,214	386	2,127
(Ratio)	(100.0)	(21.2)	(66.0)	(0.9)	(2.1)	(0.4)	(2.1)
2000	99,461	20,507	65,139	1,088	2,349	514	2,397
(Ratio)	(100.0)	(20.7)	(65.6)	(1.1)	(2.4)	(0.5)	(2.4)
2005	99,646	20,108	64,805	1,108	2,533	622	2,685
(Ratio)	(100.0)	(20.3)	(65.3)	(1.1)	(2.6)	(0.6)	(2.7)
2006	99,678	20,012	64,731	1,113	2,575	644	2,747
(Ratio)	(100.0)	(20.2)	(65.2)	(1.1)	(2.6)	(0.6)	(2.8)

(Source : Statistics Korea).

4) The evolution of the major settlement system

Throughout Korean history there have been numerous major structural changes in the settlement system. There were not only changes in administrative boundaries that redefined the settlement units, but also political and social changes that brought about changes in the names of places as well as in their functions. After World War II, the major change was the division of Korea along the 38th Parallel, creating North and South Korea. The Korean War in 1953 brought revolutionary changes not only in population redistribution, but also in the spatial organization of the settlement system. Today the border between North and South Korea is along the Demilitarized Zone (DMZ) following the cease fire line. Refugees' migration and the population shift created by the division of the country from the north to south, as well as mass migration during the Korean War, forced people to move to the southern tip of Korea.

There has been a major shift in population since the 1960s when Korea moved toward industrialization and many cities started to expand. Although industrialization brought rapid urbanization, historical inertia tended to keep the same administrative boundaries for most of the cities. Therefore, it was necessary to reexamine the settlement system in the light of the changes in transportation and communication, daily commuting systems and regional special characteristics and their changes.

4.1.3 The Present Korean Settlement System and Its Characteristics

The Korean settlement system consists of 1 capital city, 6 metropolitan cities, 8 provinces (*do*) and 1 special self-governing province (Teukbyeoljachi-*do*). Under the provincial (*do*) governments, cities (*si*) and counties (*gun*) are the lower level administrative units and under the metropolitan cities and the capital city, large neighborhood districts called *gu* are the local governing units. The capital city is Seoul and the 6 metropolitan cities are Busan, Incheon, Daegu, Daejeon, Gwangju and Ulsan. In the "smaller than metropolitan" category, there are 23 medium-level cities and 52 smaller cities those are urban-rural combinations. These 52 smallest municipalities sometimes include *myeon* (village) and *eup* (town) in their administrative areas. Jeju is a special self-governing province including the 2 cities of Jeju and Seogwipo, but it also includes many *eup* and villages. Overall, South Korea has 86 counties (*gun*) and relatively larger cities with large neighborhood units (*gu*). These cities are in the capital region, namely Suwon, Seongnam, Goyang, Bucheon, Ansan, Yongin, Anyang and other provincial cities of Cheongju, Jeonju and Pohang.

The capital city of Seoul and the surrounding Gyeonggi-*do* have the largest concentration of population in Korea with each having over 10 million people. These two land areas are only 10.79% of South Korea however, the population is 43.23% of the South Korean total population (Table 4.3). Such a skewed pattern of population distribution is also shown in terms of the number of cities by province : Gyeonggi-*do* has 27 cities ; Gyeongsangnam-*do*, 10 cities ; and Gyeongsangbuk-*do*, 10 cities ; this indicates again the strong regional concentration along the Seoul-Busan Axis.

Table 4.3 **List of integrated administration units of Korea**

	Pop. (1,000)	Ratio (%)	Area (km^2)	Ratio (%)	City	County	Gu	Eup	Myeon	Dong
Seoul	10,192	20.69	605	0.61	0	0	25	0	0	518
Busan	3,587	7.28	765	0.77	0	1	15	2	3	218
Daegu	2,493	5.06	884	0.88	0	1	7	3	6	134
Incheon	2,664	5.41	1,007	1.01	0	2	8	1	19	123
Gwangju	1,413	2.87	501	0.50	0	0	5	0	0	91
Daejeon	1,475	2.99	539	0.54	0	0	5	0	0	81
Ulsan	1,099	2.23	1,057	1.06	0	1	4	4	8	46
Gyeonggi-*do*	11,106	22.54	10,183	10.18	27	4	20	31	108	395
Gangwon-*do*	1,503	3.05	16,873	16.67	7	11	0	24	90	74
Chungcheongbuk-*do*	1,506	3.06	7,431	7.43	3	9	2	14	89	50
Chungcheongnam-*do*	1,995	4.05	8,600	8.60	7	9	0	24	147	41
Jeollabuk-*do*	1,862	3.78	8,062	8.06	6	8	2	14	145	85
Jeollanam-*do*	1,929	3.92	12,121	12.12	5	17	0	31	198	66
Gyeongsangbuk-*do*	2,681	5.44	19,025	19.02	10	13	2	35	202	104
Gyeongsangnam-*do*	3,196	6.49	10,524	10.52	10	10	0	22	177	115
Jeju special self-governing province	559	1.13	1,848	1.85	2	0	0	7	5	31
Total	49,260	100.0	100,025	100.0	77	86	95	212	1,197	2,172

(Source : Ministry of Public Administration and Security, 2008, Local Governments and Population).

As Korean society became industrialized and more urbanized, the proposed urban areas included 17,043 km2, i.e., 17.1% of the total area of South Korea, while the percent of people in the urban areas was about 90% of the total population in 2005. At the same time, the rural population was only about 10% of the nation's population, which makes South Korea an extremely urbanized society with seriously low agricultural contribution. As a result, urban areas have growing problems associated with population concentrations, such as environmental pollution, housing shortages and higher crime rates, all of which exacerbate the quality of life in the cities.

4.1.4 Functional Changes in Settlement Pattern

In Korea everyone traditionally lived in single detached homes. Since the 1970s, apartment living has become popular and by 2005, as many as 53% of all housing units were apartment types, an even higher percentage than single detached homes (Table 4.4). Korean apartments are mostly owner-occupied condominiums rather than rental units and this change to apartment life is a reflection of lifestyle changes. Such a rapid change to apartment living is unprecedented in the world and it is explained by the fast urbanization process and increased nuclear rather than extended family living, as well as an increased number of households.

As urbanization accelerated, massive housing units were constructed in the Greater Seoul area. Apartment units were the easiest type of housing units to supply the masses in a short time and the convenience of apartment life brought the apartment boom to the Korean housing market. Subsequently, there were speculative demand and supply issues that created confusion in the housing market. In the capital region, there has always been a great demand for housing regardless of the fact that it has the greatest supply of apartments in the capital region. Bundang in Seongnam, Ilsan in Goyang, Jungdong in Bucheon, Pyeongchon in Anyang, Yeongtong in Suwon, Jukjeon and Suji in Yongin and Pangyo in Seongnam all have massive high-rise apartment complexes, the equivalent of which is unseen anywhere else in the world.

Most of the new housing units were built along the Seoul-Busan Axis, which is a natural trend considering that the population and settlement concentration is along the same axis (Figure 4.4). Distribution of households strongly followed the same Seoul-Busan Axis tendency. In summary, the growth of the Seoul-Busan Axis reflects not just a simple population concentration, but also household changes and distribution, as well as new housing construction plans.

Table 4.4 **Changes in residential house type**

Kind of Residential House	1975		1985		1995		2005	
	No. of Units	Ratio	No. of Units	Ratio	No. of Units	Ratio	No. of Units	Ratio
Total	4,734,169	100	6,104,210	100	9,204,929	100	12,494,827	100
Detached House	4,381,772	93	4,719,464	78	4,337,105	47	3,984,954	32
Apartment	89,248	2	821,606	13	3,454,508	38	6,626,957	53
Row House	164,718	3	349,985	6	734,172	8	520,312	4
Apt. Unit in a Private House	–	–	–	–	336,356	4	1,164,251	9
Dwelling Unit in the Building	98,431	2	213,155	3	342,788	4	198,353	2

(Source : Statistics Korea).

CHAPTER 4

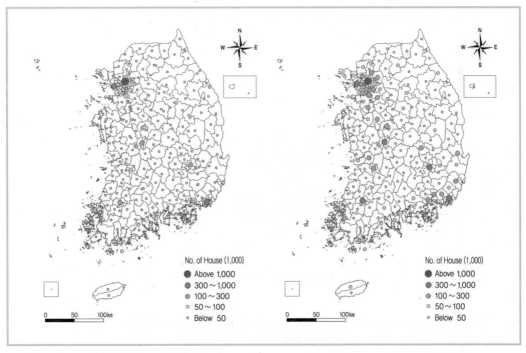

Figure 4.4 **Distribution patterns of Korean houses (Left : 1995, Right : 2005).**
(Source : Statistics Korea)

4.1.5 The Development of a Spatial Settlement Network and Its Characteristics

The framework of a spatial settlement system is determined by the transportation network. This is because the daily commuting pattern, which is the core of a settlement system, is the direct result of daily movement patterns between regions (Figure 4.5). The following is an analysis of the spatial network of a Korean settlement system based on the origin and destination matrix of express bus lines. All of South Korea is well connected by express bus lines and the analysis of its connectivity tells the story of regional connectivity.

1) Settlement connectivity of the Seoul national capital area

In this system, Seoul is the destination and the surrounding regions are the originating points. In addition to Seoul, Incheon and Suwon dominate as nodal points (Figure 4.5). The connectivity pattern mainly shows the daily commuting pattern to work and to school when people use the bus regularly. Bus commuting connectivity to the capital region also includes some interaction from the Chungcheong region and from even farther places throughout the entire country, which is expected since Seoul is the hub of the national network.

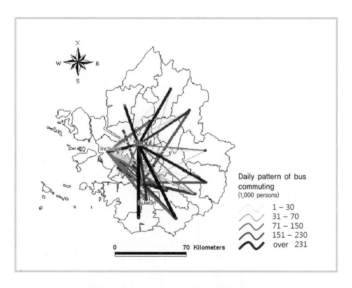

Figure 4.5 **Linkages in the Seoul National Capital Area
: Seoul is the hub of the network.**
(Source : Tour and Transportation Timetable (Train-Culture Travel ,2008))

2) Settlement connectivity in the Chungcheong (Daejeon-Cheongju) region

Daejeon metropolitan city dominated as the highest-order city in this region, followed by Cheongju. Consequently, these two cities emerged as the Daejeon-Cheongju Greater Metropolitan Area in terms of land use and the commuting pattern. The next-order cities include the local centers of Cheonan, Asan, Seosan, Chungju and Jecheon.

3) Settlement connectivity in the Gangwon region

In the mountainous Gangwon-*do* region, the transportation network is determined by the hilly landform. This region is divided into Yeongseo and Yeongdong, meaning the west side and the east side of the mountain range. Because of its hilly landform, there is no clear regional nodal core in this region, but several local cities play a role of local transportation centers. Chuncheon and Wonju are the local transportation centers in Yeongseo and Gangneung and Sokcho are identified as the local transportation centers in Yeongdong. There are smaller-order local towns nested within these cities.

4) Settlement connectivity in the Gyeongsang (Busan-Daegu) region

Busan metropolitan city is the highest-order nodal center of this region, followed by Daegu metropolitan city with its broad transportation network. The next-order nodal centers are major industrial cities, Ulsan, Pohang and Changwon, with other lower-order places connected to these four major regional nodal centers.

5) Settlement connectivity in the Honam (Gwangju-Jeonju) region

Gwangju metropolitan city is the highest-order nodal point of this region, followed by the second-order city, Jeonju. Below them in rank are Mokpo, Yeosu, Iksan, Gunsan and Gwangyang, which are important nodal points in this region as well as centers of their own hinterlands.

Figure 4.6 shows the above-mentioned major nodal points and the regional connectivity based on the daily bus traffic volume between the identified cities as they were reported in 2005. Seoul was clearly the national hub and the highest-order in the settlement system, followed by the 6 metropolitan cities of Busan, Daegu, Incheon, Daejeon, Gwangju and Ulsan, as well as the other cities of Jeonju, Chuncheon and Pohang, which emerged as regional centers. Cheongju, Gangneung, Sokcho, Samcheok, Mokpo, Yeosu, Masan and Jinju are also important local nodal points shown in Figure 4.6.

In summary, the entirety of South Korea is connected to the daily urban system centered in Seoul. All the other cities are nested, second-order cities of Seoul, which in turn make the population concentration in the capital region more extensive. The 2005 statistics indicated a slowing down of the population increase in the Greater Seoul area. The main task of the future settlement system of Korea is how to decentralize the population from the capital region. Solutions being implemented and evaluated include more use of personal cars, extension of bus lines to the suburbs of Seoul, new KTX express rails and regional air services, all of which should help to decentralize the population.

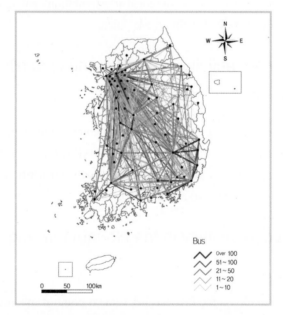

Figure 4.6 **Daily operation numbers of buses between cities.**
(Source : Tour and Transportation Timetable (Train-Culture Travel ,2008)

CHANGES IN RURAL SETTLEMENTS

4.2.1 The Formation of Rural Settlements and Their Characteristics

1) Farming villages

The location and distribution of farming villages is closely related to the distribution of agricultural land, the basis of an agricultural economy. Most Korean farming villages have been located along rivers, on the fertile alluvial fans at the bases of low lying hills or on the slopes of hills. Such physical placement is well suited to an ideal settlement location, according to the Pungsu (Feng shui in Chinese) principle of mountains in the back and water in the front (Baesan Imsu).

The naturally evolved early rural villages often had irregularly-shaped, clustered settlements. A majority of rural central places, however, were clustered along a major road, forming linear rural settlements. In direct contrast, villages established in association with the large-scale farms created from the tidal flat reclamation of the 20th century had regular settlement patterns. Such settlements initially emerged during the Japanese occupation, but they grew from utilizing 5 to 10 houses, which were dispersed near the center of the reclaimed land. After 1945, new farming villages in the tidal flat area were separated from reclaimed farm land and formed clustered villages. Typical examples of the former were the Okgu, Mimyeon and Gimje, Gwanghwal reclamation sites, while the Gyehwa site was representative of the latter.

Rural settlements could be identified as clustered or dispersed villages based on the density of population and the distance to their fields. The types of crops, especially rice, determined whether the village was dispersed or clustered. A rice crop could support more people per unit area than any other crop and it had always been the preferred grain for Koreans. Rice cultivation traditionally required much cooperative work amongst villagers. Confucian cultural practices and the Pungsu principle also helped to establish clustered villages. Intensive, large-scale rice cultivation was possible on the erosional basins or depositional plains along the middle or lower reaches of the major rivers in Korea. Clustered villages on the plains were the core of Korean agricultural settlements. Providing a direct contrast, on the western slope of the Taebaek Mountains, dispersed villages were scattered on the high plateau areas where upland dry field cultivation was practiced. The only other scattered villages not related to this high plateau situation were found in the Taean Peninsula on Chungcheongnam-*do*. The dispersed villages found in this area were more related to the large-scale tidal flat reclamation utilized to expand farm land in the 1960s (Lee, Moon-Jong 1988 ; Choi, Ki-Yeop 1985).

2) Fishing villages

Korea has many fishing villages along its three-sided coast line. Although the main focus of these villages is fishing, the characteristics of the coastal area, i.e., rocky coast or sandy beach, determine the functions of the villages. Such patterns can be easily compared along the East Coast where both types of beaches are usually interspersed. Along the area of a rocky coastline, the depth of the harbor at the entrance to the bay area is deep therefore, it is easy to build wave breakers or harbor facilities. This, in turn, accommodates the structuring of the settlement. Fishing villages are formed based on how much of their livelihood depends on fishing. The typical land use pattern of these fishing villages is as follows : the fishing-related facilities are built along the narrow strip of land near the fishing harbor, the clustered villages are established on the hillside and a small parcel of arable land is set aside farther inland from the coast for the villagers' agricultural use.

On the other hand, where sandy beach coasts are found due to the shallow sea, it is unfavorable to build a fishing port. The well-established coastal plains provide the basis for agricultural activities. Therefore, in these areas, although they are located on the coast, their economic basis is totally agricultural. Typically, villages are located near their farm land and often trees are planted as wind breakers between the beach and the farm fields. Many fishing villages along the West Coast of Korea have such situations because the shallow sea prevents them from building a good fishing harbor. This explains why there are no larger towns, but many small farming/fishing villages relying on small-scale aquaculture and fishery. Typically, traditional larger towns along the West Coast have been the salt-producing towns because of the proximity of salt flats (Kim, Ilki, 1988). With the decline of the sun-produced salt industry, these towns have lost population. The characteristics of the southern coastal towns are somewhat similar to those of these eastern and western coastal towns.

Most recently, the rapid decline of marine resources has influenced the foundation of the fishing economy. Along the west coast especially, the foundation of the fishing industry has been weakening rapidly as more land is being reclaimed for other purposes. Consequently, fishing villages that do not have other economic foundations are now rapidly declining. Most of the coastal villages look for financial alternatives in resort development and tourism as a way to maintain their economy and to satisfy the increasing demand for tourism and recreation from an affluent Korean society. For instance, any coastal areas that have sandy beaches are being converted to swimming beaches. At the same time, the tidal mud flats are also being changed from future reclamation candidates or shellfish harvesting locations to "Experiential Tourism" destinations where people actually participate in activities in these areas.

3) Mountain villages

There are 2 types of mountain villages, according to their origins : farming and mining villages. Typically, traditional mountain villages consist of the family farmstead located in a high plateau area where the slash and burn method for clearing fields has been practiced. Since 1960, the practice has been prohibited and a reforestation program has successfully recovered most of the forest area. Some of the remaining mountain villages are located in the upper reaches of rivers and practice specialized agriculture that requires cool weather. These villages are also being converted to tourist destinations while still producing specialized crops. Even with these benefits, the areas have experienced continuing out-migration of their population to the larger cities.

The other types of mountain villages were the mining-associated villages located in the very mountainous terrain. Mining towns in Korea were mostly associated with anthracite coal mines. However, after 1980, the Korean government adopted the "Rationalization of the Coal Industry" policy and closed all of the inefficient and uneconomical coal mines. These coal mining towns lost their original function and became ghost towns. Only the coal museums established in some of the mining towns remain as silent testimony to the previously important function of the towns.

4.2.2 The Changes in Farming and Fishing Villages

Rural settlements in Korea's rapidly urbanizing society are no longer the self-sufficient, self- contained, closed systems of previous years. Although there may be some degree of difference, all the villages have become a part of the reorganized open system centered on major urban settlement systems. In this process, the new characteristics of rural settlements depend on the level of influence they receive from the central place. In the urbanization process, a massive migration of the Korean population to cities has taken place at the same time that out-migration from rural settlements has been occurring. Such a population exchange has brought changes in agriculture and in the entire rural economy. The typology of the migration determines the demographic, social and economic structure of rural settlements and eventually each village becomes specialized according to its role related to the central city (Park, Young-Han and Cho, Young-Kug, 2004).The rural settlements experience quantitative as well as qualitative changes in agriculture and the agricultural labor force, in order to respond to the commerciality of the central market of their open systems. The opening of the Korean agricultural market to the world economy has also been one of the major contributing factors to the structural changes of Korean rural settlements. The changes do not follow a uniform pattern, but they vary depending on the influence of the central urban areas. As a result, the economy of rural villages has become diversified and specialized. Traditional homogeneous farming communities have now converted into economically more diversified settlements. This is a phenomenon seen in the rural economy of de-industrialized societies and Korean rural settlements are no exception.

1) Diversification process of farming and fishing villages

As Korea has moved toward being a de-industrialized society, rural settlements have evolved a new dimension. Spatial rearrangements of rural settlements now depend on the socioeconomic influence of the central city. The influence of the central cities varies depending on the accessibility to the city in terms of communication and transportation.

Accessibility to cities from rural settlements created a new epoch in the 1990s and has allowed for tremendous improvements in rural spatial arrangements. First, in regard to the transportation network : continuous new construction and expansion of expressways has diminished the differences in regional accessibility that existed previously. Though limited in some rural areas, the opening of new express rails has improved accessibility between regions. Primary and secondary highways have all been paved and major local highways have been widened, allowing most rural areas equal access to urban centers, as well as between regions.

Second, in regard to communication networking : rural information extension services have brought better accessibility to information. Provincial universities now have rural extension education services with all *guns* in the provinces and Chung-cheongbuk-*do* is the leader in programming. Such improvements in transportation and communication networking have allowed rural settlements to become nested within the hierarchies of higher order cities in the Korean urban system.

At the same time, opening the agricultural product market to free trade has brought about major changes in rural settlements and their spatial organization. As competitors producing agricultural products for the overseas market, the majority of Korean farmers who are small-scale producers can no longer compete and survive in the business. Agriculture in Korea can no longer be the traditional subsistence farming to support families, but instead has taken the new survival approach of becoming commercial farming with supplementary non-farming income. In that sense, the close ties with central urban markets have become more crucial than ever for the survival of rural settlements.

According to Yim, Seok-Hoi (2005), realizing the above-mentioned impact and the socioeconomic changes, rural farming communities have evolved into 5 types of diversified settlements. To differentiate among the types, Yim uses 5 major categories-population characteristics, industrial structure characteristics, agricultural characteristics, economic sustainability and information technology-as well as 14 other variables. He classifies the newly changing Korean rural farming settlements into 5 new types : Manufacturing-Mining (Type A), Retail-Service (Type B), Dry Fields-Orchard (Type C), Fishery (Type D) and Paddy Field-Common Farm (Type E) (Figure 4.7).

The Manufacturing-Mining settlements (Type A) are found in the capital or near the capital region, as well as in other major metropolitan areas. The remainder of the Type A settlements is located on the west coast close to the capital region, in the interior industrial area of the Southeast, or along the coastal industrial area of the Southeast. Type A settlements are heavily influenced by urbanization and industrialization ; most settlements are within the commuting zone of cities of 200,000 or more. These settlements provide vegetables to the city residents (i.e., a market gardening agriculture).

The Retail-Service settlements (Type B) include settlements that have relatively more services, retail businesses, wholesale markets, restaurants and hotel and lodging areas. Type B settlements are found in areas adjacent to the DMZ where many military facilities are located. A higher proportion of food and lodging services are found in northeastern Gyeonggi-*do* and tourism and resort areas are more visible on the East Coast and in Gangwon-*do*. The relative

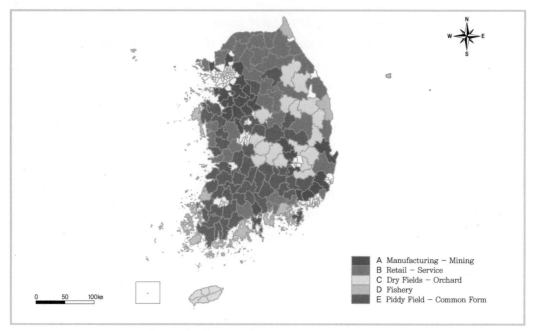

Figure 4.7 **Rural Settlement Types** *(Source : Yim, Seok-Hoi(2005))*

importance of tourism-related services, compared to other economic activities, makes these areas more specialized because of these activities.

The Dry Fields-Orchard settlements (Type C), together with the Paddy Field-Common Farm settlements (Type E), are still the most traditional farming-oriented rural settlements. The difference between Types C and E is that the former is mainly farming taking place on a dry field while the latter takes place in a rice paddy field. Type C settlements are found mainly in the interior area of Gyeongsangbuk-*do*, the northern part of the province and in southern Gangwon-*do*, as well as in the typical orchard farming area of Jeju special self-governing province. Most of the orchards are located along the hillsides or in the cooler mountainous areas.

The Fishery settlements (Type D) are found along coastal areas, but all coastal areas do not necessarily belong to this group. Type D settlements are more prominent in fishing areas than the other types are. Type D settlements are concentrated in the coastal regions of Jeollanam-*do* and Gyeongsangnam-*do*. The lower number of Fishery settlements in Gangwon-*do* does not necessarily indicate a lack of fishing villages, but reflects a higher dependency on tourism-related retail services (Type B), which have a higher percentage in this particular area.

The Rice Paddy Field-Common Farm settlements (Type E) are most typically Korean farms that have rice paddy fields. Geographically this type is distinctly separated from the

Type C settlements. The Type E settlements are mainly in Jeollanam-*do* and Jeollabuk-*do* where large-scale, mechanized rice fields are concentrated. Although the areas are identified as specifically Type E because the areas are best suited to rice cultivation, it is more important to note that the areas are solely dependent on rice cultivation, which creates a lack of opportunities for any other economic activities.

In summary, the classification of rural settlements into the 5 types is mainly determined by which is more important to the settlement's economic strength : agricultural activities or non-agricultural activities. However, the main variable that makes rural settlements diversely specialized into these groups is not the agricultural practice itself, but the supporting factor of the settlements' integration into the central cities' economy, especially the distance to the metropolitan areas or the core industrial centers.

2) Changes in the remote farming settlements

In the process of rapid urbanization, rural settlements witnessed an extreme population decline, which in turn caused the lack of an adequate labor force and the weakening of all types of service functions within the rural settlements. This eventually reached the "severe depopulation" stage, where even sustaining life could be a challenge. Such severe depopulation processes and compounded problems associated with these phenomena were even more severe in a country such as Korea, where urbanization and industrialization had taken place in such a short time (Park, Young-Han and Joh, Young-guk, 2004).

Since the late 1960s, a rapid decline of rural population in absolute numbers has been caused by the rapid out-migration from all rural settlements. Consequently, the population of most rural settlements today has declined to less than half of that found 40 years ago and the decline is even more severe in remote farming communities. The shortage of an adequate labor force in remote farming villages is even more serious than in other rural areas. The severe depopulation process and selective migration have brought about a serious shortage in the farming labor force and farming is left to an elderly population. Some young men who have remained in farming have difficulties in finding Korean young women willing to live in rural areas and a growing number of mail-order international brides from Vietnam or the Philippines have brought about new social concerns. Language barriers, cultural adjustment, the loneliness of these women and discrimination against the children of these couples in more or less homogeneous Korean rural villages are some of the problems associated with the lack of population in remote rural farming villages.

In modern-day Korea a majority of farming households have no one to continue the family farm. Therefore, idling farms or relinquishing the farming rights are widespread practices. If this trend continues, some of these villages will cease to exist due to the lack of a working population or anyone performing farming practices. Outside factors, such as free trade, have worsened the situation of the remote farming villages and made them struggle even further for existence.

The struggles of farmers in an industrialized society have already been witnessed in more developed countries. Presently, the Japanese and some European governments subsidize farmers who struggle to survive in disadvantaged farming communities. Recently, the Korean government has provided subsidies for rice farmers who are affected by the free trade agreement in order for them to maintain the acreage of rice paddy fields. Farmers in remote areas need similar supportive programs from the government in order to be able to maintain traditional family farming.

3) Changes in farming settlements adjacent to urban centers

Urban sprawl is the typical settlement pattern found when a society moves to the advanced industrialized stage. The spatial range of the urban area is typically within an hour's commuting time from an urban center. The areas of urban sprawl often include many rural settlements of various functions and different landscapes. There are many situations relating to urban sprawl. In some rural villages most of the fields have been converted to residential, commercial and industrial land and only a few residents remain involved in farming. Other rural areas that appear to have operational farming activities actually have industrial and commercial buildings, as well as some warehouses along major roads. These areas are typically already owned by urban residents for speculative purposes. Some of these rural landscapes may appear to remain the same ; however, one can find the urban influence everywhere. More commuters (who work in the city), rather than farmers, live in the area, and most of the land has already been purchased by urban residents. In short, the degrees of influence from the central city may vary from the largest city, Seoul, to smaller urban areas, but the effect scan be found everywhere.

Rural settlements within the urban realm have close ties to the central urban area in many aspects of their economy. There are two contrasting land use patterns and the rural cultural landscape is influenced by the urban center. The first contrasting pattern is that the land is usually left idle at the edge of an urban area without being used as farm land because of the low monetary return on farm land. The landowner farmers wait until the zoning of the parcel is converted to urban land use, at which time they can sell the land for a large profit. These new landowners, if they do decide to cultivate, have a very small scale "hobby farm" and most of the land remains untended. The second pattern includes the most intensively used farms. Their close proximity to the urban area gives them the competitive advantage of market gardening. They can provide fresh vegetables and flowers to the city residents with a decided profit. Often many parcels of land are owned by speculative urban landowners so that they can rent the large plots of land to be used for hot houses where cultivation can take place all year round. Speculators, well aware of the fact that the land cannot be maintained as farm land for too long, make the most intensive use of chemicals to produce the best yield within the limited time (Park, Younghan and Cho, Youngkug, 2004). This provides a positive return on their investment and reinforces the benefits derived from this type of speculation. These two contrasting agricultural land use patterns can most commonly be found outside of metropolitan areas, especially near Seoul. Abundant, large-scale hot houses in the midst of empty lots with tall weeds comprise the common rural cultural landscape today.

There is a new phenomenon evolving at the edge of metropolitan areas as society becomes de-industrialized and more environmentally friendly. Consumers now demand fresh, healthier, organic agricultural products regardless of the higher prices. Despite the higher production cost and lower yield involved in the initialization of organic farming, the higher price of the organic product can overcome the difference and organic farming is on the rise.

4) Changing characteristics of Korea's rural society

Urbanized Korean society has methodically changed the composition of Korean rural society. Korean rural society has changed from a traditional homogeneous society to a diverse heterogeneous one. Rural communities located at the edges of urban areas are now occupied by not only the farmers who have lived and farmed there for generations, but also the commuters to the city or the workers employed by the businesses newly located there. Although they all live in the same community, there is little interaction among them due to their different lifestyles, social relationships and value systems. As a result, previously homogeneous rural communities have changed to diverse, heterogeneous residential spaces. There are other factors reinforcing the heterogeneity of rural settlements-one is the migration of urban residents to single homes in the country to escape high-rise condominiums. Living in a single detached home in a rustic rural setting can be reached either by moving into an existing farm house or residing in a newly established subdivision. In the case of the capital region, residential suburbs can range along a radius of 25-30 kilometers from Seoul, while the newly established exurban (or suburban) subdivisions are concentrated within a radius of 30-

60 kilometers (Park, Younghan and Joh, Youngkug, 2004). Rural settlements within the range of an urban center can vary greatly in terms of resident composition and farming practice.

The changing Korean rural settlements near the urban areas can be divided into 4 groups of concentric rings according to settlement patterns and their agricultural practices (Lee, Jaeduk, 1996). The first area, just outside of the city, is the rapid conversion ring of farms to urban areas, where agriculture has become obsolescent. This is called the "obsolescent agriculture type." The second area is the gradual suburbanization area where traditional agriculture declines while commercial agriculture emerges. This is known as the "urban-farming type." The third area farther out from the city is where rice fields are still important, yet intensive commercial farming has changed the area into the "commercial suburban farming type." The fourth ring, farthest from the city, is where both rice and dry fields are coexisting, the "traditional farming type." These 4types of farming and agricultural practices have a close relationship and can be found in all rural areas of Korea today. The main difference is in the extent to which the influence of each central city reaches into the surrounding farming communities. That is usually determined by and varies according to the hierarchy and the size of the central urban area.

Chapter 4.3.

GROWTH AND CHANGES IN URBAN AREAS

4.3.1 Location and Growth of Korean Cities

1) Origin and growth of cities

The earliest cities in the world were established in the Fertile Crescent along the Tigris and Euphrates River Valley around 3,000-4,500 B.C. The early cities, such as Eridu and Ur, had an infrastructure of temple grounds, fortresses, harbors, canals and warehouses, as well as a social structure that consisted of a well-established social system for conducting trade. Often scholars have overemphasized the location's fertile farm land and the surplus agricultural products. Such a traditional emphasis has been viewed as over-accentuating the agricultural environment. It would be more appropriate to recognize the importance of innovation and the political power structure that helped the movement of the population, the dissemination of information and the distribution of goods, which were the more important functions of the cities.

In Korea, the definition of a city is established by law, which states that it must be a place that has a population of at least 50,000 (Local Government Act ; 7-1 Clause). The location of the earliest city that Dangun (the legendary founder of ancient Korea) was supposed to have established is not clear. The creation of this first city is in the Korean creation mythology. The earliest capital cities that were well documented in written Korean history are Jolbonseong and Guknaeseong of the Goguryeo Dynasty in Manchuria. Goguryeo's territory reached most of the Manchu Plain, including Laohe and the Songhua River, a tributary of the Amur River. During the Three Kingdoms (Goguryeo, Baekje and Silla) period (B.C. 57-935 A.D.), within the Korean Peninsula, the capital cities of Gyeongju, Gongju, Buyeo and Pyeongyang each emerged in turn. These early pre-industrial cities, such as Gyeongju and Pyeongyang,

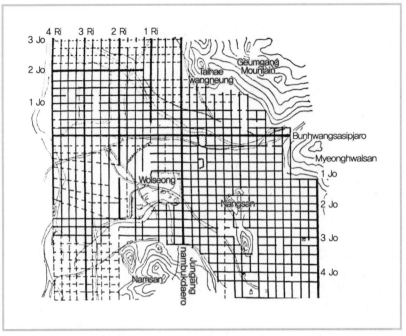

Figure 4.8 **Restored map of the planned city of Gyeongju and its Bang-ri (grid format) system.**
(Source : Lee, 1999)

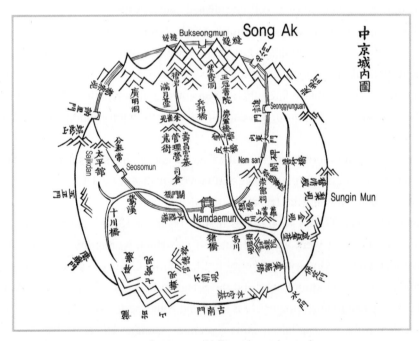

Figure 4.9 **Gaeseong's Pungsu urban plan.**
(Source : Joseon Kwangmunhoe, 1915)

established major dykes and managed the layout of the capital cities according to careful planning. They also had many functional districts within the city limits. Figure 4.8 shows a restored map of the planned city of Gyeongju and its Bang-ri (grid format) system.

2) The Location and Development of Pre-Industrial Cities

① The development of cities in the Goryeo Dynasty

When the first king of the Goryeo Dynasty, King Wang Geon, united the Korean Peninsula from The Later Three Kingdoms, he established Gaeseong as its capital and built all the functional areas of the city according to Pungsu principles (Figure 4.9). The Goryeo Dynasty kept most of the Korean Peninsula as its territory and established an excellent administrative system while developing new production technologies. As agricultural productivity increased, providing plentiful regional specialties and surplus products, rural periodic markets developed for the purpose of exchanging goods and surplus products. To transport agricultural products to the region's capital city of Gaeseong (formerly Gaegyeong), a water transportation network was established utilizing the nearby Yeasung River. In addition, a new road network was established as part of the infrastructure centered in Gaeseong. The entire country was also connected by a torch-based communication network (Bongsu network). Gaeseong was more accessible to the rest of the country than any other city under Goryeo control and due to its central location, it had the best connectivity with all the other cities of the Goryeo regime. For the greatest protection of the capital city, Gaeseong was built with double fortress walls and the functional division of the city was separated into 5 districts and 35 sub-districts. It also had a capital city market. To utilize the market, international trade was well developed with many dynasties in China, mainly the Song Dynasty, but with connections extending as far away as Arabian countries.

② Development of cities during the Joseon Dynasty

The first king of the Joseon Dynasty, Taejo Yi Seong-gye, moved the capital of the new kingdom to Seoul (formerly called Hanseong, then Hanyang) in 1394. He divided the new state into 8 provinces and built a major road network centered in Seoul, utilizing a star-shaped (or X-shaped) thoroughfare. These thoroughfares became the main framework of the settlement system at the time by providing connections to the local transportation network. Later, this same framework became the basic structure of today's transportation network in Korea. By the time of King Sejong, the fourth and most well-known king of the Joseon Dynasty, a Korean settlement system for the entire Korean Peninsula, along with a major

169

transportation network, was already established. During his reign, waterways were built for the entire country to transport regional staples and rice for tax to Seoul's warehouses.

The location of the capital city, Seoul, was chosen by the ideal Pungsu principle of the crouching tiger, Inwang Mountain, to the right and of the hidden dragon, Nak Mountain, to the left, with the Han River in front and Bukhan Mountain behind. The location of other regional cities also followed the Pungsu principle and smaller towns were established wherever local government branch offices were located. Occasionally, a *eup* was located on the plains however, with rare exceptions. All the cities in Korea followed the Pungsu principle of "Baesan Imsu," meaning "mountains in back and water in front" (Figure 4.10). Since the Korean landform frequently has Quaternary erosion basins carved by rivers, it is natural to find "Baesan Imsu" locations being used for villages and towns. The Korean landform is very mountainous and there are plenty of basins open to the south for rivers or streams. Well protected by the hills from the prevailing northwest wind in winter, traditional towns and cities all followed the ideal Pungsu principle. Hills and mountains in the back provided secondary or tertiary lines of fortification, while a river in front provided both drinking water and easy access to transportation. Hillsides often provided more variety of flora and fauna, while mountains provided firewood and lumber, or other special products of the region. At the summit of the mountains, fortresses or torch platforms were built for protection or emergency communication networks. At other times sacred symbolic places or other necessary locations were placed there. The wide open basin, created by the main river in front and tributaries, provided the plain where agricultural and other productive activities were performed. Any

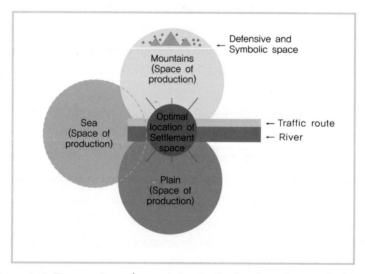

Figure 4.10 **Baesan Imsu (mountains in the back and water in front)
: Ideal environment for human habitation.**

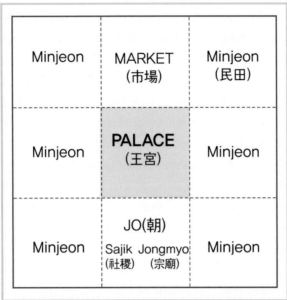

Figure 4.11 **Internal structure of Han Seong Bu urban area (following the Pungsu principles and Ju Rye)**
(Source : http://seoul600.visitseoul.net)

special or excess products from the region were then transported by the river and often exchanged for products from the ocean. Such nodal points were where the traditional markets were held. Korea had a well-developed traditional periodic (5-day) market network covering the entire Korean Peninsula. These markets were located in Baesan Imsu sites and they provided important functioning market points in the urban settlements, which became the traditional Korean urban system.

The spatial organization of cities in the Joseon Dynasty, shown in Figure 4.11, followed the Ju Rye (Neo Confucian I-ching), Pungsu principle (Gogonggi). In front of the palace the Jo Jeong (The Royal Court) was located, where the Sajik is on the right and the Jongmyo on the left. Behind the palace was the place for markets. In Seoul, the mountains were very close to the palaces, which did not allow sufficient space for marketplaces. So, the markets were located on the left front side of the city, the southeastern part of Seoul. Within the city wall were located 5 districts (Bu). The area within the surrounding walls of Seoul, which were located 4 kilometer outside the city wall, was designated as a special district belonging to Seoul.

The internal structure of pre-industrial cities was relatively simple ; however, places had lots of symbolic importance. The social status of the pre-industrial cities had a pyramidal structure based on occupying the series of concentric zones surrounding the city center, where small concentrations of elites were located (Sjoberg, 1960). In Joseon society the elite group, called "Yangban," had special privileges and they had a separate residential area near the palace, while other social classes owned designated areas that were farther away. Gyeongbok Palace was located very close to the mountains in the back rather than being in the center of the city, so the northernmost area of Seoul, near the palaces, was occupied by the powerful Yangban class. South of Jongro Street, which traverses Seoul East and West, was South town and it was the home of the lower Yangban class and the middle class, who were often the mixed blood of Yangban and commoners. Further south along the slope of Namsan (South Mountain) were people of the Yangban families who did not get official jobs or titles. These separate quarters of different classes were similar to the ones discussed by Vance, who noted the specific mosaic of various craft quarters and vertical structuring of space found in the internal structure of pre-capitalist cities (Vance, 1971).

③ Urbanization and development of modern cities

Urbanization is a process that evolved through the increase in size and number of cities, the diffusion of an urban lifestyle and a population concentration in cities. It is also a process driven by a series of interrelated changes. It has a close relationship to a variety of factors : the expansion of markets in a capitalistic economy, technological changes, social and demographic changes, expansion of democracy and cultural changes (Knox and McCarthy, 2005).

In the later Joseon Dynasty, during the 18th century, a new group of intellectuals who called themselves "Practical Scholars (Sil Hak Pa)" unlike the traditional Confucian scholars, brought Western scientific and practical knowledge to Korean society. As a result, agricultural productivity was increased and various surplus products were exchanged by itinerant merchants and a well-developed periodic market network emerged. This was the dawning of a capitalistic economy ; however, Korean traditional Confucianism considered artisans and merchants as lower class and suppressed merchandising. Such a policy discouraged artisans from developing new technologies or products.

When Japan occupied Korea in 1910, modern technology was introduced, which led to the colonial exploitation of resources. Railroads were built in order to transport raw materials, minerals and agricultural products to Japan. South Korea was the major rice-producing source for the Japanese and most of it was shipped to Japan through the new ports they built. Japan also developed Korea as the marketplace for their manufactured goods. More manufacturing plants and mines were established in the north, while major roads, railroads and port cities were built on the south or southwest coast to ship the goods to Japan. The location decisions for the manufacturing or transportation facilities were based solely on how best to take goods and products to Japan in preparation for World War II.

After 1945, the infrastructure and manufacturing facilities established under Japanese occupation continued namely, North Korea was industrialized and South Korea was the rice-producing agricultural area. Korea was divided into North and South Korea and each entity established a separate government. The Democratic People's Republic of Korea (North Korea) was led by Kim Il Sung and the Republic of Korea (South Korea) was established in 1948 south of the 38th Parallel. During the Korean War (1950-53), most of the nation was destroyed, along with what little material wealth that had existed in South Korea.

Industrialization in South Korea started in the 1960s. The regional development strategy, which began in the Seoul National Capital Area (the capital region), extended to the southeastern industrial complex and from there, inland. Investment priorities were initiated, chronologically, with light industries, then petrochemical industries, machine industries, electronics and finally, information industries. Such industrialization brought population concentrations to the cities and cities started to grow very rapidly. The fastest-growing cities were in the capital region, the regional metropolitan areas, the southeastern coastal industrial cities and transportation and distribution centers.

Such fast industrialization made South Korea one of the Four Dragons of Asia, along with Hong Kong, Singapore and Taiwan. However, other newly industrializing countries (NICs) in Asia were either small city-states or countries without a civil war. As a result, their locations were much more easily urbanized or industrialized. In addition, South Korea had to recover from its colonial legacy, the Korean War and an economy switching from agriculture to manufacturing, along with a migrating settlement pattern of a population moving from rural villages to industrial urban settlements within the very short time period of under 20 years.

Yet, one other major change has taken place in South Korean society during recent years : a shift from the mass production of Fordism to a flexible production system of a post-industrial society. The Korean economy is now centered on service industries and the globalization of its economy has brought restructuring of industries and changes in production processes-all of which have brought about an increased class and regional socioeconomic gap.

Figure 4.12 shows the changes in the pre-industrial traditional Korean cities of 1901. Before the Japanese Occupation, there were only 6 cities with a population of 380,000 people. The urbanization rate at the time was only 2.9%. Until the 1930s the urbanization rate remained less than 5%. In 1945 the urban population reached 5 million and the urbanization rate soared to about 20%. As a result of the massive migration of population after World War II and the Korean War, most refugees stayed in the cities, which caused rapid urbanization.

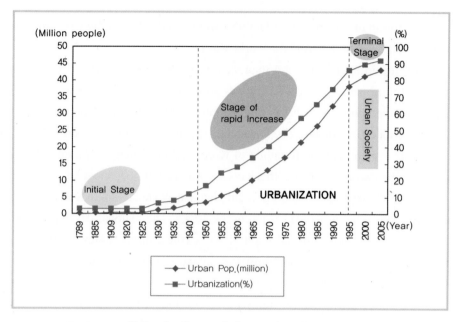

Figure 4.12 **Urbanization and change in urban population.**
(Source : Statistics Korea)

The rapid industrialization in the 1960s also brought rapid urbanization. By the 1970s about half the country's population lived in the cities and by 2005 the urbanization rate had reached approximately 90% and the population growth started to slow down.

The urbanization process follows an s-shaped innovation adoption process. In the beginning there is some resistance to change, so the adoption process moves very slowly. However, after a certain point in time, rapid adoption takes place. Nonetheless, in Korea during the early urbanization process (or the innovation adoption period) the urbanization rate was very low for a long period of time. Such a long delayed process was the direct result of the exploitive colonial influence. In contrast, the rapid urbanization that took place after the division of the country and the Korean War was not due to industrialization, but to the massive migration of refugees to the cities. This is a very common urbanization pattern in the developing world, which is considered to be pseudo-urbanization, where people look for opportunities in the cities because they cannot survive in the agricultural villages without land to farm.

4.3.2 The Urban System and Its Changes

The study of urban systems can be divided into 2 approaches. The first is the study of the system of cities within a region or a country and their sets of interactions. The second is looking at a city as a system and studying the functional regions within it and the internal structure of that city. In the first approach, the daily urban system is the lower order city system, above which the regional cities and national cities, in that order, are studied when determining the national urban system (Bourne and Simmons, 1978). Most urban system studies are conducted at the national level ; however, as globalization has become more widespread, studies on a world urban system have appeared (Kim, 2005 ; Nam, 2006).

1) Rank order and population sizes

Rank-size changes of South Korean cities for the last 30 years are shown in Table 4.5. There were 3 cities with a population of over 1 million in 1975 and the number increased to 6 by 2005. The total number of cities grew from 36 to 84 during the same period, especially in the capital region and southeastern cities grew most rapidly.

The urban rank-size rule is often applied in studying the urbanization process of a country

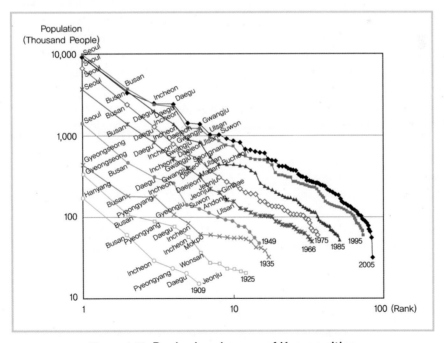

Figure 4.13 **Rank-size changes of Korean cities.**
(Source : Statistics Korea)

Table 4.5 **Changes in rank-size distribution of Korean cities (1975-2005)**

Year / Rank	1975		1985		1995		2005	
1	Seoul	6,879,464	Seoul	9,625,755	Seoul	10,217,177	Seoul	9,762,546
2	Busan	2,450,125	Busan	3,512,113	Busan	3,809,618	Busan	3,512,547
3	Daegu	1,309,131	Daegu	2,028,370	Daegu	2,445,288	Incheon ▲	2,517,680
4	Incheon	797,143	Incheon	1,384,916	Incheon	2,304,176	Daegu ▽	2,456,016
5	Gwangju	606,468	Gwangju	905,673	Daejeon ▲	1,270,873	Daejeon	1,438,551
6	Daejeon	506,223	Daejeon	865,687	Gwangju ▽	1,257,063	Gwangju	1,413,644
7	Masan	371,597	Ulsan ▲	550,207	Ulsan	966,628	Ulsan	1,044,934
8	Jeonju	311,237	Bucheon ▲▲	456,148	Seongnam ▲	868,268	Suwon ▲	1,039,233
9	Seongnam	272,470	Masan ▽	448,498	Bucheon ▽	778,693	Seongnam ▽	931,019
10	Ulsan	252,281	Seongnam ▽	447,647	Suwon ▲	754,670	Goyang ▲	864,402
11	Suwon	223,718	Suwon ▲▲	430,487	Annyang ▲	590,545	Bucheon ▽	833,931
12	Gimhae	203,377	Jeonju ▽	426,382	Jeonju	562,832	★Yongin	686,842
13	Mokpo	192,888	Annyang	361,503	Cheongju ▲	530,933	Ansan ▲	669,839
14	Cheongju	192,453	Cheongju	350,044	★Goyang	517,930	Cheongju ▽	640,631
15	Jinju	154,575	Pohang ▲▲	260,538	★Ansan	508,799	Jeonju ▽	622,092
16	Gunsan	154,456	Mokpo ▽	236,038	Pohang ▽	508,627	Annyang ▽▽	609,886
17	Chuncheon	140,397	Jinju ▽	227,281	Changwon ▲▲	480,433	Cheonan ▲	518,171
18	Jeju	134,921	★Gwangmyeong	219,544	Masan ▽▽	441,030	Changwon ▽	499,414
19	Annyang	134,746	Jeju ▽	202,707	Gwangmyeong ▽	350,465	Pohang ▽	488,433
20	Pohang	134,276	Iksan ▲	192,008	Jinju ▽	329,771	Gimhae ▲▲	428,893
21	Yeosu	130,405	Gunsan	185,474	Cheonan	329,622	Masan	426,784
22	Wonju	120,133	Changwon	173,283	Iksan	322,134	Namnyangju	424,446
23	Iksan	116,864	Yeosu	171,874	Pyeongtaek	311,940	Uijeongbu	397,694
24	Bucheon	109,093	Cheonan	170,085	Gumi	309,968	Siheung	384,304
25	Gyeongju	108,351	Chuncheon	162,869	Uijeongbu	275,717	Gumi	381,583
26	Uijeongbu	108,223	Uijeongbu	162,572	Gyeongju	273,733	Pyeongtaek	374,262
27	Suncheon	107,995	Wonju	150,994	Gunsan	266,340	Jinju	336,355
28	Chungju	105,084	Gumi	142,052	Jeju	258,307	Gwangmyeong	319,452
29	Jinhae	103,563	Gangneung	132,812	Gimhae	255,641	Jeju	310,713
30	Cheonan	96,663	Gyeongju	127,459	Suncheon	249,190	Iksan	306,974
31	Andong	95,243	Suncheon	121,880	Mokpo	247,362	Wonju	283,583
32	Gangneung	84,843	Jinhae	121,291	Wonju	237,089	★Hwaseong	282,124
33	Sokcho	71,351	Andong	114,157	★Gunpo	234,885	Yeosu	277,420
34	Gimcheon	67,031	★Taebaek	113,972	Chuncheon	234,362	Gunpo	268,917
35	Chungmu	66,828	Chungju	113,227	★Namnyangju	228,835	Gyeongju	266,131
36	Samcheonpo		★Jecheon	102,141	Gangneung ▽▽	220,246	Suncheon ▽▽	261,519
37			★Donghae	91,673	Chungju ▽	204,933	Chuncheon ▽	260,234
38			Chungmu	87,439	Andong ▽▽	188,364	Gunsan ▽▽	249,212
39			★Yeongju	84,724	Yeosu ▽▽	183,515	Mokpo ▽▽	244,543
40			★Seogwipo	82,268	★Gyeongsan	173,155	Gyeongsan	240,371

Year\Rank	1975	1985		1995		2005	
41		★Jeongeup	79,258	★Asan	154,331	★Paju	239,823
42		Gimhae ▽▽	77,889	★Geoje	147,484	Gangneung ▽▽	220,706
43		Gimcheon ▽▽	77,190	Gimcheon	146,923	★Yangsan	215,845
44		Sokcho ▽▽	69,430	★Guri	141,952	Asan ▽	206,851
45		★Dongducheon	68,610	Jeongeup ▽▽	138,984	★Gwangju	204,266
46		★Songtan	66,310	Jecheon ▽▽	136,983	Chungju ▽▽	204,248
47		★Sacheon	62,458	★Seosan	134,662	Geoje ▽▽	193,398
48		★Namwon	61,422	★Siheung	133,324	★Gimpo	192,716
49		★Naju	58,855	Tongyeong	131,694	★Icheon	187,514
50		★Yeongcheon	52,758	★Gongju	131,173	Guri ▽▽	186,954
51				Yeongju ▽▽	131,039	Andong ▽▽	169,436
52				Jinhae ▽▽	125,805	★Icheon	157,632
53				★Sangju	124,094	★Yangju	149,931
54				★Boryeong	122,541	Jinhae ▽	149,128
55				★Gwangyang	122,035	Seosan ▽▽	143,692
56				★Miryang	121,409	Uiwang ▲▲	143,568
57				★Hanam	115,773	★Pocheon	139,472
58				★Gimje	115,407	Gwangyang ▽	135,583
59				Sacheon ▽▽	113,475	Gimcheon ▽▽	135,166
60				Yeongcheon ▽▽	113,303	Jecheon ▽▽	132,483
61				★Uiwang	108,700	Osan ▲▲	131,792
62				Naju ▽▽	107,762	Gongju ▽▽	126,484
63				Namwon ▽▽	103,527	★Nonsan	124,779
64				Donghae ▽▽	95,449	Hanam ▽▽	121,646
65				★Mungyeong	92,204	Tongyeong ▽▽	121,115
66				★Samcheok	83,791	Jeongeup ▽▽	115,416
67				Seogwipo ▽▽	82,241	Yeongju ▽▽	113,670
68				Sokcho ▽▽	81,979	Sacheon ▽▽	106,532
69				★Yeocheon	75,883	Miryang ▽▽	105,651
70				Dongducheon ▽▽	71,305	Sangju ▽▽	105,600
71				★Osan	70,330	Yeongcheon ▽▽	103,289
72				Gwacheon	68,005	Boryeong ▽▽	96,992
73				Taebaek ▽▽	59,374	Donghae ▽▽	93,018
74						Gimje ▽▽	90,376
75						Naju ▽▽	86,823
76						Namwon ▽▽	85,828
77						Sokcho ▽▽	84,706
78						Dongducheon ▽▽	78,897
79						Seogwipo ▽▽	78,133
80						Mungyeong ▽▽	70,813
81						Samcheok ▽▽	67,957
82						Gwacheon ▽▽	56,587
83						Taebaek ▽▽	55,241
84						★Gyeryong	31,646

< Legend >

▲ Rank up

▽ Rank down

▲▲ Over 5 Rank up

▽▽ Over 5 Rank down

★ Newly designated city

[Source : Statistics Korea]

Table 4.6 **Regression analysis for rank-size distribution and change of slope parameter (q).**

Year	q Coefficient	Year	q Coefficient	Year	q Coefficient
1773	1.19	1985	1.23	1997	1.05
1975	1.20	1987	1.23	1999	1.04
1977	1.21	1989	1.21	2001	1.04
1979	1.23	1991	1.25	2003	1.06
1981	1.20	1993	1.26	2005	1.07
1983	1.20	1995	1.09	2007	1.07

(Source : Statistics Korea)

(Figure 4.13). The graph indicates the rank order distribution of the Korean urban system since 1909. In classic theory, countries shift through stages from primate-city distribution to the ideal rank-size rule when they reach the developed stage (Berry, 1961). During this process, some scholars believe that there is a correlation, following "The Principle of Least Effort," between the rank order of the cities and the population sizes (Zipf, 1949). As seen in the figure, the Korean urban system had a somewhat primate city distribution until 1935. As South Korea has become more urbanized, the series of graphs indicate that the Korean urban system has followed the rank-size rules.

However, any change in an urban system is the result of complex factors, such as the size of a country's population and its historical background, economic development, technological changes and self-sufficiency in local government. The results of analyses indicate changes in the q-value (slope parameter) for the last 30 years (Table 4.6). In 1973 the q-value was 1.19. It changed minutely, but increased by 1993. It started to decline in 1995 from 1.1 to nearly 1.0. This decline is connected to population decline within the municipal boundaries of Seoul and population increase in the capital region. Often countries with a colonial legacy have a primate city distribution (Linsky, 1965), while countries with larger territories usually follow the rank-size rule of a log-normal distribution (Berry, 1961).

2) Changes in urban function

As the effects of industrialization became clearly visible in the Korean landscape in the 1980s, the functions of Korean cities changed drastically. Industrialization of the society brought rapid changes in the Korean settlement system, which in turn brought a deepening gap between the different hierarchies of cities and regions. These changes can be seen from

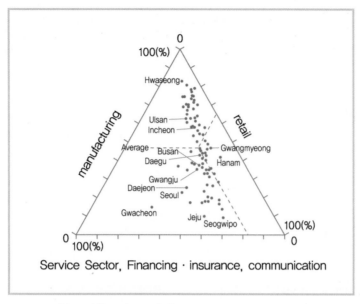

Figure 4.14 **Classification of Korean cities by urban functions.**
(Source : Statistics Korea)

the functional classification of cities.

The triangle graph in Figure 4.14 indicates the functions of Korean cities including manufacturing, retail and wholesale and financing, insurance and communication services. The figure shows that Seoul and the metropolitan cities of Ulsan, Incheon and Daejeon, are apart from the average of city functions for Korean cities, indicating their special functions. Other metropolitan cities, such as Gwangju, Daegu and Busan, are closer to the average of city functions for Korean cities, indicating that as the city size increases, the city functions become more diversified and become specialized in multiple functions. For all the cities in the study, on average, industry in South Korean cities was comprised of 48% manufacturing and 35% retail and wholesale, while the service sector of financing, insurance and communication services comprised 17% of industry. The graph clearly indicates that finance and other service sectors rank higher in major metropolitan areas than in the rest of the cities. Noyelle and Stanback in their study (1984) indicate that such growth in the finance and producer services sectors is the direct result of service industrialization and globalization of the urban system

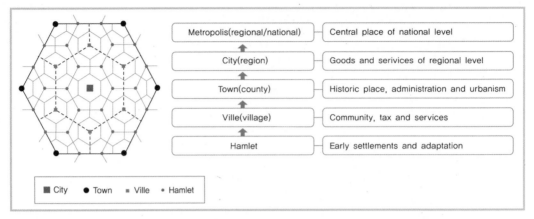

Figure 4.15 **Distribution pattern of central places (urban size and economic independence) : Characteristics of Korean urban system.**
(Source : The Structure of Urban System, Marshall 1989)

3) Arrangement and changes of central places

The spatial arrangements of cities that provide goods and services to the hinterland are commonly based on 3 principles : market, transportation and administration. Central places have a hierarchical division from the lowest order of villages (*myeon*-sized central places), to the next order of regional cities and to the highest order of the metropolitan cities, all of which have been closely interdependent in the Korean urban system (Figure 4.15).

The Korean urban system has historically evolved from a strong central dynastic control and the hierarchical distribution of central places has always been based on the administrative principle. Rapid industrialization and its subsequent urbanization, along with the development of transportation networks, have brought changes to traditional central places. New places have emerged based on transportation principles that connect the basins where most cities are located in Korea. The smaller cities near the larger metropolitan cities lose their function as central places when consumers decide to travel farther using the advanced transportation network. In particular, the availability of cars for everyone and the structural changes in transportation have brought a further decline in the existing smaller central places and the rapid growth of larger metropolitan centers. The mushrooming growth of one-stop shopping behavior, large box stores and major chain discount stores in suburban locations has reinforced the transportation principle of central places. For instance, the distribution of central places between Daejeon and Cheongju indicates that many small and large central places are strung along the thread of cities, the typical linear settlement pattern along the major highways. This is a good example of the "beads of cities" transportation principle applied in central place

Table 4.7 **Central place system of Korea by the centrality indices.**

Class*	Centrality Indices(Sum)	Classified Cities
I	over 99.1	Seoul
II	23.5 - 99.0	Busan
III	23.4 - 12.87	Daegu, Incheon, Gwangju, Daejeon
IV	8.92 - 3.37	Ulsan, Suwon, Seongnam, Buchun, Cheongju, Jeonju, Annyang, Goyang, Pohang, Changwon, Ansan, Cheonan, Masan, Jeju, Jinju, Gumi, Pyeongtaek
V	Under 3.11	Yongin, Gimhae, Wonju, Uijeongbu, Mokpo, Chuncheon, Gangneung, Yeosu, Gyeongju, Suncheon, Siheung, Iksan, Gunsan, Hwaseong, Chungju, Namnyangju, Yangsan andong, Gwangmyeong, Geoje, Gyeongsan, Paju, Gunpo, Icheon, Guri, Asan, Gimpo, Jecheon, Tongyeong, Pocheon, Seosan, Gwangju, Gwangyang, Gimcheon, Nonsan, Yeongju, Sokcho, Jinhae, Gongju, Donghae, Anseong, Sacheon, Jeongeup, Yangju, Boryeong, Seogwipo, Miryang, Sangju, Osan, Yeongcheon, Namwon, Hanam, Naju, Mungyeong, Gimje, Samcheok, Dongducheon, Uiwang, Taebaek, Gwacheon, Gyeryong

Classification of cities by the natural break points

distribution and the gradual decline of small cities around the metropolitan area.

As the interaction between central places for social and cultural events became more frequent and their activity realms widened, the Korean settlement system centered on the metropolitan cities. Within the metropolitan boundary, the internal structure of the cities has also changed. Due to urban sprawl, the suburban population has increased and edge cities and satellite cities have grown at the outer edge of the metropolis, while inner cities have lost population. In fact, the population of the capital region has grown continuously while the population of the city of Seoul has relatively declined.

To investigate the central-place hierarchy of Korean cities, centrality indices have been calculated from the analysis of the number counts of establishments of service industries (Table 4.7). The methodology used to calculate the centrality is the Davies standardized functional indices (1967). The centrality index is positively related to the establishment counts, so the larger metropolitan areas have higher functional indices. Korean cities have been divided by the centrality indices into 5 levels of hierarchy. The capital city Seoul is the first order city, followed by Busan (the second order city), then the 4 metropolitan cities of Daegu, Incheon, Daejeon and Gwangju (third order central places). These cities are followed by the fourth order regional central places, Cheongju, Jeonju, Ulsan, Pohang, Changwon, Masan, Cheonan and Jeju cities, which have higher centrality indices, with the fifth order being comprised of the medium-sized and smaller cities.

4.3.3 The Characteristics of the Urban System and Its Hierarchical Structure

1) The characteristics of the Korean urban system

A country's urban system changes as social, economic, cultural, political and technological changes occur. Numerous studies have been conducted with regard to the characteristics of an urban system, the urbanization processes and the factors related to the processes. The factor analysis method has often been used for analysis of the urban system.

In the study of the Korean urban system, 19 statistical variables were selected to be used for factor analysis. The variables related to population characteristics include the following : total population, population density, single-person households and teenager-headed and serving households. Social welfare related variables include the following : the number of highly educated residents, the number of lower educated residents, incidences of 5 major crime types, the number of welfare recipients and the number of divorces. Variables related to the basic urban characteristics include the following : local tax revenue receipts, financial self-sufficiency and change rates of land values. Economic variables include the following : employment in manufacturing, employment in wholesale and retail businesses, employment in construction, employment in the hotel and restaurant service industries and employment in the business service industry. In actual analysis these raw data were converted to percentage scales.

Principal component analysis, Kaiser's criterion and varimax rotation were chosen as analysis methods and 5 factors were extracted from the analysis as major characteristics of the urban system (Table 4.8). Factor I explained 24.0% of the characteristics of the urban system. The variables with high loadings on this factor were population-related variables, local tax, financial self-sufficiency, business services and high educational level. They could be labeled collectively as the "City Size and Economic Self-Sufficiency" factor. Cities with a high score in Factor I were Seoul, Busan, Daegu, Incheon, Daejeon and the Gwangju metropolitan cities, along with other major large cities.

Factor II explained 16.8% of the characteristics of the urban system. The variables included in this factor were welfare recipients, single-person households, lower educational level, teenager-headed and serving households, all of which could be labeled collectively as the "Social Welfare" factor. Cities with a high score in Factor II were Seogwipo, Gimje, Namwon, Jeongeup, Yeongju, Naju and Andong, all of which had lack of social welfare systems. All of these cities have had difficult financial and economic situations and less

Table 4.8 **Dimensions (characteristics) of Korean urban system : Rotated factor loadings**

Id. No. and Definition of Variables	Factor Loadings				
	I	II	III	IV	V
1. Total Population (in 10000)	.965	- .054	.027	- .069	- .015
10. Local Tax (10 thousand Won)	.941	- .114	- .063	.050	- .012
11. Financial Independence (%)	.791	- .433	- .254	.021	.079
2. Population Density (/km²)	.724	- .367	.043	.152	.143
5. No. of Lower Schooling (per 100 thousand)	- .720	.429	.145	- .098	.128
17. Business Service Worker (%)	.642	.046	.255	.581	- .052
8. Basic Living Standard Aid (Per 1000)	- .314	.842	.230	- .058	- .025
3. Single Family (per 1000))	- .180	.808	.281	- .095	- .095
4. Juvenile Family Head (per 100 thousand)	- .134	.777	- .024	.155	.225
12. Change of Land Values (%)	.243	- .484	- .251	.340	.087
13. Manufacturing Workers (%)	- .025	- .242	- .852	- .399	- .008
14. Workers in Retail and Whole Sales (%)	.150	.250	.784	.065	.247
15. Workers in Hotels and Restaurants (%)	- .274	.192	.772	- .018	.351
16. Workers in Construction (%)	- .101	- .026	.662	.084	- .384
18. Workers in Public Administration (%)	- .135	.059	.223	.886	- .036
6. No. of Higher Schooling (per 1000)	.408	- .383	.066	.679	- .086
9. No. of Divorce (per 100 thousand)	- .095	- .025	- .069	- .297	.816
7. No. of crime (per 100 thousand)	.109	.054	.273	.220	.679
Eigen Value	6.167	3.590	1.175	1.419	1.036
Variance %	34.260	19.946	9.858	7.882	5.753
Cumulative Variance %	34.260	54.205	64.063	71.946	77.699
Identification of Factor	Size and Economic Independ - ence of Cities	Social and Well - bei ng State of Cities	Supply of Urban Service	Public Administr ation and Service	Social Ill - being

(Data : 2005)

(Methods : Principal Factor Analysis/ Kaiser's Criterion/Varimax Rotation).

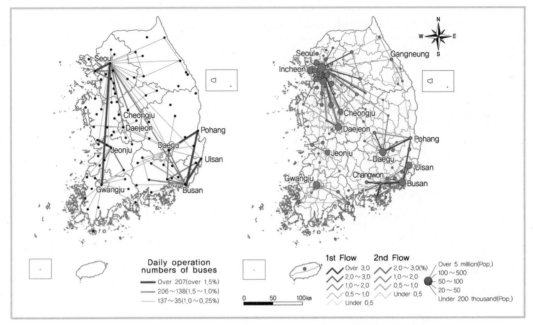

Figure 4.16 **Urban linkage patterns by daily bus operation**
(Source : Left: Ok-Hee Lee 1990
Right:Tour and Transportation Timetable 2008 (Train-Culture Travel)

chance to improve social welfare.

Factor Ⅲ explained 15.8% of the total variance in urban systems and the variables rated high in this factor were manufacturing employment, retail and wholesale employment, hotel and restaurant employment and construction employment, all of which could be labeled collectively as the "Urban Services and Tourism Industries" factor. Taebaek, Gangneung, Sokcho, Boryeng and Jeju are such tourism-inclined cities that shown high factor Ⅲ scores.

2) The connectivity of Korean cities

It is crucial to understand the interactions and connectivity among cities in the urban system. Reviewing the distribution, variable changes, or classifications of city functions does not provide the whole picture of cities, especially the interactions between cities. The urban system in Korea grew and was transformed very fast as a result of the seventh 5-year economic development plan, which provided direction for preparing for future growth by recommending development of new industrial sites, indicating growth management techniques for cities and preparing for an information society.

Lee (1990) studied the connectivity of the Korean urban system and nodal points by analyzing the intercity express bus line network in 1985. Seoul dominated the system with 2 important connections, which were from Seoul to Busan and from Seoul to Gwangju. The next most important connections were Daegu-Pohang, Busan-Pohang, Busan-Ulsan and Jeonju-Gunsan. These lines made the first-level connections in the hierarchy. While cities at this level established their own hinterlands in their regions, they simultaneously maintained connectivity with each other. These hinterlands were the capital region and Chungcheong, Jeolla and Gyeongsang regions. The Gangwon region was basically nested under the capital region (Figure 4.16).

Recently updated research on the connection has been conducted with the origin and destinations of intercity express bus lines. The study shows patterns relatively similar to those of 1985. However, the main difference is that the influence of the capital region has now spilled over into the Chungcheong region (Figure 4.16). The pattern indicates that despite all the efforts to diffuse the concentration of the capital region, the strong hub characteristics of the capital region remain part of the nodal connectivity of Korea. The rest of the country has varying nodes : Daejeon as the center for the Chungcheong region, Busan for the southeast (Busan) region, Daegu for the Gyeongsangbuk region, and Gwangju-Jeonju for the southwest region. And Gangneung in the east central areas shows weak connectivity. Unlike Seoul, these metropolitan cities have less connectivity with other regions, but are playing the role of a major hub for each of their own regions.

4.3.4 Spatial Distribution of Korean Cities

1) The changes in the Korean urban system

In 1909 before the colonial occupation, the distribution of Korean traditional cities was that of pre-industrial cities and the number of cities was small. Cities at the time were regional administrative centers. The distribution of cities in 1944, complete with port cities, railroad junction cities and mining cities of northern Korea, were clearly the result of Japanese colonization. Cities in 1966 reflected the results of the division of Korea and the Korean War in 1950. At this time, cities were following the central place hierarchy.

In 1985, distribution of cities indicated not only an increase in the total number of cities, but also the emergence of regional centers. By that time the Seoul-Busan axis was established, connecting Seoul-Daejeon-Daegu-Busan. Figure 4.17 reveals the spatial distribution of cities in Korea for 2005. The major characteristics and the changes during the 2 decades were first,

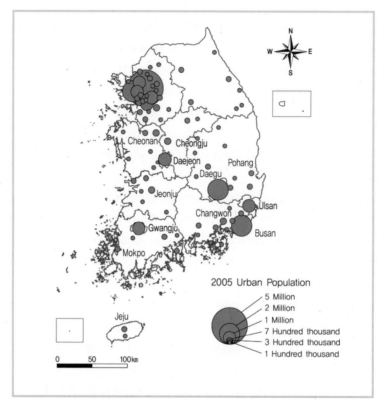

Figure 4.17 **Distribution patterns of Korean cities (2005).**
(Source : Statistics Korea)

the increase in the number of cities with over a million in population (Incheon, Daejeon and Gwangju entered this category in 2005) second, the formation of the corridor between Seoul and Busan, which resulted in the emergence of a secondary axis along the southeastern coastal-industrial complex ; and third, newly developed cities clustered around the capital region. These cities grew much larger in size than conventional suburban satellite cities. The service-and information-related functions of Seoul also dispersed to these so-called "edge cities" of Seoul and this phenomenon reflected the "suburbanization process of city functions."

2) Changes in the internal structure of Korean cities

The internal structures of cities were arranged by economic principles such as competition, efficiency and accessibility that were well adjusted to fluctuating land prices. As a city grew, businesses with similar activities in the city tended to aggregate to certain functional districts. Eventually, the city had a central business district, a commercial district, a residential district,

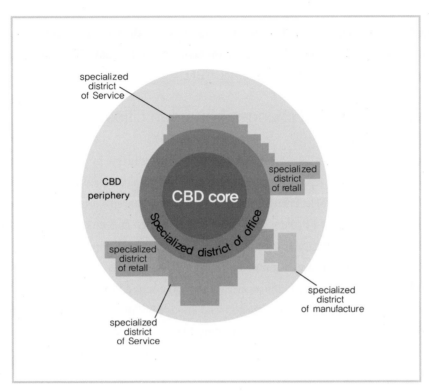

Figure 4.18 **Schematic spatial structure of Seoul's CBD.**
[Source : Kyungsik Joo,Min-Cheoul Seo 1988]

an educational district, a recreational district and some mixed-use areas (Figure 4.18). The Central Business District (CBD), especially, was located in the city center where land prices were the highest, had the highest order central functions and became the core center of the city, with lots of activities and often high accessibility.

Murphy and Vance (1954) conducted the classic study of delimiting the CBD by analyzing functional business indices. Park (1973) studied CBDs of Korean cities and delimited the area from 10 functional groups. A more recent study based on the survey of CBD functions indicated that the spatial structure of the Seoul CBD was similar to the previous findings. First, the area surrounding the CBD core had specialized office areas extending outward. From this core, which followed the main thoroughfare, there were special retail districts and finally, adjacent to the retail area was a special district for personal services. Light manufacturing areas were concentrated in one corner of the CBD. In a transitional bordering area of the CBD, one can find a residential area and non-CBD areas (Seo and Joo, 1998).

In addition to these findings, the metropolitan areas have evolved from a single core area to multiple nuclei cities. The recent urban renewal projects and the Newtown development in

Seoul reinforced the multiple nuclei pattern in the city. To disperse the population from the central city and to ease the inequality in development, edge cities have been carefully planned and constructed to disperse the functions of the CBD.

3) Globalization and changes in Korean cities

The changes in capitalism and technology, especially in the information and communication revolution, have overcome the spatial and geographical limitations of the city. The industrial process has also changed to specialization-required variability and the flexible production systems of post-Fordism that favor individuality and customized design. In the CBD, cultural centers and regional special characteristics become important.

As a result of the rapid progression of urban sprawl, businesses, management, information and service functions, providing better accessibility, have moved to the suburbs and emerging edge cities (Joo, 1998). As the urbanization and metropolitanization of settlement systems moves Seoul toward further suburbanization, new town developments and urban renewal are taking place in the city. Such gentrification processes often push low-income residents from the area, which creates sociopolitical issues. The newly replaced deluxe residential areas often have gated communities with guards.

4) Regional disparity and the future of the Korean urban system

The core concern of the Korean urban system is the unbalanced growth of Seoul, with 20 million people (about 48% of the nation's population) concentrated in the capital region and the trend continuing (Table 4.9). While the population of Seoul has actually declined, the capital region, with many satellite and edge cities, continues to grow. Consequently, the Korean settlement system is divided into the capital region and the non-the capital region rural region. Urban services, as well as social welfare, in the capital region have been better than the rest of the non-the capital region and the regional disparity is recognized more seriously as a social issue. The future of the Korean urban system relies on the balanced development of Korea through regional self-sufficiency to turn the tide of the migration to the capital region.

Table 4.9 **Weight changes of the urban the capital region vs. total urban population**

Kobayashi (1931)	Tada (1941)	Yoshikawa (1947)		Kim, Sang Ho (1973)	
Yukbaeksan	Yukbaeksan	Yukbaeksan Odaesan		Yukbaeksan Odaesan	Yukbaeksan Odaesan
Yeoju	Yeoju	Yeoju	570m Daegwallyeong	Middle Surface	Jecheon, Daehwa, Pyeongchang, Jeongseon, Hajinbu, Hoenggye etc.
			380m Hajinbu		
			260m Jecheon		
			160m Chungju	Low Surface	Chungju Gimpo

[Source : Statistics Korea].

Chapter 5.
RESOURCES AND INDUSTRY

Chapter 5.1.

USE OF RESOURCES

5.1.1 Mineral Resources

Mineral resources can be classified into metallic minerals, nonmetallic minerals, and coalmines. The total mineral reserves of Korea in 2006 were estimated at 13.16 billion tons, 11.68 billion tons of which comprised nonmetallic reserves. This means that nonmetallic minerals had the biggest portion of Korea's total mineral reserves (88.7%). Coal reserves were estimated to be 1.37 billion tons (10.4%), while metallic reserves were 0.11 billion tons (0.9%). Converting the volume of the reserves into their potential monetary value would amount to roughly 147,524.4 billion won. By percentage, the shares of the potential value of coal and metallic reserves were at 20.0% and 3.1%, respectively, while the share of nonmetallic reserve was at 76.9% in 2006 (Figure 5.1).

Among the metallic reserves, iron ore has the biggest share at 26.2% ; rare earth follows at 22.0% ; zinc ore at 16% ; and tungsten at 14%. The other types of ores are lesser in volume and are less than 10% of the total (Table 5.1). Total potential value of metallic reserves is estimated at 4,518.9 billion won. Zinc has the

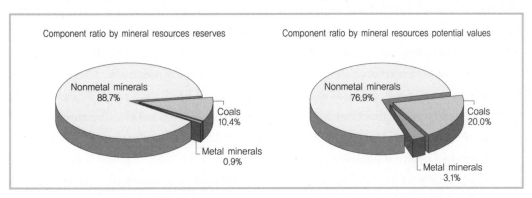

Figure 5.1 **Component ratio by mineral resources reserves and potential values**
(Source : Ministry of Knowledge Economy, 2007, Mineral Resources Reserves.)

Table 5.1 **Metallic mineral reserves and R/P (Reserves/production)**

	mine (number)	grade	reserves (1000 ton)[*]	R/P (year)
Gold	98	Au 6.6g/t	6,253.0	0.8
Silver	10	Ag 188.4g/t	8,397.6	1.1
Cooper	26	Cu 2.5%	2,269.6	0.1
Lead	31	Pb 2.2%	18,383.9	10.6
Iron	31	Fe 38.3%	30,913.4	0.4
Tungsten	17	WO30.5%	16,539.0	-
Molybdenum	4	MoS20.4%	4,936.6	2.3
Manganese	2	Mn 19.6%	360.0	0.3
Antimony	1	Sb 2%	22.0	-
Tin	2	Sn 2%	947.0	-
Placer gold**	9	Au 0.887g/m^2	2,860.5[*]	
Rare earth	1	R2O32.13%	25,972.0	

Reserves indicate both proved ore reserves and possible ore reserves.
** unit (kg)
(Source : Ministry of Knowledge Economy, 2007.)

highest share at 21.8% ; followed by molybdenite at 16.6% ; tungsten at 16.5% ; gold ore at 2.9% ; and iron ore at 12.6%. Iron ores are mostly found in Gangwon-*do* and Gyeonggi-*do*. Most of the zinc ores are found in Gyeongsanbuk-*do* and Gangwon-*do*, while tungsten is found in Gangwon-*do*. Gold ores are found throughout the nation. As seen in Table 5.1, the proved years of mining of metallic ores are not long and the economic efficiency of mining is low. The total production of metallic minerals from 1930 to 2006 was only 33.74 million tons, of which the share of iron ore share was at 73.2%, followed by titanium at 15.3%, and zinc at 2.9%.

Nonmetallic reserves in Korea are relatively diverse and important because they take up 88.7% of the total mineral reserves and 76.9% of the total potential value. Limestone's share is at 85.4% of the total mineral reserves, followed by silicon dioxide at 11.2%, and kaolinite at 0.9% (Figure 5.2). Limestone is mostly found in Gangwon-, Chungcheongbuk-, and Gyeongsangbuk-*do*, while silicon dioxide and kaolinite are generally found throughout the nation. The total production of nonmetallic minerals during the period of 1930 to 2005 was estimated at 2,198.2 million tons, of which the share of limestone was at 90.0%, followed by silicon dioxide at 2.5%, kaolinite at 2.5%, and silica at 1.6%. The proved years of mining of nonmetallic reserves are relatively longer compared with that of metallic reserves (Table 5.2).

The total coal reserve is estimated at 1,367.03 million tons. The largest coalfield is the Samcheok coalfield, which takes up 35.5% of the total reserves. It is followed by Jeongseon coalfield with a 33.0% share, Chungnam coalfield with an 8.5% share, and Honam coalfield with 6.6% share. The production of coal reached more than one million tons by the time Korea proclaimed its increase in production of major

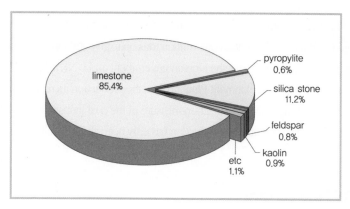

Figure 5.2 **Component ratio by nonmetal minerals reserves**
(Source : Ministry of Knowledge Economy, 2007, Mineral Resources Reserves.)

Table 5.2 **Non-metallic mineral reserves and R/P (Reserves/production)**

	mine (number)	reserves (1000 ton)	R/P (year)
Limestone	271	9,973,614.4	92.9
Pyropyllite	32	70,207.3	89.2
Silica stone	244	1,303,369.6	314.8
Feldspar	48	94,932.8	170.9
Kaolin	128	106,335.9	28.2
Mica	10	12,341.1	93.2
Talc	25	8,152.2	36.0
Flaky graphite	14	2,595.5	158.4
Fluorite	38	477.0	6.0
Zeolite	16	29,164.9	128.9
Diatomite	6	3,439.7	83.9
Wollastonite	7	4,234.5	157.4
Alunite	5	29,308.6	170,966.6
Serpentine	6	33,245.9	108.0
Asbestos	5	695.5	11,371.1
Crystal[*]	3	45.1[*]	-
Barite	1	842.1	24.0
Andalusite	1	1,041.0	65.6
Quartz sand	16	6,131.0	1.6

* : unit (ton)

(Source : Ministry of Knowledge Economy, 2007.)

minerals in 1938. However, the production decreased to less than one million tons during the liberation and Korean War. It again increased to more than one million tons up to five million tons with the conclusion of the coal development agreements between the Korean government and UNKRA in 1954. After the launch of the First Five-Year Economic Development Plan in 1962, the production increased rapidly and peaked at 24.29 million tons in 1988. Since the rationalization measure of the coal industry in 1989, the production of coal has rapidly decreased. The annual coal production has only been about 3 million tons since 2000.

5.1.2 Energy Resources

The trend in energy consumption has been closely related with the changes in the economic structure of Korea. Since the industrialization in the 1960s, energy consumption has been rapidly increasing, with some exception during the oil crisis of the 1970s and the financial crisis in 1997. After the considerable decrease in energy consumption (-8.1%) in 1998, the consumption recovered in 2000, but the consumption level kept getting lower than the former peak level of consumption.

In the 1960s, coal and charcoal were the major sources of energy, but petroleum became the major energy source in the 1970s when there was rapid progress of industrialization. Petroleum has kept its position of being the major energy source since the 1980s, but its share in total energy sourcing was reduced to less than 50% in 2002 when there was a rapid increase in LNG consumption. Along with the increase in electricity consumption, the shares of atomic energy and bituminous coal in energy sourcing have gradually increased. Bituminous coal now takes up 21.8% of the total energy sources, while the share of anthracite coal has decreased to 2.1% from 40% of the total energy sources since the 1960s. Such

Table 5.3 **Major energy indicators**

	1980	1990	2000	2005
Primary energy consumption (M toe)	43.9	93.2	192.9	229.3
Increasing rate (%)[*]	(1.6)	(14.1)	(6.4)	(4.1)
Final energy consumption (M toe)	37.6	75.1	149.9	172.1
Increasing rate (%)	(14.0)	(14.0)	(4.7)	(3.7)
Dependence on petroleum (%)	61.1	53.8	52.0	44.3
Energy imports (100 million US $)	66.2	109.1	378.9	667.0
Increasing rate (%)			(66.6)	(33.5)
Dependence on energy imports (%)	73.5	87.9	97.2	96.4
Share of energy imports to total imports (%)	29.6	15.6	23.6	25.5
GDP growth rate (%)	- 1.5	9.2	8.5	4.0

* : Increasing rate represents percentage growth compared with the previous year.
(Source : KEEI (Korea Energy Economics Institute) (Various years))

changes in energy sourcing pattern resulted in the increase in the importation of other energy sources, which was roughly 96.4% from import in 2005 (Table 5.3).

The industrial sector's share in the total energy consumption was more than half (51.2%) during that period and has always been around 55% since then. The share of the transportation sector consumption was around 21% and that of commercial and household consumption was about 22% in 2005 (Table 5.4). The energy sources of Korea are mostly imported from other countries. In recent years, more than 95% of the energy consumed domestically has been sourced from outside the country. The strong dependency on imported energy source is related with the increase in the prices of petroleum and bituminous coal, as well as in the increase in the importation of LNG (Table 5.5).

Table 5.4 **consumption structure, by sector**

By sector	2002		2003		2004		2005 (estimate)	
	amount	%	amount	%	amount	%	amount	%
Industry	89.20	55.6	90.81	55.4	92.99	56.0	95.06	55.2
Transport	33.76	21.0	34.63	21.1	34.62	20.9	35.44	20.6
household - commerce	34.30	21.4	34.97	21.3	34.81	21.0	37.84	22.0
public - other	3.19	2.0	3.59	2.2	3.60	2.2	3.81	2.2
Total	160.45	100.0	164.00	100.0	166.01	100.0	172.14	100.0

Note : The sum of the percentages may not be 100.0 in some of the Tables in this chapter.
(Source : Ministry of Knowledge and Economy, 2005 ; KEEI (Various years))

Table 5.5 **Trend of energy imports**

	1990	2000	2005	Increasing rate (%)		
				1990 - 2000	2000 - 2005	1990 - 2005
Dependence on energy imports(%)	87.9	97.2	96.4			
Energy imports (million US $)	10,908	37,888	66,697	247.3	76.0	511.5
- Crude petroleum (million US $)	6,386	25,216	42,605	294.9	69.0	567.2
• amount of resources(million B)	308.4	893.9	843.2	108.9	- 5.7	173.4
• unit cost ($/B,CIF)	21.0	28.2	50.4			
- other petroleum products (million US $)	2,773	6,379	9,716	130.0	52.3	250.4
- LNG (million US $)	459	3,882	8,646	745.8	122.7	1783.7
- Bituminous coal (million US $)	1,217	2,033	4,803	67.1	136.3	294.7
- Anthracite (million US $)	52	72	429	38.5	495.8	725.0

(Source : Ministry of Knowledge Economy, 2005 ; KEEI (Various years).)

5.1.3 The Development of New Energy and Foreign Sources

Due to Korea's strong dependency on imported energy sources, it is necessary to develop new and renewable energy sources and find other foreign sources. New and renewable energy sources may be produced by converting energies from existing fossil fuels or by using renewable energies that come from the sun, water, geothermal fields, precipitation, bioorganic matters, and other similar sources. Despite the high cost of initial investment, the development of new and renewable energy is becoming more important because of the decrease in fossil fuel deposits as well as the environmental problems arising from the use of fossil fuels. The Korean government has been exerting efforts in developing new and renewable energies since the promulgation of the "Promotion Law of Alternative Energy Development" in 1987. However, the share of new and renewable energy in the total energy supply in Korea is only 2.15%, which is considerably lower compared with that of the more advanced or industrialized countries (Table 5.6).

Stabilizing the supply of energy resources has always been regarded as an important goal, particularly during the two oil crises in the 1970s. Korea strongly depends on foreign countries for its supply of energy and mineral resources. Thus, it needs to develop further its foreign resources to ensure a stabilized supply, which is necessary for economic development. Since the first advancement in foreign resource development in the uranium exploration in Paraguay in 1977, the number of foreign resource development projects has increased to 321 projects, 142 of which have already been completed. At present, Korea has more than 150 development or exploration projects on petroleum, natural gas, bituminous coal, and metallic ores in Yemen, Australia, Indonesia, Canada, China, and other countries (Table 5.7).

Table 5.6 **Renewable energy* supply, 1993-2005**

	1993	1997	2000	2003	2005
Amount of resources (thousand toe)	650	1,421	2,131	4,436	5,013
Total energy consumption (thousand toe)	126,879	180,639	192,888	215,067	229,334
Share of supply (%)	0.51	0.80	1.11	2.06	2.19

* : Some sectors among renewable energy resources in 2005 include waste (69.4%), bio (10.2%),
  solar electricity (0.8%), wind electricity (0.7%), and waterpower (26.1%).
(Source : Ministry of Knowledge Economy, 2005 ; KEEI (various years))

Table 5.7 **Investment in overseas resource development**

	production	development	exploration	total	Country
petroleum (including gas)	25	7	33	65	United States, Libya, Yemen, Indonesia etc. (26 countries)
Bituminous coal	14	5	5	24	United States, Australia, Indonesia etc. (7 countries)
Uranium	-	-	1	1	Canada (1 country)
Stone	-	5	-	5	China, Saudi Arabia, Philippines (3 countries)
Silica stone	1	1	2	4	Malaysia, Vietnam, Indonesia, China (4 countries)
Sulfur	-	1	-	1	Costa Rica (1 country)
Aluminum	1	1	-	2	Venezuela, China (2 countries)
Copper	1	4	5	10	Philippines, Peru etc. (6 countries)
Zinc	3	2	2	7	United States, Canada, Australia (3 countries)
Gold	1	11	29	41	Mali, Papua New Guinea, Mongolia etc. (16 countries)
Manganese	-	2	1	3	Indonesia, Philippines (2 countries)
Talc	-	1	-	1	China (1 country)
Mica	-	2	-	2	South Africa, China (2 countries)
Sapphire	-	1	-	1	Laos (1 country)
Halite	-	1	-	1	Australia (1 country)
Magnesite	1	-	-	1	China (1 country)
Limestone	-	2	-	2	China (1 country)
Iron	1	-	-	1	Australia (1 country)
Phosphorus	-	1	-	1	Mongolia (1 country)
Perlite	-	1	-	1	China (1 country)
Rare earth	1	-	-	1	China (1 country)
Tin	1	-	-	1	Indonesia (1 country)
Fluorite	-	2	-	2	Mongolia (1 country)
Ruby	-	1	-	1	Cambodia (1 country)
Total	48	43	68	159	

[Source : Ministry of Knowledge Economy, 2005.]

Chapter 5.2.

CHARACTERISTICS AND CHANGES IN THE INDUSTRIAL STRUCTURE

5.2.1 Changes in Overall Industrial Structure

The industrial structure of Korea has been significantly changing along with the rapid industrialization and "compressed economic growth" since the launch of the First Economic Development Plan (1962-1966). The manufacturing industry became the major driving force of the Korean economy during the rapid industrialization period from the late 1960s to the 1980s. The changes in the industrial structure are seen in the continuous decline of primary industries, structural changes in the manufacturing sector, and the recent rapid growth and structural changes in tertiary activities.

The changes in industrial structure are shown in Table 5.8 and Figure 5.3. Table 5.8 shows the structural changes brought about by the economically active population and gross domestic product (GDP) based on the value added. The share of primary industries has

Table 5.8 **Changes of economic structure, by sector, 1985-2005**

Criteria	Sector	1985	1990	1995	2000	2005
By economically active population	Primary (Agriculture etc.)	24.9%	18.3%	12.5%	10.9%	7.6%
	Secondary (Mining & Manufacturing)	24.5%	27.3%	23.5%	20.2%	18.4%
	Tertiary (Services)	50.6%	54.4%	64.0%	68.9%	74.0%
Value added by activity* (GRDP)	Primary (Agriculture etc.)	13.2%	9.0%	6.1%	4.6%	3.3%
	Secondary (Mining & Manufacturing)	27.6%	27.5%	27.6%	29.3%	28.8%
	Tertiary (Services)	59.2%	63.5%	66.3%	66.0%	67.9%

*: The shares of each sector are calculated by dividing the value added in each sector by total value added, based on current prices.
[Source : Statistics Korea (Various years), [kostat.go.kr]]

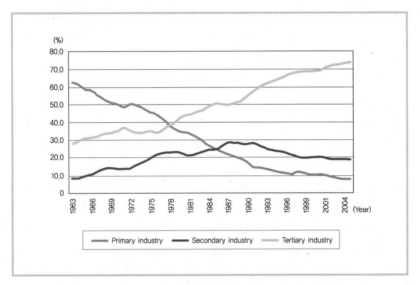

Figure 5.3 **Trend of the industrial structure variation**
* estimated by the weights of employees in each industries during 1963-2005.
(Source : Statistics Korea, each year, Statistics of Employment.)

decreased to 7.6% by economically active population and to 3.3% by GDP. The share of the secondary industry (manufacturing and mining) stabilized at around 28%-29% of the GDP, but it has considerably decreased since 1990 to 18.4%. On the other hand, the share of tertiary industry has continuously increased to 74% by economically active population and about 68% by GDP.

The dramatic changes in the industrial structure in terms of employment during the last four decades are presented in Figure 5.3. The working population in the primary industries in 1963 was estimated at 4,764 thousands, covering a share of 63% of the total working population. The value decreased to 1,815 thousands, covering a share of only 7.9% in 2005. The working population in the secondary industries in 1963 was 657 thousands, covering a share of only 8.7%. The working population in the secondary industry peaked at 5,220 thousands or 28% of the total in 1991, but the value continuously decreased to 4,251 thousands, covering 18.1% of the total in 2005. On the other hand, the working population in the tertiary industry was 2,144 thousands, covering 28.3% of the total in 1963, but the value increased to 16,789 thousands, covering 73.5% of the total in 2005.

5.2.2 Major Characteristics and Changes by Sectors

1) Agriculture and fishery

With the progress of industrialization, primary industries were restricted. The number of agricultural and fishery households rapidly decreased from 1,920 thousands in 1985 to 1,270 thousands in 2005. The cultivated acreage also decreased to about 15% in the period of 1985 to 2005.

Along with the restriction of the primary industrial activities, the structure of the agricultural sector has significantly changed as well. Traditionally, the agricultural sector of Korea has always centered on rice farming. After all, rice is still the most important agricultural product. However, vegetable and fruit farming have continuously gained importance in terms of contribution to agricultural household income. As seen in Table 5.9, the area of cultivated land with rice farms takes up more than half of the total cultivated land area. However, the share of rice farming income to gross agricultural household income is only 35.9%, while the share of vegetable farming income is 33.6%. This is ironic, considering that the area for vegetable farming is smaller at 12.0% compared with the land cultivated with rice.

There has been a gradual change in the fishery sector's structure as well. In general, cultivation has been extended and there had been changes in fishery types brought about by impacts of climate change. Although there have been some fluctuations, the share of coastal

Table 5.9 **Cultivation area by crop and farm household income**

	Cultivation area		Farm household income	
	Area (ha)	Share (%)	Income (1000 won)	Share (%)
Rice	950,250	51.2	7,296	35.9
Barley	55,664	3.0	190	0.9
Cereals	27,233	1.5	135	0.7
Legume	88,120	4.7	424	2.1
Sort of potato	39,838	2.1	591	2.9
Vegetables	222,661	12.0	6,817	33.6
A crop for a special use	79,915	4.3	957	4.7
Fruit	148,398	8.0	3,192	15.7
Others	243,867	13.1	704	3.5
Total	1,855,946	100.0	20,306	100.0

(Source : Ministry for Food, Agriculture, Forestry and Fisheries, 2007 ; Statistics Korea

fishery production generally decreased from 56.9% in 1985 to 40.4% in 2005, while the share of the cultivation production increased from 22.4% in 1980 to 38.4% in 2005 (Table 5.10).

The restriction of the primary industry seems to suggest significant issues beyond the changes in industrial structure itself. The degree of self-sufficiency in the agricultural sector continuously decreased from 54.3% in 1980 to 28.9% in 2005. Due to the tradition of rice farming-centered agriculture and the relative decrease of rice consumption in Korea, the degree of self-sufficiency in rice is around 100%. However, there seems to be a very low self-sufficiency rate in most of the other agricultural products as shown in Table 5.11. Due to this low degree of self-sufficiency in the primary industry, the importation of primary industrial products radically increased from $3,164 million in 1980 to $14,276 million in 2005, resulting in a trade deficit of $10,860 million in the primary industrial sector.

Such restriction in the primary industrial sector can be an inevitable phenomenon if a country pursues structural changes towards the advancement in its industries and services.

Table 5.10 **Share of production in fishing industry, by type of fishery, 1980-2005**

		1980	1985	1990	1995	2000	2005
Share of production (%)	General marine fisheries	56.9	48.2	46.0	42.6	47.3	40.4
	Fish farming	22.4	25.4	24.2	29.8	26.0	38.4
	Deep-sea fisheries	19.0	24.7	28.7	26.8	25.9	20.3
	Inland water fisheries	1.6	1.7	1.1	0.9	0.8	0.9
Total production (million tons)		2,410,346	3,102,605	3,198,234	3,348,178	2,514,225	2,714,050

(Source : Ministry for Food, Agriculture, Forestry and Fisheries, 2007 (Various years))

Table 5.11 **Degree of food self-support of major crops, 1980-2005**

	1980	1985	1990	1995	2000	2005
Rice	88.8	103.3	108.3	91.1	102.9	95.7
Barley	57.6	63.7	97.4	67.0	46.9	60.0
Wheat	4.8	0.4	0.0	0.3	0.1	0.2
Sort of potato	100.0	100.0	95.6	98.4	99.3	98.6
Corn	5.9	4.1	1.9	1.1	0.9	0.9
Bean	-	-	20.1	9.9	6.8	9.8
Other grains	41.5	19.1	13.9	3.8	5.2	10.0
Total	54.3	48.4	43.1	29.1	29.7	28.9

(Source : Statistics Korea (Various years). [kostat.go.kr])

However, a careful consideration should be given to decreasing self-sufficiency in the agricultural sector in light of national food security. Effective planning for a consistent supply of food is needed especially considering the changes in agricultural demands and environments vis-á-vis climate change.

2) Manufacturing

Korea has experienced rapid industrialization and structural changes in the manufacturing sector since the launch of the First Economic Development Plan in 1962. Manufacturing industries have grown due to changes and growth in key industries over time : labor intensive and light industries in the 1960s, heavy and chemical industries in the 1970s and 1980s, and high-technology and knowledge-intensive industries in the 1990s and beyond. The structural changes were closely related with the government's industrial policies. In addition, the firms' industrial restructuring strategies in the early 1990s, brought about by the labor movements in the late 1980s, significantly contributed to the structural changes in the manufacturing sector. Since the financial crisis in 1997, the manufacturing sector in Korea has moved towards the technology and knowledge-intensive industries.

More details on the structural changes in the manufacturing sector by two-digit Standard Industrial Classification (SIC) level are presented in the Table 5.12. The total number of manufacturing establishments continuously increased from 218,952 in 1986 to 340,183 in 2005. The total number of employees increased from 3,290 thousand in 1986 to 3,709 thousand in 1995. However, the number decreased to 3,451 thousand in 2005, revealing that there was a considerable decrease in average employment size in firms in the period of 1995 to 2005. The decrease in employment size in establishments in the period of 1995 to 2005 is related to the increase of small high-technology firms and the restructuring of the large establishments due to the financial crisis of 1997.

During the last two decades, the share of labor intensive industries such as those engaged in the manufacturing of apparels, shoes, and furniture has continuously decreased, while that of technology-intensive industries such as electrical and electronics, computer, and medical and precise machinery has significantly increased in terms of both the number of establishments and employees (Table 5.12). The number of establishments engaged in printing, which is related to the knowledge-intensive industry, automobile and transportation equipment and fabricated metals increased during the last two decades as well.

There are various ways to represent the structural changes in the manufacturing sector, but for convenience, this chapter will examine the structural changes by the type of industry. In

Table 5.12 **Changes of manufacturing structure by industry, 1986-2005**

Division of industry	Number of firms						Increasing rate(%)		
	1986		1995		2005		1986 - 1995	1995 - 2005	1986 - 2005
	No.	%	No.	%	No.	%			
Manufacture of Food Products and Beverages	41,453	18.9	49,612	15.9	59,818	17.6	19.7	20.6	44.3
Manufacture of Tobacco Products	30	0.0	20	0.0	13	0.0	- 33.3	- 35.0	- 56.7
Manufacture of Textiles, Except Sewn Wearing apparel	18,270	8.3	28,042	9.0	24,009	7.1	53.5	- 14.4	31.4
Manufacture of Sewn Wearing Apparel and Fur Articles	44,162	20.2	38,253	12.2	23,189	6.8	- 13.4	-39.4	-47.5
Tanning and Dressing of Leather , Manufacture of Luggage and Footwear	9,432	4.3	7,138	2.3	4,555	1.3	- 24.3	- 36.2	- 51.7
Manufacture of Wood and of Products of Wood and Cork, Except Furniture	11,191	5.1	11,685	3.7	7,497	2.2	4.4	- 35.8	- 33.0
Manufacture of Pulp, Paper and Paper Products	2,803	1.3	4,991	1.6	5,489	1.6	78.1	10.0	95.8
Publishing, Printing and Reproduction of Recorded Media	10,907	5.0	21,202	6.8	22,751	6.7	94.4	7.3	108.6
Manufacture of Coke, Refined Petroleum Products and Nuclear Fuel	4,130	1.9	109	0.0	180	0.1	14.4	65.1	85.7
Manufacture of Chemicals and Chemical Products			4,617	1.5	7,489	2.2		62.2	
Manufacture of Rubber and Plastic Products	5,363	2.4	10,134	3.2	15,409	4.5	89.0	52.1	187.3
Manufacture of Other Non - metallic Mineral Products	7,258	3.3	9,905	3.2	9,916	2.9	36.5	0.1	36.6
Manufacture of Basic Metals	1,880	0.9	3,421	1.1	5,294	1.6	82.0	54.8	181.6
Manufacture of Fabricated Metal Products, Except Machinery and Furniture	19,010	8.7	38,633	12.3	51,914	15.3	103.2	34.4	173.1
Manufacture of Other Machinery	15,161	6.9	27,787	8.9	34,246	10.1	202.5	23.2	301.6
Manufacture of Computers and Office Machinery			1,061	0.3	1,481	0.4		39.6	
Manufacture of Electrical Machinery and Apparatuseses n.e.c.			10,928	3.5	16,412	4.8		50.2	
Manufacture of Electronic Components, Radio, Television and Communication equipment			6,088	1.9	8,753	2.6		43.8	
Manufacture of Medical, Precision and Optical Instruments, Watches	1,508	0.7	4,199	1.3	6,596	1.9	178.4	57.1	337.4
Manufacture of Motor Vehicles, Trailers and Semitrailers	3,337	1.5	5,960	1.9	6,119	1.8	134.5	2.7	140.2
Others			1,866	0.6	1,895	0.6		1.6	
Manufacture of Furniture; Manufacturing of Articles n.e.c.	23,057	10.5	26,704	8.5	26,247	7.7	18.4	- 1.7	17.8
Recycling			585	0.2	911	0.3		55.7	
Total	218,952	100.0	312,940	100.0	340,183	100.0	42.9	8.7	55.4

Division of industry	Number of employment								
	1986		1995		2005		Increasing rate(%)		
	No.	%	No.	%	No.	%	1986 - 1995	1986 - 1995	1986 - 1995
Manufacture of Food Products and Beverages	281,150	8.5	312,350	8.4	297,441	8.6	11.1	- 4.8	5.8
Manufacture of Tobacco Products	11,746	0.4	5,399	0.1	3,222	0.1	- 54.0	- 40.3	- 72.6
Manufacture of Textiles, Except Sewn Wearing apparel	445,323	13.5	353,962	9.5	189,232	5.5	- 20.5	- 46.5	- 57.5
Manufacture of Sewn Wearing Apparel and Fur Articles	370,417	11.3	258,681	7.0	149,704	4.3	- 30.2	- 42.1	- 59.6
Tanning and Dressing of Leather , Manufacture of Luggage and Footwear	198,680	6.0	98,728	2.7	39,172	1.1	- 50.3	- 60.3	- 80.3
Manufacture of Wood and of Products of Wood and Cork, Except Furniture	65,227	2.0	62,727	1.7	40,785	1.2	- 3.8	- 35.0	- 37.5
Manufacture of Pulp, Paper and Paper Products	64,856	2.0	83,813	2.3	68,372	2.0	29.2	- 18.4	5.4
Publishing, Printing and Reproduction of Recorded Media	99,704	3.0	141,329	3.8	137,877	4.0	41.7	- 2.4	38.3
Manufacture of Coke, Refined Petroleum Products and Nuclear Fuel	176,128	5.4	15,013	0.4	10,326	0.3	16.4	- 31.2	2.7
Manufacture of Chemicals and Chemical Products			190,022	5.1	170,550	4.9		- 10.2	
Manufacture of Rubber and Plastic Products	151,822	4.6	155,012	4.2	217,358	6.3	2.1	40.2	43.2
Manufacture of Other Non - metallic Mineral Products	131,479	4.0	162,582	4.4	107,162	3.1	23.7	- 34.1	- 18.5
Manufacture of Basic Metals	92,347	2.8	123,469	3.3	126,871	3.7	33.7	2.8	37.4
Manufacture of Fabricated Metal Products, Except Machinery and Furniture	206,262	6.3	286,814	7.7	325,472	9.4	39.1	13.5	57.8
Manufacture of Other Machinery	548,603	16.7	381,571	10.3	362,961	10.5	58.4	- 4.9	78.8
Manufacture of Computers and Office Machinery			37,210	1.0	43,142	1.3		15.9	
Manufacture of Electrical Machinery and Apparatuseses n.e.c.			155,554	4.2	169,869	4.9		9.2	
Manufacture of Electronic Components, Radio, Television and Communication equipment			294,771	7.9	404,853	11.7		37.3	
Manufacture of Medical, Precision and Optical Instruments, Watches	45,471	1.4	60,552	1.6	71,683	2.1	33.2	18.4	57.6
Manufacture of Motor Vehicles, Trailers and Semitrailers	198,098	6.0	261,695	7.1	256,423	7.4	79.9	- 2.0	88.0
Others			94,762	2.6	116,002	3.4		22.4	
Manufacture of Furniture; Manufacturing of Articles n.e.c.	202,722	6.2	168,704	4.5	134,360	3.9	- 14.7	- 20.4	- 29.7
Recycling			4,156	0.1	8,056	0.2		93.8	
Total	3,290,035	100.0	3,708,876	100.0	3,450,893	100.0	12.7	-7.0	4.9

• Classification of industries of 1986 differs from that of 1995 and 2005. Therefore, data from 1986 has been reorganized to fit the statistics.
(Source : Statistics Korea, [kostat.go.kr])

Table 5.13 **Changes of manufacturing structure by types of industry, 1986-2005**

Type	1986		1991		1995	
	No.*	ratio (%)	No.	ratio (%)	No.	ratio (%)
Resource based	506,415	15.4	630,789	14.9	622,748	16.8
Assembly	1,108,830	33.7	1,768,512	41.8	1,751,764	47.2
Labor intensive	1,258,568	38.3	1,259,454	29.8	856,252	23.1
Capital intensive	142,680	4.3	211,501	5.0	299,911	8.1
Other	273,542	8.3	360,824	8.5	178,201	4.8
Total	3,290,035	100.0	4,231,080	100.0	3,708,876	100.0

Type	2000		2005		1986-2005
	No.	ratio (%)	No.	ratio (%)	Increasing rate (%)
Resource based	513,417	15.4	521,147	15.1	2.9
Assembly	1,697,815	50.9	1,986,241	57.6	79.1
Labor intensive	665,612	20.0	493,990	14.3	- 60.7
Capital intensive	289,282	8.7	280,090	8.1	96.3
Other	166,892	5.0	168,825	4.9	- 38.3
Total	3,333,018	100.0	3,450,893	100.0	4.8

Number of employees in manufacturing in enterprises more than 5 employees.
-Resource based : Manufacture of Food Products, Manufacture of Wood and of Products of Wood and Cork (except Furniture), Manufacture of Pulp, Paper and Paper Products, Manufacture of Other Non-metallic Mineral Products, Manufacture of Basic Nonferrous Metals.
-Assembly : Manufacture of Plastic Products, Manufacture of Fabricated Metal Products (except Machinery and Furniture), Manufacture of Other Machinery, Manufacture of Computers and Office Machinery, Manufacture of Electrical Machinery and Apparatuses n.e.c., Manufacture of Electronic Components, Radio, Television and Communication equipment, Manufacture of Medical, Precision and Optical Instruments, Watches, Manufacture of Motor Vehicles, Trailers and Semitrailers, Others, Manufacture of Furniture ; Manufacturing of Articles n.e.c.
-Labor intensive : Manufacture of Textiles (except Sewn Wearing apparel), Manufacture of Sewn Wearing Apparel and Fur Articles, Tanning and Dressing of Leather, Manufacture of Luggage and Footwear, Manufacture of Rubber products, Others.
-Capital intensive : Manufacture of Coke, Refined Petroleum Products and Nuclear Fuel, Manufacture of Chemicals and Chemical Products, Manufacture of Basic Steel.
-Other : Manufacture of Beverages, Manufacture of Tobacco Products, Publishing, Printing and Reproduction of Recorded Media, Recycling.
(Source : Statistics Korea, [kostat.go.kr])

order to clarify the changes in the manufacturing sector's structure, the 23 manufacturing industries are classified into five types : resource-intensive industry, assembly type, labor-intensive type, capital-intensive type, and the other special type. The classification is based on the factor analysis of the manufacturing industries by their structural characteristics (Park,

1993a). Table 5.13 reveals the structural changes during the last two decades. There is a contrasting trend between the labor-intensive type and assembly type, which includes high-tech industries such as plastics, office automation machinery, electrical and electronics machinery, audio-video equipment, communication equipment, and medical precision and optical instruments. In 1986, the labor-intensive industry type comprised the largest share with 38.3% of the total employment, but the value continuously decreased and reached 14.3% in 2005. The share of the assembly type continuously increased from 33.7% in 1986 to 57.6% in 2005. In general, the capital-intensive type has increased its share, but that of the other special type has decreased. There have been no significant changes in the share of resource-intensive type.

Such structural changes in the manufacturing sector are closely related with the changes in the government's industrial policies. In the early stage of economic development, the government emphasized export-oriented industrial development focusing on labor-intensive industries, where Korea had comparative advantages due to cheap labor in the 1960s and early 1970s. The industrial structure began to shift towards the heavy and chemical industrial structure due to the government's heavy and chemical industrial policy in the 1970s. Since the 1980s, the government policies have focused on R&D investments and training high-quality human resources for the development of technology-intensive industries, which resulted to the continuous growth of the assembly-type industries that include the technology-intensive industries (Park, 1999).

3) Service industries

Along with the trend in the service industries in advanced countries (Bryson, et. al, 2004), the share of the service sector in the total national employment has continuously increased since the 1980s in Korea. The share of the service industries in the total establishments and total employment in Korea in 2005 were 89.3% and 76.9%, respectively.

Wholesale and retail trade shared the largest portion (26.0%) of the total employment in the service industries, followed by the accommodation and food service activities (18.1%) and education services (12.7%) in 2005. However, there have been considerable changes in the structure of service industries due to the different growth rates in the individual service industry. During the last two decades, all the service industries showed considerable growth in terms of the number of establishments and employment size, as shown in Table 5.14. There was an increase in the number of establishments and employees by 71.6% and 112.7%, respectively, in the service industry during the period of 1986 to 2005. Business services represented the highest growth rate (984.4%), while wholesale and retail trade showed the lowest growth rate (48.6%). In addition to the business services, telecommunications, human health and social work activities, and art, sports, and recreation-related services showed high growth rate (Table 5.14). Such changes in the service sector show that the service industry in

Table 5.14 **Changes of Service structure by service industry, 1986-2005**

Number of firms									
Division of industry	1986		1995		2005		Increasing rate(%)		
	No.	%	No.	%	No.	%	1986 - 1995	1995 - 2000	2000 - 2005
Wholesale and Retail Trade	716,498	50.9	944,131	43.6	864,687	35.8	31.8	- 8.4	20.7
Hotel and Restaurants	288,833	20.5	522,323	24.1	621,279	25.7	80.8	18.9	115.1
Post and Telecommunications	1,379	0.1	4,326	0.2	9,371	0.4	213.7	116.6	579.6
Financial Institutions and Insurance	17,587	1.2	35,169	1.6	34,690	1.4	100.0	- 1.4	97.2
Real estate and Renting and leasing	50,645	3.6	92,213	4.3	116,190	4.8	82.1	26.0	129.4
Business activities	12,671	0.9	51,657	2.4	87,671	3.6	307.7	69.7	591.9
Education	52,986	3.8	99,273	4.6	127,284	5.3	87.4	28.2	140.2
Health and Social work	20,281	1.4	45,905	2.1	76,074	3.1	126.3	65.7	275.1
Recreational, Cultural and Sporting activities	49,191	3.5	86,991	4.0	128,637	5.3	76.8	47.9	161.5
Other community, Repair and Personal service activities	198,852	14.1	282,096	13.0	352,317	14.6	41.9	24.9	77.2
Total	1,408,923	100.0	2,164,084	100.0	2,418,200	100.0	53.6	11.7	71.6
Number of employment									
Division of industry	1986		1995		2005		Increasing rate(%)		
	No.	%	No.	%	No.	%	1986 - 1995	1995 - 2000	2000 - 2005
Wholesale and Retail Trade	1,642,775	37.3	2,538,897	33.8	2,440,701	26.0	54.5	- 3.9	48.6
Hotel and Restaurants	809,984	18.4	1,289,317	17.2	1,696,133	18.1	59.2	31.6	109.4
Post and Telecommunications	46,188	1.0	85,560	1.1	138,577	1.5	85.2	62.0	200.0
Financial Institutions and Insurance	367,280	8.3	710,518	9.5	591,969	6.3	93.5	- 16.7	61.2
Real estate and Renting and leasing	163,845	3.7	302,456	4.0	404,290	4.3	84.6	33.7	146.8
Business activities	98,311	2.2	475,382	6.3	1,066,107	11.4	383.5	124.3	984.4
Education	492,356	11.2	777,175	10.3	1,193,363	12.7	57.8	53.6	142.4
Health and Social work	188,097	4.3	353,613	4.7	647,746	6.9	88.0	83.2	244.4
Recreational, Cultural and Sporting activities	120,495	2.7	237,700	3.2	396,290	4.2	97.3	66.7	228.9
Other community, Repair and Personal service activities	479,381	10.9	747,117	9.9	803,313	8.6	55.9	7.5	67.6
Total	4,408,712	100.0	7,517,735	100.0	9,378,489	100.0	70.5	24.8	112.7

[Source : Statistics Korea, [kostat.go.kr]]

CHAPTER 5

Korea has been undergoing significant shift towards knowledge-intensive advanced services. It is noticeable that financial and insurance activities and wholesale and retail trade showed a negative growth rate during the period of 1995 to 2005, that represents the restructuring of the service sector due to the financial crisis in 1997 in Korea.

If we examine the growth rate of the sub sectors within the service sector during the last decade, it clearly shows the direction of the changes in the service sector in Korea. During the period of 1995 to 2005, the service sector as a whole increased the number of establishments and employees by 11.7% and 24.8%, respectively. These rates are much lower than the growth rate during the period 1986 to 1995 (Table 5.14), revealing the impact of the 1997 financial crisis. Business service, however, showed an increase in the number of establishments and employees during the period of 1995 to 2005 by 69.7% and 124.3%, respectively. Within the business service, the number of establishments and employees in information service and computer operation-related service activities increased by 340.8% and 351.2%, respectively (Table 5.15). Business support services also showed a high growth rate in the number of establishments (150.2%) and employees (305.9%). It is noticeable that the number of establishments in R&D activities increased by 148.4%, which is higher than the growth rate of the number of employees (101.9%). The higher growth rate of the establishments compared with that of the employees is closely related with the increase of the small R&D labs of small high-technology firms during the restructuring period after the financial crisis. Many small high-technology firms (called "venture firms" in Korea) were established in the period of 1999 to 2001, when the government supported the venture firms and their R&D activities.

Table 5.15 **Growth of business services**

Division of industry	1995		2005		1995 - 2005 Increasing rate(%)	
	F(No.)*	E(No.)**	F(No.)	E(No.)	F(No.)	E(No.)
Business activities	51,657	475,382	87,671	1,066,107	69.7	124.3
Computer and Related Activities	2,145	35,699	9,456	161,083	340.8	351.2
Research and Development	948	38,965	2,355	78,673	148.4	101.9
Professional, Scientific and Technical Services	40,053	288,082	54,564	369,186	36.2	28.2
Business Support Services	8,511	112,636	21,296	457,165	150.2	305.9

* number of firms
** number of employment
[Source : Statistics Korea, [kostat.go.kr]]

All the subsectors within the business service showed a higher growth rate than that of the average growth rate in all the service sectors during the period of 1995 to 2005. The higher growth rate in all the business services (Table 5.15) suggests that Korea was under the process of reshaping its service activities towards a knowledge-based economy, information society, and globalization. Such shift towards a knowledge-based economy and information society will further reshape the industrial structure in Korea in the future.

5.2.3 Spatial Characteristics of the Industries

1) Changes of the spatial structure of the manufacturing sector

In the initial industrialization phase, there was a trend towards industrial concentration in Seoul and its surrounding areas. During the rapid industrialization phase in the 1970s, there was a bipolar concentration of industries in the capital region, which includes Seoul, Incheon, and Gyeonggi-*do*, and the Southeast region, which includes Busan, Daegu, Ulsan, Gyeongsangnam-*do*, and Gyeongsangbuk-*do*. However, with industrialization, the spatial changes became dynamic. Generally, there was a trend towards industrial decentralization in large metropolitan areas such as Seoul and Busan, on the one hand, and dispersion to non-Capital regions from the capital region, on the other.

During the last two decades, the share of employment in the manufacturing sector in Seoul to the national total dramatically decreased from 26.8% in 1986 to 13.7% in 2005, with a decreasing rate of -85.8% (Table 5-16). Busan also decreased its share from 13.9% in 1986 to 5.8% in 2005. However, Gyeonggi-*do*, the surrounding areas of Seoul, increased its share in the national total from 17.9% in 1986 to 28.8% in 2005. Gyeongsangbuk-*do*, Ulsan and Gyeongsangnam-*do*, which are the surrounding areas of Daegu and Busan, increased their share from 5.5% and 10.8% in 1986 to 7.7% and 14.2% in 2005, respectively. Such changes can be considered a decentralization trend in the manufacturing sector in large metropolitan areas.

On the other hand, Chungcheongbuk-*do* and Chungcheongnam-*do* experienced a considerable growth in manufacturing employment. The growth of the Chungcheong provinces can be regarded as the extension of the decentralization trend and dispersion beyond the capital region to Mid-region, including the Chungcheong provinces and Daejeon situated along the express highways from Seoul. It reveals a wave-like expansion of manufacturing activities from Seoul to the Middle Region over time : concentration in the center of Seoul

Table 5.16 **Share of manufacturing employment by region, 1986-2005**

Region	1986		1995		2005		Increasing rate(%)		
							86 - 95	95 - 05	86 - 05
	No.	%	No.	%	No.	%	%	%	%
Seoul	880,229	26.8	729,057	19.7	473,643	13.7	- 17.2	- 35.0	- 85.8
Busan	457,047	13.9	287,571	7.8	200,895	5.8	- 37.1	- 30.1	- 127.5
Daegu	196,365	6.0	213,987	5.8	155,484	4.5	9.0	- 27.3	- 26.3
Incheon	204,626	6.2	284,478	7.7	225,663	6.5	39.0	- 20.7	9.3
Gwangju	28,387	0.9	61,312	1.7	69,606	2.0	116.0	13.5	59.2
Daejeon	-	-	56,987	1.5	47,326	1.4	-	- 17.0	-
Ulsan[*]	-	-	-	-	140,668	4.1	-	-	-
Gyeonggi - *do*	588,512	17.9	859,827	23.2	995,534	28.8	46.1	15.8	40.9
Gangwon - *do*	41,984	1.3	50,295	1.4	42,120	1.2	19.8	- 16.3	0.3
Chungcheongbuk - *do*	62,701	1.9	118,439	3.2	122,416	3.5	88.9	3.4	48.8
Chungcheongnam - *do*	122,530	3.7	129,884	3.5	184,533	5.3	6.0	42.1	33.6
Jeollabuk - *do*	84,820	2.6	98,833	2.7	82,279	2.4	16.5	- 16.7	- 3.1
Jeollanam - *do*	81,598	2.5	94,580	2.6	89,118	2.6	15.9	- 5.8	8.4
Gyeongsangbuk - *do*	181,411	5.5	243,893	6.6	265,013	7.7	34.4	8.7	31.5
Gyeongsangnam - *do*[*]	353,890	10.8	471,786	12.7	348,015	10.1	33.3	- 26.2	- 1.7
Jeju special self-governing province	5,935	0.2	7,947	0.2	8,580	0.2	33.9	8.0	30.8
Total	3,290,035	100.0	3,708,876	100.0	3,450,893	100.0	12.7	- 7.0	4.7

* Ulsan included in Gyeonsangnam-do in 1995.
(Source : Statistics Korea, [kostat.go.kr])

before the 1960s, decentralization from the city center to the inner city of Seoul in the 1960s, decentralization from Seoul to nearby suburbs in the 1970s, decentralization to the far away suburbs of Seoul, and decentralization to the Chungcheong provinces. The extension of the decentralization trend from Seoul to the far away suburbs and Chungcheong provinces is presented in Figure 5.4.

Along with the spatial changes of manufacturing activities in Korea, there was a diverse trend in the structural changes by region. Although the continuous structural shift from labor-intensive to technology and knowledge-intensive industries can be identified in the nationwide level, there are considerable differences in the structural changes by regions. The Southeast region, which includes Busan, Daegu, Ulsan, Gyeongsangbuk-*do*, and Gyeongsangnam-*do*, has had highly specialized assembly type industries during the last three decades. The Middle Region saw the significant transformation of industries from labor-intensive to technology-

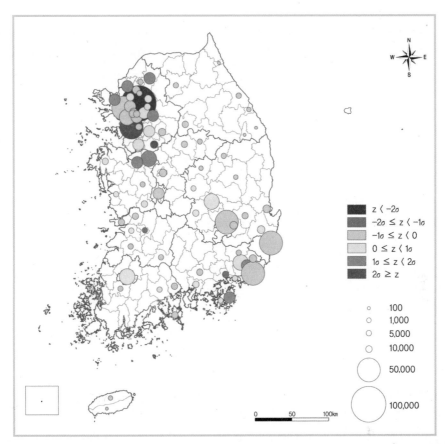

Figure 5.4 **Changes of the number of manufacturing industry workers (1994-2005)**
(Source : Park, 2009, World Bank.)
* Using data on the number of manufacturing industry employees in the Census of Basic Characteristics of Establishments in 1994 and in 2005.

intensive industries in the 1990s. The rapid transformation of industrial structure in the Middle region is closely related with the expansion of industrial agglomeration from the capital region to the nearby Chungcheong region as well as the development of Daedeok Research Park in Daejeon in the 1990s. A trend towards technology-intensive industries is also recognized in the Southwest region, which includes Gwangju, Jeollabuk-*do*, and Jeollanam-*do*, but the degree of the shift is lower compared with the nationwide trend. The Southwest region is rather specialized with more resource-intensive type industries (Park, 2009).

It is also noticeable that the trend of changes in the industrial structure of Seoul is significantly different from that seen nationwide. Seoul concentrated in labor-intensive industries during the early industrialization phase of Korea. Although the share of technology-intensive industries has been slightly increasing since the early 1990s, the increase is lower than the share of labor-intensive industries in Seoul. In 2005, the share of the number of employees in the textile and apparel industry in the national total number was 36.6%, which was much higher than Seoul's manufacturing employment share in the national total (13.7%) or Seoul's technology intensive industries (such as those involved in computer, electronics, and precision machinery) share in the national total (11.2%). This is presented in Table 5.17. In Seoul, the structural changes within an industry have been more intensive than the changes of industrial composition among industry types. For example, within an apparel industry, Seoul has specialized in fashion design and high-value added products rather than standardized mass production activities. This suggests that Seoul's specialization in the labor-intensive industries is not only sustaining the traditional industries, but restructuring towards knowledge-intensive industries instead of technology intensive industries as well.

However, Gyeonggi-*do*, regarded as the suburban areas of Seoul, transformed its industries towards technology-intensive industries. Gyeonggi-*do* has a share of 41.8% of the national total in technology-intensive industries. This is higher than the share of manufacturing in the national total manufacturing employment. Such specialization in Gyeonggi-*do* was brought about by the relocation of branch plants of the technology-intensive industries from Seoul.

Industries in Ulsan and Gyeongsangnam-*do*, which are in the surrounding areas of Busan, are highly specialized in transportation-related industries. Ulsan and Gyeongsangnam-*do* have shares of 20.2% and 21.9%, respectively, in the national total number of employment in the transportation related-industries. These are higher than the shares in the national total of the manufacturing employment (4.1% and 10.1%, respectively) (Table 5.17). The Chungcheong provinces have also considerably specialized in technology-intensive industries, although the degree of concentration of the industries in Chungcheong provinces is relatively weaker than that of Gyeonggi and Gyeongsangnam provinces. Daegu has been the traditional textile industrial center, and it continues to specialize in the textile industry. However, Gyeongsangbuk-*do*, which is located in the surrounding area of Daegu, has specialized in technology-intensive industries through the formation of electronics industry clusters in Gumi and in the suburban areas of Daegu. The Jeolla provinces are specialized in the resource-intensive industry such as food-related products. There is a recent trend towards concentrating in transportation-related industry in the Southwest region, which includes Gwangju and Jeolla provinces.

The spatial changes in the industry are closely related with the industrial policies and structural changes. In the early industrialization phase, export-oriented industrial policies and heavy and chemical industrial policies reinforced the spatial disparity, that is, the bipolar concentration of industries in the capital region and Southeast region (Park and Wheeler,

Table 5.17 **Changes of regional share of manufacturing employment, 2005**

Region	Food/Tobacco products		Textile/Apparel /Leather		Wood/Paper/ Publishing		Chemistry		Other Non - metallic products	
	No.	%	No.	%	No.	%	No.	%	No.	%
Seoul	30,257	10.1	138,402	36.6	87,731	35.5	32,725	18.1	16,229	5.0
Busan	17,436	5.8	40,972	10.8	10,086	4.1	4,448	2.5	13,274	4.1
Daegu	9,522	3.2	37,891	10.0	9,306	3.8	1,925	1.1	11,168	3.4
Incheon	10,305	3.4	9,879	2.6	15,012	6.1	8,400	4.6	18,932	5.8
Gwangju	5,509	1.8	4,282	1.1	4,218	1.7	609	0.3	9,093	2.8
Daejeon	6,075	2.0	4,790	1.3	5,300	2.1	3,341	1.8	4,837	1.5
Ulsan	3,550	1.2	3,557	0.9	2,245	0.9	18,070	10.0	5,264	1.6
Gyeonggi - do	63,583	21.1	73,722	19.5	63,529	25.7	50,374	27.9	104,404	32.2
Gangwon - do	15,153	5.0	1,526	0.4	2,686	1.1	1,685	0.9	7,214	2.2
Chungcheongbuk - do	18,730	6.2	6,046	1.6	6,334	2.6	9,875	5.5	19,749	6.1
Chungcheongnam - do	24,343	8.1	7,699	2.0	6,979	2.8	12,193	6.7	23,698	7.3
Jeollabuk - do	18,793	6.3	8,903	2.4	7,224	2.9	5,839	3.2	9,540	2.9
Jeollanam - do	23,424	7.8	3,059	0.8	3,627	1.5	12,732	7.0	12,223	3.8
Gyeongsangbuk - do	23,266	7.7	23,541	6.2	9,772	4.0	11,182	6.2	31,662	9.8
Gyeongsangnam - do	27,390	9.1	13,432	3.6	11,718	4.7	7,262	4.0	35,888	11.1
Jeju special self-governing province	3,327	1.1	407	0.1	1,267	0.5	216	0.1	1,345	0.4
Total	300,663	100.0	378,108	100.0	247,034	100.0	180,876	100.0	324,520	100.0

Region	Metals/Fabricated Metal Products		Computers/ Precision		Motor Vehicles/ other transport		Others		Total	
	No.	%	No.	%	No.	%	No.	%	No.	%
Seoul	53,084	6.5	77,440	11.2	6,471	1.7	31,304	22.0	473,768	13.7
Busan	63,758	7.8	21,545	3.1	20,800	5.6	8,576	6.0	200,939	5.8
Daegu	49,413	6.1	16,195	2.3	16,011	4.3	4,053	2.8	155,518	4.5
Incheon	87,856	10.8	42,273	6.1	19,667	5.3	13,339	9.4	225,708	6.5
Gwangju	20,930	2.6	11,888	1.7	10,871	2.9	2,206	1.5	69,621	2.0
Daejeon	9,860	1.2	8,699	1.3	2,136	0.6	2,288	1.6	47,338	1.4
Ulsan	20,176	2.5	10,299	1.5	75,054	20.2	2,453	1.7	140,707	4.1
Gyeonggi - do	237,895	29.2	288,150	41.8	65,016	17.5	48,861	34.3	995,749	28.8
Gangwon - do	4,270	0.5	4,332	0.6	3,282	0.9	1,972	1.4	42,132	1.2
Chungcheongbuk - do	18,460	2.3	33,798	4.9	5,815	1.6	3,609	2.5	122,447	3.5
Chungcheongnam - do	33,051	4.1	47,953	7.0	23,389	6.3	5,228	3.7	184,577	5.3
Jeollabuk - do	10,235	1.3	6,293	0.9	12,164	3.3	3,288	2.3	82,302	2.4
Jeollanam - do	17,805	2.2	2,401	0.3	10,781	2.9	3,066	2.2	89,144	2.6
Gyeongsangbuk - do	61,973	7.6	78,448	11.4	19,260	5.2	5,909	4.1	265,071	7.7
Gyeongsangnam - do	125,565	15.4	39,477	5.7	81,658	21.9	5,625	3.9	348,091	10.1
Jeju special self-governing province	973	0.1	356	0.1	50	0.0	639	0.4	8,582	0.2
Total	815,304	100.0	689,547	100.0	372,425	100.0	142,416	100.0	3,451,693	100.0

-The major manufacturing sectors are as follows.
-Food/Tobacco products : Manufacture of Food Products and Beverages, Manufacture of Tobacco Products.
-Textile/Apparel / Leather : Manufacture of Textiles, Manufacture of Sewn Wearing Apparel and Fur Articles, Tanning and Dressing of Leather, Manufacture of Luggage and Footwear.
-Wood /Paper/Publishing : Manufacture of Wood and of Products of Wood and Cork, Manufacture of Pulp, Paper and Paper Products, Publishing, Printing and Reproduction of Recorded Media.
-Chemistry : Manufacture of Coke, Refined Petroleum Products and Nuclear Fuel, Manufacture of Chemicals and Chemical Products.
-Other Non-metallic products : Manufacture of Rubber and Plastic Products, Manufacture of Other Non-metallic Mineral Products.
-Metals/ Fabricated Metal Products : Manufacture of Basic Metals, Manufacture of Fabricated Metal

CHAPTER 5

Products, Except Machinery and Furniture, Manufacture of Other Machinery.
-Computers/Precision : Manufacture of Computers and Office Machinery, Manufacture of Electrical
  Machinery and Appar atuseses n.e.c., Manufacture of Electronic Components, Radio, Television and
  Communication equipment, Manufacture of Medical, Precision and Optical Instruments, Watches.
-Motor Vehicles/other transport : Manufacture of Motor Vehicles, Trailers and Semitrailers, Others,
  Manufacture of Furniture ; Manufacturing of Articles n.e.c., Recycling
(Source : Statistics Korea, [kostat.go.kr])

1983). the capital region increased its share of manufacturing employment in the 1960s and reached a peak at 48.3% in 1975. In the heavy and chemical industrialization phase, the Southeast region increased its share sharply and reached a peak in 1980 with 40.4%. This shows that the heavy and chemical industrial development policy in the 1970s aggravated the spatial disparity (Park, 2009).

Furthermore, the government's heavy and chemical industrial development policy has resulted in the spatial division of labor, with the concentration of the headquarters of Jaebols in Seoul and decentralization of the production functions to non-Capital regions, especially in the Southeast region. The high technology industrial policy of the 1980s resulted in a slight re-concentration in the capital region in the 1980s due to the locational advantages that the capital region has for high-technology industries. The concentration of high-technology industries and advanced services including R&D activities in the capital region intensified the spatial division of labor in Korean production systems and space economy in the 1980s (Park, 1993b).

It is also noticeable that the shares of the Middle and Southwest regions, considered the peripheral region of Korea at that time, decreased until the mid-1980s, while that of the Middle region has increased considerably since that time. The Southwest region increased its share in manufacturing employment from the mid-1980s to the mid-1990s, but no significant change was observed since the mid-1990s.

2) Changes of the spatial structure in the service industry

The changes of the spatial structure in the service industry have progressed along with the structural changes in the service industry. In order to understand easily the structural changes in the service industry, it is classified according to producer services and consumer services. For convenience of using the data, telecommunication, finance and insurance, real estate leasing service, and business services are considered producer services, while the other services are considered consumer services.

From 1995 to 2005, consumer services increased by only 1.3% in the number of establishments and 8.1% in the number of employees. However, producer services increased considerably in the same period : 35.2% in the number of establishments and 39.8% in the number of employees (Table 5.18). the capital region, which includes Seoul, Incheon, and Gyeonggi-*do*, had a share of about half of the consumer services and 62.1% of producer services in the number of employees, revealing more agglomeration of producer services in the capital region in 2005. There are two distinctive characteristics in the changes in spatial distribution.

First, Gyeonggi-*do* experienced a considerable growth of consumer services and accordingly its national share increased from 13.7% to 16.8% in the number of establishments and from 12.7% to 17.9% in the number of employees. However, Seoul and Busan experienced a negative growth in both the number of establishments and employees during the same period. The rapid growth of consumer services in Gyeonggi-*do* seems to be related with the growth of population in Gyeonggi-*do* due to the immigration influx from the non-Capital region. Chungcheongnam-*do* also showed a considerable increase in the number of consumer services

Second, there is a continuous concentration of producer services in Seoul and Gyeonggi-*do*. Seoul's share increased from 39.2% in 1995 to 42.5% in 2005 in the number of employees, while that of Gyeonggi increased from 11.8% to 16.1% in the same period. All the other metropolises and provinces showed less than average growth rate in the number of employees in the producer services, representing the overwhelming concentration trend of producer services in the capital region. The metropolises in the non-Capital region have seen an increase in the number of employees in the producer services, but the growth rate was lower than the national average during the period of 1995 to 2005. This reveals that the share of metropolises of the non-Capital region in the total national number of employees in the producer services decreased during the same period (Table 5.18). The Chungcheong provinces showed a considerable growth in the number of employees in the producer services, but their national share decreased. Jeollanam-*do* experienced a negative growth rate, and its national share decreased from 6.1% in 1995 to 4.0% in 2005.

In addition to the overwhelming agglomeration of producer services in Seoul, there was a continuous concentration of producer services in Seoul and its surrounding satellite cities in Gyeonggi-*do*, as shown in Figure 5.5. It is clear that all the cities in the non- Capital region displayed a growth rate less than the average of the national growth regardless of the size of the city. Such trend towards a continuous concentration of producer services in the capital region suggests the evolution of another spatial division of labor, beyond the spatial division of labor between the control and management functions in Seoul and of the manufacturing

Table 5.18 **Changes of regional share of service activities, 1995-2005**

Region	Number of firms									
	Consumer service					Producer service				
	1995		2005		Increasing rate(%)	1995		2005		Increasing rate(%)
	No.	%	No.	%		No.	%	No.	%	
Seoul	366,418	25.0	339,631	22.9	- 7.3	56,058	30.6	79,640	32.1	42.1
Busan	138,502	9.4	126,903	8.5	- 8.4	15,945	8.7	18,296	7.4	14.7
Daegu	83,891	5.7	81,165	5.5	- 3.2	10,299	5.6	11,818	4.8	14.7
Incheon	65,556	4.5	67,161	4.5	2.4	8,796	4.8	10,845	4.4	23.3
Gwangju	41,329	2.8	43,178	2.9	4.5	5,753	3.1	7,023	2.8	22.1
Daejeon	44,503	3.0	42,656	2.9	- 4.2	5,957	3.2	7,389	3.0	24.0
Ulsan*	-	-	31,583	2.1	-	-	-	4,255	1.7	-
Gyeonggi - do	200,865	13.7	250,147	16.8	24.5	28,290	15.4	49,922	20.1	76.5
Gangwon - do	59,456	4.1	62,400	4.2	5.0	5,258	2.9	7,302	2.9	38.9
Chungcheongbuk - do	46,901	3.2	46,243	3.1	- 1.4	4,966	2.7	6,229	2.5	25.4
Chungcheongnam - do	57,490	3.9	62,430	4.2	8.6	6,009	3.3	7,989	3.2	33.0
Jeollabuk - do	59,351	4.0	56,163	3.8	- 5.4	6,669	3.6	6,928	2.8	3.9
Jeollanam - do	67,283	4.6	63,500	4.3	- 5.6	6,240	3.4	5,978	2.4	- 4.2
Gyeongsangbuk - do	86,189	5.9	88,972	6.0	3.2	8,008	4.4	9,239	3.7	15.4
Gyeongsangnam - do*	129,398	8.8	102,033	6.9	- 21.1	13,067	7.1	12,671	5.1	- 3.0
Jeju Special Self-Governing Province	19,322	1.3	21,801	1.5	12.8	2,050	1.1	2,398	1.0	17.0
Total	1,466,454	100.0	1,485,966	100.0	1.3	183,365	100.0	247,922	100.0	35.2

Region	Number of employment									
	Consumer service					Producer service				
	1995		2005		Increasing rate(%)	1995		2005		Increasing rate(%)
	No.	%	No.	%		No.	%	No.	%	
Seoul	1,264,082	33.0	1,141,046	27.6	- 9.7	616,821	39.2	935,969	42.5	51.7
Busan	347,768	9.1	339,376	8.2	- 2.4	133,365	8.5	151,865	6.9	13.9
Daegu	203,830	5.3	212,234	5.1	4.1	77,481	4.9	91,814	4.2	18.5
Incheon	159,557	4.2	180,390	4.4	13.1	59,014	3.7	76,660	3.5	29.9
Gwangju	108,372	2.8	123,124	3.0	13.6	44,820	2.8	59,711	2.7	33.2
Daejeon	115,842	3.0	120,707	2.9	4.2	64,924	4.1	74,491	3.4	14.7
Ulsan*	-	-	80,790	2.0	-	-	-	41,352	1.9	-
Gyeonggi - do	486,490	12.7	738,608	17.9	51.8	185,904	11.8	353,556	16.1	90.2
Gangwon - do	133,943	3.5	147,863	3.6	10.4	39,327	2.5	47,940	2.2	21.9
Chungcheongbuk - do	102,891	2.7	113,147	2.7	10.0	35,454	2.3	45,695	2.1	28.9
Chungcheongnam - do	120,457	3.1	147,482	3.6	22.4	39,925	2.5	48,590	2.2	21.7
Jeollabuk - do	131,361	3.4	137,218	3.3	4.5	47,862	3.0	50,790	2.3	6.1
Jeollanam - do	136,161	3.6	142,367	3.4	4.6	50,435	3.2	47,063	2.1	- 6.7
Gyeongsangbuk - do	179,721	4.7	202,192	4.9	12.5	64,737	4.1	68,993	3.1	6.6
Gyeongsangnam - do*	284,155	7.4	246,982	6.0	- 13.1	95,718	6.1	87,052	4.0	- 9.1
Jeju Special Self-Governing Province	53,584	1.4	63,308	1.5	18.1	18,129	1.2	19,402	0.9	7.0
Total	3,828,214	100.0	4,136,834	100.0	8.1	1,573,916	100.0	2,200,943	100.0	39.8

* Ulsan included in Gyeongsangnam-do in 1995.
• Each industry within two services group is as follows.
-Consumer services : Wholesale and Retail trade, Hotels and Restaurants.
-Producer services : Post and Telecommunications, Financial institutions and Insurance, Real estate and Renting and leasing, Business activities.
(Source : Statistics Korea, [kostat.go.kr])

function in the areas outside Seoul. This new trend towards spatial division of labor can be understood if we compare the maps of the changes in the manufacturing sector (Figure 5.4) and the changes in producer services (Figure 5.5).

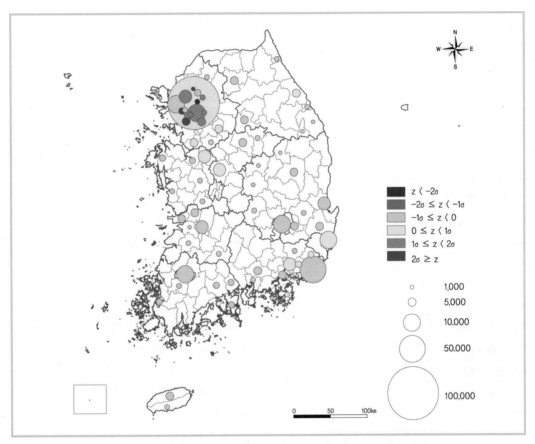

Figure 5.5 **Increasing rate of producer services employment**
(Source : Park, 2009, World Bank.)

Using data on the number of wholesale trade, financial and insurance activities, real estate activities and renting and leasing, and business services workers in the Census of Basic Characteristics of Establishments in 1994 and in 2005.

Chapter 5.3.

GROWTH AND DEVELOPMENT OF THE NEW INDUSTRY

5.3.1 Scope of the New Industry

The definition and scope of the new industry vary with time, region, and level of economic development. The scope also varies depending on the researchers or academic fields because the term "new industry" is not an academic one. There are diverse definitions of and approaches to the new industry. In general, the new industry involves the technological reorganization of existing industries and newly developed industries. That is, the new industry includes not only the newly developed industries from new technology and the new management method based on new knowledge, but it also includes the reorganized existing industries with high value added and knowledge-intensive industries based on professional knowledge and technology (Kim, 1998). In Korea, particularly in the 1980s and 1990s, the high-technology industry was the main focus of discussion on the new industry, while in the beginning of 21st century, the producer services was included in the mainstream of the new industry. With the progress in knowledge-based economy and information society in the years following 2000, knowledge-based industries have been regarded as the new industry or as the representative of the new industry. Knowledge-based industries are classified according to core technology such as Information Technology (IT), Biology Technology (BT), Nano Technology (NT), Space Technology (SP), Environment Technology (ET), and Culture Technology (CT) ; they are regarded as an important growth engine for the future.

Due to the rapid development of Information and Communication Technology (ICT), the high-technology industry and advanced service industry have experienced rapid and diverse development with the creation and diffusion of new technology and knowledge during the last decade. In working towards the definition and scope of knowledge-based industry, the content of technology with regard to the creation of new knowledge through R&D activities and diffusion and use of knowledge is significantly considered. That is, if the creation, diffusion and use of the new knowledge have a critical role in the development of the industry, then the industry tends to be considered as a new industry. In this chapter, the new industry is considered a knowledge-based industry and classified by two sectors : knowledge-based manufacturing industry and knowledge-based service. In addition, industry related with the core technology such as IT, BT, CT, and ET is regarded as new industry as shown in Table 5.19.

Table 5.19 **Industrial classification of knowledge-based industry**

Classification	Industry	Category of business
By business	Knowledge - based manufacture	Computer, Semiconductor, High - tech Electronic Components, Communication Instrument, Fine Chemicals, Advanced Materials, Mechatronics, Precision, High - tech Transport Equipment
	Knowledge - based service	Knowledge & information service(IT service, software, e - commerce, Newspaper and broadcast), Manufacturing support service(business service, R&D and engineering, advertisement, design), Cultural service(culture: video and record, publishing, tourism etc.)
By core technology	IT	IT device, Software and computer - related
	BT	New drug development
	CT	Game, animation and musical record industry
	ET	Environmental plant industry, Environmental resource industry, Environmental service industry

(Source : Kim, 2003 ; Park et al., 2003)

5.3.2 Growth of the New Industry

The type of industries included in the new industry may differ according to the purpose of classification and the degree of breakdown of the industry or the level of SIC. In order to understand the overall spatial changes of the new industry, data on the two-digit SIC level are used for the analysis of the new industry. As defined in the previous section, the new industry is categorized into two groups : high-technology industry from the manufacturing sector and producer services from the service sector. The high-technology industry in this chapter includes manufacturers of computer and office machinery (SIC 30), manufacturers of electrical machinery and apparatuses (SIC 31), manufacturers of electronic components, radio, television, and so on (SIC 32), and manufacturers of medical, precision, and optical instruments and watches (SIC 33). The producer services in this chapter include computer and related activities (SIC 72), research and development (SIC 73), professional scientific and technical services (SIC 74), and business support services (SIC 75).

The overall trend of the new industry is presented in Table 5.20. The share of the new industry in the manufacturing sector increased from 6.1% to 9.8% in the number of establishments and from 12.9% to 20.0% in the number of employees during the period of 1993 to 2005. The share of the new industry in the service sector increased from 2.1% to 3.1% in the number of establishments and from 4.3% to 9.2% in the number of employees during the same period. Both high-technology industries and producer services showed higher growth rates than the manufacturing industry and service industry, and increased their share compared with the manufacturing and service industries. The share of new industry in the number of employments increased more rapidly than that of the number of establishments. The share of the high-tech industry in the manufacturing sector is higher than that of producer services in the service sector in both the number of establishments and employees despite of the higher growth rate in the producer services compared with that of the high-technology industries. Such trend suggests a higher growth rate in the service sector compared with the manufacturing sector as a whole and a trend towards service world during the period of 1993 to 2005. In this sector, based on the SIC code, the regional distribution of the new industry included in manufacturing sector (high-tech industry) and in service sector (producer services)

Table 5.20 **Changes of new industry*, 1993-2005**

		1993	1995	1997	2000	2003	2005
New industry (Manufacture)	Firm (No.)	17,235	22,276	23,315	26,918	30,422	33,242
	Share of total manufacture (%)	6.1	7.1	7.7	8.6	9.3	9.8
	Employment (No.)	499,512	548,087	520,187	601,755	645,475	689,547
	Share of total manufacture employees (%)	12.9	14.8	15.7	18.1	18.9	20.0
New industry (Service)	Firm (No.)	42,220	51,657	56,008	69,741	84,275	87,671
	Share of total services (%)	2.1	2.1	2.2	2.6	3.0	3.1
	Employment (No.)	354,922	475,382	562,045	619,007	926,229	1,066,107
	Share of total services employees (%)	4.3	4.8	5.6	6.1	8.2	9.2

* New industry classifies by industry based on KSIC.
-Manufacture : Manufacture of Computers and Office Machinery (30), Manufacture of Electrical Machinery and Appara tuseses n.e.c. (31), Manufacture of Electronic Components, Radio, Television and Communication equipment (32), Manufacture of Medical, Precision and Optical Instruments, Watches (33).
-Service : Computer and Related Activities (72), Research and Development (73), Professional, Scientific and Technical Services (74), Business Support Services (75)
(Source : Statistics Korea (Various years), [kostat.go.kr])

will be examined. The new industries identified as the new growth industries for the future will also be explored.

1) Regional distribution of the new industry in the manufacturing sector (high-technology industry)

Table 5.21 shows the distribution of the high-technology industry by metropolis and province. The average growth rate of the high-technology industry was higher during the period of 1986 to 1995 than that of the period of 1995 to 2005 in both the number of establishments and the number of employees. This may be due to the impact of the financial crisis in 1997.

The most distinctive characteristics of the distribution and changes therein are that the national share of Seoul dramatically decreased from 48.7% to 20.1%, while Gyeonggi-*do* (which is in the surrounding area of Seoul) rapidly increased its national share from 21.8% to 36.1% during the period of 1986 to 2005. These changes represent the decentralization trend in the high-technology industry from Seoul to nearby Gyeonggi-*do*, which eventually became the center of high-technology industrial agglomeration in Korea. The Middle region, which includes Daejeon, Chungcheongbuk-*do*, and Chungcheongnam-*do*, also showed a rapid increase in the high-technology industry, demonstrating that the area of high-technology agglomeration extends well beyond the Gyeonggi-*do* to the Middle region. The rapid increase in the high-technology industry in the Middle region is also related with the development of the Daedeok Special Research Park located in Daejeon.

The trend of concentrating in the high-technology industry in the capital region and recently in the Middle region reveals the importance of the location factor of the high-technology industry. Generally, the important location factors of the high-technology industries are easy access to qualified research centers and university for networking, agglomeration of scientists and engineers, venture capital, and so on. the capital region is the most appropriate region for the agglomeration of the high tech industry in Korea because it meets these location factors, although the Middle region is gaining its locational advantage for the high-technology industries because of the development of the Daedeok Special Research Park and easy access to Seoul by the newly constructed high speed railway.

Table 5.21 **Changes of regional share of new industry in manufacturing sector, 1986-2005**

	Number of firms										
	Firm (No.)			Share of total region (%)			Share of total manufacture (%)			Increasing rate(%)	
	1986	1995	2005	1986	1995	2005	1986	1995	2005	86-95	95-05
Seoul	3,815	6,062	6,694	48.7	27.2	20.1	5.6	7.4	9.6	58.9	10.4
Busan	640	1,701	2,053	8.2	7.6	6.2	3.1	5.7	7.3	165.8	20.7
Daegu	436	1,480	1,887	5.6	6.6	5.7	2.7	5.9	7.9	239.4	27.5
Incheon	403	1,906	3,000	5.1	8.6	9.0	5.4	11.2	14.0	373.0	57.4
Gwangju	49	289	729	0.6	1.3	2.2	1.1	4.3	9.7	489.8	152.2
Daejeon	-	408	800	-	1.8	2.4	-	5.8	12.3	-	96.1
Ulsan	-	0	419	-	-	1.3	-	-	8.2	-	-
Gyeonggi-*do*	1,710	6,956	12,012	21.8	31.2	36.1	6.5	12.2	14.0	306.8	72.7
Gangwon-*do*	29	209	394	0.4	0.9	1.2	0.4	3.1	6.0	620.7	88.5
Chungcheongbuk-*do*	63	463	740	0.8	2.1	2.2	1.1	6.3	8.5	634.9	59.8
Chungcheong*nam-do*	140	361	735	1.8	1.6	2.2	1.1	3.3	6.2	157.9	103.6
Jeollabuk-*do*	54	216	347	0.7	1.0	1.0	0.6	2.0	3.7	300.0	60.6
Jeollanam-*do*	21	137	297	0.3	0.6	0.9	0.2	1.2	2.8	552.4	116.8
Gyeongsangbuk-*do*	213	880	1,497	2.7	4.0	4.5	1.7	5.5	8.1	313.1	70.1
Gyeongsang*nam-do*	258	1,152	1,573	3.3	5.2	4.7	1.7	4.9	6.4	346.5	36.5
Jeju special self-governing province	8	56	65	0.1	0.3	0.2	0.5	3.1	3.2	600.0	16.1
Total	7,839	22,276	33,242	100.0	100.0	100.0	3.6	7.1	9.8	184.2	49.2

	Number of employment										
	Employment (No.)			Share of total region (%)			Share of total manufacture (%)			Increasing rate(%)	
	1986	1995	2005	1986	1995	2005	1986	1995	2005	86-95	95-05
Seoul	121,257	102,972	77,440	28.4	18.8	11.2	13.8	14.1	16.3	-15.1	-24.8
Busan	14,663	16,237	21,545	3.4	3.0	3.1	3.2	5.6	10.7	10.7	32.7
Daegu	9,382	14,690	16,195	2.2	2.7	2.3	4.8	6.9	10.4	56.6	10.2
Incheon	35,461	39,465	42,273	8.3	7.2	6.1	17.3	13.9	18.7	11.3	7.1
Gwangju	2,205	7,197	11,888	0.5	1.3	1.7	7.8	11.7	17.1	226.4	65.2
Daejeon	–	4,280	8,699	–	0.8	1.3	–	7.5	18.4	–	103.2
Ulsan	–	–	10,299	–	–	1.5	–	–	7.3	–	–
Gyeonggi-*do*	126,706	200,726	288,150	29.7	36.6	41.8	21.5	23.3	28.9	58.4	43.6
Gangwon-*do*	2,257	4,286	4,332	0.5	0.8	0.6	5.4	8.5	10.3	89.9	1.1
Chungcheongbuk-*do*	9,376	27,418	33,798	2.2	5.0	4.9	15.0	23.1	27.6	192.4	23.3
Chungcheongnam-*do*	7,585	21,523	47,953	1.8	3.9	7.0	6.2	16.6	26.0	183.8	122.8
Jeollabuk-*do*	2,940	7,008	6,293	0.7	1.3	0.9	3.5	7.1	7.6	138.4	-10.2
Jeollanam-*do*	2,684	1,406	2,401	0.6	0.3	0.3	3.3	1.5	2.7	-47.6	70.8
Gyeongsangbuk-*do*	35,100	53,766	78,448	8.2	9.8	11.4	19.3	22.0	29.6	53.2	45.9
Gyeongsangnam-*do*	56,820	46,934	39,477	13.3	8.6	5.7	16.1	9.9	11.3	-17.4	-15.9
Jeju special self-governing province	59	179	356	0.0	0.0	0.1	1.0	2.3	4.1	203.4	98.9
Total	426,495	548,087	689,547	100.0	100.0	100.0	13.0	14.8	20.0	28.5	25.8

Manufacture in new industry classifies by industry based on KSIC. Classification of industries of 1986 differs from that of 1995 and 2005. Therefore, data from 1986 has been reorganized to fit the statistics.

-1986 : Manufacture of electrical and electronic machinery, apparatus, appliances and supplies

(383), Manufactureof medical, photographic and optical, professional, scientific, measuring and controlling equipment and goods (385), Manufacture of electrical appliances and housewares (3833). cf.)Manufacture of office, computing and accounting machinery (3825) is omitted from the statistics due to lack of data.
-1995, 2005 : Manufacture of Computers and Office Machinery (30), Manufacture of Electrical Machinery and Appar atuseses n.e.c. (31), Manufacture of Electronic Components, Radio, Television and Communication equipment (32), Manufacture of Medical, Precision and Optical Instruments, Watches (33)
(Source : Statistics Korea (Various years), [kostat.go.kr])

2) Distribution of the new industry in the service sector (producer services)

The distribution and growth rate in the producer services are presented in Table 5.22. The overall growth rate in the producer services was higher than that of the high-technology industries, as shown in Table 5.21. As in the case of the high-technology industries, the growth rate in the producer services in the period of 1986 to 1995 was higher than that in the period of 1995 to 2005 in both the numbers of establishments and employees. This could also be due to the impact of the 1997 financial crisis.

Contrary to the case in the high-technology industries, the producer services are overwhelmingly concentrated in Seoul. Their national share is around 40% in the number of establishments and around 50% in the number of employees. There was a slight decentralization trend in the producer services from Seoul to its surrounding areas in the capital region, including Gyeonggi-*do* and Incheon, during the period of 1986 to 1995. However, there was a slight trend of reconcentration towards Seoul during the period of 1995 to 2005. Such reconcentration trend in the producer services since 1995 reveals the evolution of the new spatial division of labor especially under the economic restructuring period with relation to the 1997 financial crisis (Park, 2009). Gyeonggi-*do* continuously increased its national share in producer services during the period of 1986 to 2005, with a more rapid increase during the period of 1986 to 1995 in the number of employees (Table 5.22).

Since the 1980s, there has been a clear trend of decentralization in the manufacturing industries and even in the high-technology industries specifically in Seoul. However, advanced services such as those in the producer services have continued to concentrate in Seoul. The continuous concentration of the producer services in Seoul during the last two decades suggests the evolution of a new spatial division of labor brought about by the development of knowledge-based economy in Korea. That is, the spatial division of labor has been intensified with the evolution of spatial division between the knowledge-based industries in Seoul versus the manufacturing industries, including high-technology industries in the other

Table 5.22 **Changes of regional share of new industry in service sector, 1986-2005**

Number of firms											
	Firm (No.)			Share of total region (%)			Share of total services (%)			Increasing rate(%)	
	1986	1995	2005	1986	1995	2005	1986	1995	2005	86 - 95	95 - 05
Seoul	6,388	19,636	35,165	41.5	38.0	40.1	1.6	3.1	5.2	207.4	79.1
Busan	1,703	4,498	6,595	11.1	8.7	7.5	1.3	2.0	2.8	164.1	46.6
Daegu	849	2,948	4,553	5.5	5.7	5.2	1.1	2.1	2.9	247.2	54.4
Incheon	465	2,018	2,911	3.0	3.9	3.3	0.9	1.8	2.2	334.0	44.3
Gwangju	500	1,584	2,783	3.2	3.1	3.2	1.4	2.2	3.2	216.8	75.7
Daejeon	-	1,613	2,671	-	3.1	3.0	-	2.1	3.2	-	65.6
Ulsan	-	-	1,610	-	-	1.8	-	-	2.7	-	-
Gyeonggi - *do*	1,404	6,376	13,187	9.1	12.3	15.0	0.9	1.9	2.6	354.1	106.8
Gangwon - *do*	367	1,392	2,209	2.4	2.7	2.5	0.6	1.5	2.0	279.3	58.7
Chungcheongbuk - *do*	353	1,200	2,058	2.3	2.3	2.3	0.8	1.6	2.3	239.9	71.5
Chungcheongnam - *do*	776	1,448	2,266	5.0	2.8	2.6	0.8	1.5	2.0	86.6	56.5
Jeollabuk - *do*	581	1,673	2,222	3.8	3.2	2.5	0.9	1.6	2.0	188.0	32.8
Jeollanam - *do*	543	1,576	1,863	3.5	3.1	2.1	0.7	1.4	1.6	190.2	18.2
Gyeongsangbuk - *do*	574	1,911	3,001	3.7	3.7	3.4	0.6	1.4	1.9	232.9	57.0
Gyeongsangnam - *do*	788	3,254	3,785	5.1	6.3	4.3	0.7	1.6	2.0	312.9	16.3
Jeju special self-governing province	110	530	792	0.7	1.0	0.9	0.6	1.7	1.9	381.8	49.4
Total	15,401	51,657	87,671	100.0	100.0	100.0	1.1	2.1	3.1	235.4	69.7
Number of employment											
	Employment (No.)			Share of total region (%)			Share of total services (%)			Increasing rate(%)	
	1986	1995	2005	1986	1995	2005	1986	1995	2005	86 - 95	95 - 05
Seoul	61,879	229,942	540,908	53.9	48.4	50.7	3.7	7.3	16.1	271.6	135.2
Busan	12,146	36,450	69,670	10.6	7.7	6.5	2.7	4.2	7.7	200.1	91.1
Daegu	5,039	20,186	38,036	4.4	4.2	3.6	2.0	3.9	6.8	300.6	88.4
Incheon	2,926	13,934	31,552	2.5	2.9	3.0	1.8	3.5	6.3	376.2	126.4
Gwangju	2,388	11,785	24,005	2.1	2.5	2.3	1.8	4.2	6.7	393.5	103.7
Daejeon	-	24,936	40,990	-	5.2	3.8	-	7.9	11.5	-	64.4
Ulsan	-	-	23,819	-	-	2.2	-	-	10.0	-	-
Gyeonggi - *do*	7,197	53,045	154,074	6.3	11.2	14.5	1.5	4.2	7.5	637.0	190.5
Gangwon - *do*	1,825	8,187	14,925	1.6	1.7	1.4	1.0	2.4	3.9	348.6	82.3
Chungcheongbuk - *do*	1,729	7,047	18,143	1.5	1.5	1.7	1.3	2.6	5.6	307.6	157.5
Chungcheongnam - *do*	3,830	7,385	16,969	3.3	1.6	1.6	1.3	2.3	4.2	92.8	129.8
Jeollabuk - *do*	2,170	8,160	15,052	1.9	1.7	1.4	1.1	2.2	3.8	276.0	84.5
Jeollanam - *do*	3,139	11,794	13,853	2.7	2.5	1.3	1.4	3.0	3.4	275.7	17.5
Gyeongsangbuk - *do*	4,445	16,668	26,341	3.9	3.5	2.5	1.7	3.4	4.8	275.0	58.0
Gyeongsangnam - *do*	5,440	22,587	31,031	4.7	4.8	2.9	1.6	3.0	4.7	315.2	37.4
Jeju special self-governing province	660	3,276	6,739	0.6	0.7	0.6	1.1	2.5	4.3	396.4	105.7
Total	114,813	475,382	1,066,107	100.0	100.0	100.0	2.4	4.8	9.2	314.0	124.3

Service in new industry classifies by industry based on KSIC. Classification of industries of 1986 differs from that of 1995 and 2005. Therefore, data from 1986 has been reorganized to fit the statistics.

-1986 : Legal, accounting and other clerical services (841), Architectural, engineering and technical

testing services (842), Surveying and information related services (843), Other business services,
except machinery and equipment rental and leasing (844).
-1995, 2005 : Computer and related activities (72), Research and development (73), Professional,
scientific and technical services (74), Business support services (75).
[Source : Statistics Korea (Various years), (kostat.go.kr)]

areas beyond the former spatial division of labor between the headquarters versus manufacturing activities (Park, 1993b ; Park 2009).

3) New growth industry (6T)

The knowledge-based industry, which is related with the six core technologies, used to be considered the new growth industry in the future in Korea (Small and Medium Business Administration and Federation of Small and Medium Enterprises, 2007). The knowledge-based industry can be classified into industries based on six core technologies : Information Technology (IT), Biology Technology (BT), Nano Technology (NT), Space Technology (ST), Environment Technology (ET), and Culture Technology (CT). The IT industry includes telecommunication equipment, software and computer-related products and other similar tools. The BT industry includes the development of new medicine and bio internal organs. The CT industry includes games, comic pictures, records, and similar products, while the ET industry includes environmental facilities, environment resources, and other providers of environmental services.

According to the survey of the Small and Medium Business Administration and Federation of Small and Medium Enterprises (2007), about 38.3% of the Small and Medium Enterprises (SMEs) that performed technological development activities are related with the 6Ts. IT-related firms had a share of 18.2%, while ET-related firms had a share of 11.1% in the national total in terms of number of establishments as shown in Table 5.23. The share of the new growth industry in the total SMEs that performed technological development activities is high in Daejeon (65.4%), Seoul (60.8%), and Gyeonggi-*do* (46.3%). The highest share of Daejeon is closely related with the development and growth of the Daedeok Research Park. IT-related SMEs are mostly concentrated in Seoul, Gyeonggi-*do*, Daejeon, and Daegu, where IT clusters are developed.

IT-related industry is the representative of the new growth industry in Korea. As shown in Table 5.24, the number of IT-related enterprises increased from about 3,500 in 1990 to about 17,000 in 2005. The growth rate is even higher in terms of production and value added. If we classify the IT-related firms into telecommunication services, telecommunication equipment,

CHAPTER 5

Table 5.23 **Distribution of new growth industry* by region**

	Firm (No.)	Unit: percentage							
		Information Technology (IT)	Biology Technology (BT)	Nano Technology (NT)	Space Technology (ST)	Environment Technology (ET)	Culture Technology (CT)	6T total	Other
Seoul	2,132	37.6	4.7	4.2	1.0	12.4	0.9	60.8	39.2
Busan	1,249	9.4	2.5	1.3	0.2	13.4	1.1	27.9	72.1
Daegu	1,479	8.7	-	6.9	-	6.9	1.0	23.5	76.5
Incheon	1,817	10.6	0.4	1.1	0.5	10.9	0.8	24.3	75.7
Gwangju	584	10.6	4.9	3.6	7.3	5.5	1.2	33.1	66.9
Daejeon	749	42.5	6.2	2.3	0.1	13.0	1.3	65.4	34.6
Ulsan	249	1.1	-	14.4	-	20.4	0.6	36.5	63.5
Gyeonggi - *do*	3,980	25.9	3.6	4.2	0.0	12.0	0.6	46.3	53.7
Gangwon - *do*	243	5.3	16.1	-	-	11.2	1.6	34.2	65.8
Chungcheongbuk - *do*	628	7.4	12.2	7.6	-	11.7	1.0	39.9	60.1
Chungcheongnam - *do*	770	9.2	6.6	5.9	0.2	12.7	-	34.6	65.4
Jeollabuk - *do*	415	10.3	5.5	2.8	0.7	16.5	1.6	37.4	62.6
Jeollanam - *do*	387	4.4	9.8	3.1	-	17.0	1.1	35.4	64.6
Gyeongsangbuk - *do*	1,214	18.6	3.5	3.4	-	5.5	-	31.0	69.0
Gyeongsangnam - *do*	1,981	9.0	2.7	3.1	1.4	9.8	-	26.0	74.0
Jeju special self-governing province	0	-	-	-	-	-	-	-	-
Total	17,875	18.2	3.8	3.9	0.6	11.1	0.7	38.3	61.7

*17,875 SMEs which conduct technological development were selected from the total SMEs (5 to 299 employees). From those 17,875 SMEs conducting technological development, 2,881 were selected as sample of survey.
(Source : SMBA (Small and Medium Business Administration), 2007 ; Kbiz, 2007.)

Table 5.24 **Changes of information and technology (IT) industry, 1990-2005**

	1990	1995	2000	2005	Increasing rate(%)		
					1990 - 1995	1995 - 2000	2000 - 2005
Firm* (No.)	3,579	7,226	14,883	17,149	101.9	106.0	15.2
Employment (No.)	121,329	395,487	548,017	717,665	226.0	38.6	31.0
Output (100 million won)	152,990	514,526	1,531,873	2,381,081	236.3	197.7	55.4
Value added (100 million won)	-	411,429	697,164	1,148,762	-	69.5	64.8

* Number of firms in IT industry in enterprises more than 5.
(Source : KAIT, 2006 (Various years), [http://www.kait.or.kr])

Table 5.25 **Changes of information and technology (IT) industry by sub-sector**

Division by industry	Number of firms			Number of employment		
	Number (No.)*	Share (%)	Share of capital region (share of seoul)	Number (No.)**	Share (%)	Share of capital region (share of seoul)
IT service	2,876	16.8	70.7 (60.0)	127,053	17.2	90.3 (56.6)
IT device	8,969	52.3	75.0 (14.3)	481,432	65.3	58.2 (5.7)
Software and computer - related service	5,304	30.9	77.1 (65.9)	128,604	17.5	91.4 (77.5)
Total	17,149	100.0	74.9 (39.5)	737,089	100.0	69.3 (26.2)

Number of firms in enterprises more than 5 employees.
** *Number of employment is based on those who work in IT industry.*
(Source : KAIT, 2006, [http://www.kait.or.kr])

and software and computer-related services, it is clear that IT-related services are overwhelmingly concentrated in the capital region, especially in Seoul. More than 90% of the total employment of telecommunication services and software and computer-related services are concentrated in the capital region (Table 5.25). Seoul's share is more than half of the total national IT-related service firms. On the other hand, the telecommunication equipment industry, which is regarded as a high-technology industry, is less concentrated in the capital region (58.2%). Seoul has a share of only 5.7% of the total national employment of the manufacturers of telecommunication equipment, representing a great contrast between the IT-related services and IT-related manufacturing. The knowledge-based service industries are concentrated in Gangnam and Seocho district within Seoul, which have been developed as the new core of Seoul since the late 1980s (Park and Nahm, 1998). The concentration of the knowledge-based services in Gangnam and Seocho district is mainly due to the collective learning processes through formal and informal meetings, inter-firm networks, and the supply of professional manpower (Hwang, 2000 ; Hong, 2008).

The CT-related industry has been developing in recent years in Korea. The culture industry has considerably contributed to the creation of employment and value added in recent years. Culture-based firms engaged in printing, comic pictures, games, animation, broadcasting, advertisement, digital education, and similar projects have strong effects on the creation of employment and value added with strong inter-industry linkages. The culture industry is highly oriented towards urbanized economies because these are where the accumulation of culture, cluster of creative manpower, effective communication, and socialization exist (Choo, 2006). The culture-based industry in Seoul has a share of 66.1% and 53.9% in the total national sales and employment, respectively. This overwhelming concentration in Seoul is even stronger than that for the knowledge-based services. Overall, more than 80% of the national total sales of the printing, comic pictures, music, movies, and animation are concentrated in the capital region.

The Korean government drives the policy towards the development of the 10 next-generation growth engine industries related to the 6Ts. The selection of the next-generation growth engine industries is based on the size of the global market, trend of changes in market and technology, available strategies, assurance of competitiveness, and other similar factors (Choi et al, 2005). These industries include the players in digital TV/broadcasting, display, intelligent robot, future automobile, next-generation semiconductor, next-generation mobile communication, intelligent home-network, digital contents/software solution, next generation battery, and new bio medicine and internal organs. It is expected that the spatial structure of economic activities will still change with the promotion of the development of the 10 next-generation growth-engine industries. The development of the innovative industrial clusters, the progress of regional innovation systems, cooperation among diverse actors, and inter-industry networks will be more important in the development of new growth engine industries in the future in Korea.

Chapter 6.
TRANSPORTATION, COMMUNICATION AND ENERGY

Chapter 6.1.

REGIONAL DISTRIBUTION OF TRANSPORTATION AND COMMUNICATION

6.1.1 Development of Transportation Routes and Distribution of Traffic Flow

1) Expansion of ground transportation routes and transportation flow

① Modal split by transportation modes

The modal split of domestic transportation modes is well represented in Table 6.1. In terms of passenger traffic, the automobile was the dominant mode in 1990 with 66.3% of the total transportation flow. However, the automobile share decreased substantially in 2000. A metropolitan subway is mainly responsible for the decrease in automobile and railroad use. The share of passenger traffic by subway has increased over time. The inverse relationship seen between automobile and subway is also observed between aviation and railway, specifically the high-speed electric train. For example, the passenger traffic by air increased

Table 6.1 **Trends of traffic share by transportation mode between passenger and freight**

Mode	Passenger (million persons · km)			Freight (ton)		
	1990	2000	2006	1990	2000	2006
Railway	22.1	21.6	19.5	17.2	6.7	6.3
Subway	8.3	13.8	15.3	-	-	-
Automobile	66.3	57.8	60.7	63.8	73.4	76.6
Ship	0.4	0.5	0.4	18.9	19.9	17.1
Aviation	3.0	6.2	4.1	0.1	0.1	0.1
Total	135,336	128,837	161,281	337,145	676,315	690,779

(Source : Statistics Korea, 2007, Statistical Yearbook of Korea).

233

until the advent of the high-speed electric train in 2004. Travel by ship constitutes the lowest share of passenger traffic. In terms of freight traffic, automobile freight is the dominant transportation mode and its share increases over time. Accordingly, the shares by both railway and ship or waterway freight have declined. Note that the share of aviation freight is not significant (Table 6.1).

② Road transportation

A. The development of a road network

Figure 6.1 shows the changes in the total road length in Korea between 1980 and 2006. The road types include national expressways, national highways, special-greater city roads, provincial roads and city and county roads. Compared to the total road length in 1980 (43,936.6 kilometers), the total road length had doubled by 2006 (90,832.4 kilometers). In particular, the city and county roads have played a major role in the overall increase, especially since 1994. During the same period, the road density (road length/area) has also increased from 0.44 km/km² to 0.91 km/km² due to the industrial development and increase in automobile ownership.

According to the 2006 road status data, Gyeonggi-*do* has the most nationwide roads (12.5%), followed by Gyeongsangnam-*do* (12.1%), Gyeongsangbuk-*do* (11.9%), Jeollanam-*do* (9.9%) and Gangwon-*do* (9.3%). Most of the national expressways are located in Gyeongsangnam-*do* (487 kilometers), whereas most of the national highways are located in Gyeongsangbuk-*do* (2,213 kilometers) (Table 6.2).

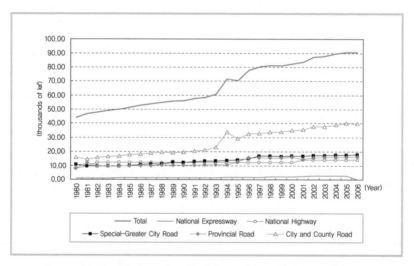

Figure 6.1 **Yearly trends of total road length by road types**

[Source : Statistics Korea, 1980-2007, National Statistical Portal [www.kosis.kr]].

Table 6.2 **Road status by city and province (2006)**

City/Province	Total Length of Road(km)	%	National Expressway (km)	National Highway (km)	Special - Greater City Road(km)	Provincial Road (km)	City Road (km)	County Road (km)
Seoul[#]	8,073	7.9	23	167	7,869	14	-	-
Busan[#]	2,742	2.7	27	125	2,435	55	-	100
Daegu[#]	2,238	2.2	94	108	1,885	15	-	136
Incheon[#]	2,307	2.3	78	77	1,633	63	-	456
Gwangju[#]	1,368	1.3	20	90	1,258	-	-	-
Daejeon[#]	1,703	1.7	70	87	1,523	23	-	-
Ulsan[#]	1,620	1.6	42	183	1,133	13	-	249
Gyeonggi-*do*	12,747	13.0	468	1,488	-	2,710	6,359	1,722
Gangwon-do	9,506	9.3	286	1,978	-	1,648	2,700	2,894
Chungcheongbuk-*do*	6,608	6.5	257	965	-	1,459	1,566	2,361
Chungcheongnam-*do*	7,552	7.4	302	1,311	-	1,817	1,735	2,387
Jeollabuk-*do*	7,761	7.6	282	1,428	-	1,901	1,970	2,180
Jeollanam-*do*	10,129	9.9	227	2,013	-	2,293	2,216	3,380
Gyeongsangbuk-*do*	12,132	12.0	440	2,213	-	3,018	2,691	3,770
Gyeongsangnam-*do*	12,368	12.0	487	1,538	-	2,349	4,557	3,437
Jeju special self-governing province	3,203	3.1	-	453	-	300	1,565	885
Nation	102,061	100.0	3,103	14,225	17,738	17,677	25,360	23,958

Metropolitan Area.
(Source : Ministry of Construction and Transportation, 2007, Statistical Yearbook of Ministry of Construction and Transportation [National Statistical Portal : www.kosis.kr])

Table 6.3 shows the road distribution status by province. In general, 77.6% of nationwide roads were paved as of 2006. However, the ratio of paved to unpaved roads shows the regional differences. For example, all the roads in Seoul and Gwangju are paved while less than the national average are paved in most other provinces. On the other hand, Gyeonggi-*do* and Jeju special self-governing province contain more paved roads than the national average. Similar to the paved road distribution, the road density is highest in Seoul with 13.33 km/km2. Most other provinces have a lower road density than the national average of 1.02 km/km2 except Gyeonggi-*do*, Gyeongsangnam-*do* and Jeju special self-governing province. The national average length of roads (the total length of roads divided by the number of persons) is 2.16 meters per person. It is not surprising that most areas, except the metropolitan areas and Gyeonggi-*do*, provide more road per capita than the national average. For example, Gangwon-*do*, one of the least populated areas, provides the most road per capita at 6.49 meters per person, followed by Jeju special self-governing province at 6.02 meters per person. Just as the metropolitan areas and Gyeonggi-*do* provide less roads per capita than the national average,

CHAPTER 6

they also provide less roads per car than the national average. Similar to the road length per capita, Gangwon-*do* has the most road per car at 17.62 meters per car, followed by Jeollanam-*do* (16.52 meters per car). By contrast, Daegu has the least road per car at 2.59 meters per car.

Table 6.3 **Road distribution status by city and province (2006)**

City/Province	Area (km²)	Population (thousand persons)	Length of Road (km)	Paved Road		Road Density (km/km²)	Length of Road per Person (m/person)	Number of Motor Vehicles (thousand Motor Vehicles)	Length of Road per Motor Vehicle (m/Motor Vehicle)
				Length (km)	%				
Seoul[#]	605	9,820	8,073	8,071	100.0	13.33	0.82	2,857	2.83
Busan[#]	764	3,524	2,742	2,653	96.8	3.59	0.78	994	2.76
Daegu[#]	884	2,465	2,238	2,212	98.8	2.53	0.91	865	2.59
Incheon[#]	994	2,531	2,307	2,120	91.9	2.32	0.91	822	2.81
Gwangju[#]	501	1,418	1,368	1,368	100.0	2.73	0.96	450	3.04
Daejeon[#]	540	1,443	1,703	1,703	100.0	3.15	1.18	521	3.27
Ulsan[#]	1,057	1,049	1,620	1,549	95.8	1.53	1.54	395	4.1
Gyeonggi-*do*	10,131	10,415	12,748	10,658	83.6	1.26	1.22	3,651	3.49
Gangwon-*do*	16,613	1,465	9,506	6,561	69.0	0.57	6.49	540	17.62
Chungcheongbuk-*do*	7,431	1,460	6,608	4,805	72.7	0.89	4.52	532	12.43
Chungcheongnam-*do*	8,601	1,889	7,553	5,585	73.9	0.88	4	700	10.79
Jeollabuk-*do*	8,055	1,784	7,761	5,464	70.4	0.96	4.35	618	12.57
Jeollanam-*do*	12,073	1,820	10,130	6,936	68.5	0.84	5.57	613	16.52
Gyeongsangbuk-*do*	19,026	2,608	12,133	8,473	69.8	0.64	4.65	984	12.33
Gyeongsangnam-*do*	10,521	3,056	12,368	8,365	67.6	1.18	4.05	1,131	10.93
Jeju special self-governing province	1,848	532	3,203	2,671	83.4	1.73	6.02	222	14.43
Nation	99,646	47,279	102,061	79,194	77.6	1.02	2.16	15,895	6.42

 # Metropolitan Area.
(Source : Ministry of Construction and Transportation, 2007, Statistical Yearbook of Ministry of Construction and Transportation [National Statistical Portal : www.kosis.kr])

B. Geographical distribution of motor vehicle spread

The number of passenger cars among other vehicles constantly increases over time as can be seen in Figure 6.2. The types of motor vehicles include passenger cars (73.0%), freight trucks (19.7%), buses (7.0%) and special motor vehicles (0.3%). In 2006, most motor vehicles (94.5%) were used for private purposes and only 5.1% and 0.4% were used for commercial and governmental purposes, respectively. Notice that the number of automobiles shows a steady increase, although the rate of increase slowed down between 1997 and 2000 due to the economic downturn. Meanwhile, the number of freight trucks gradually increased after 1999, surpassing the number of motorcycles and becoming the second-ranked motor vehicle in quantity. The bus, one of the major forms of public transit, has maintained a relatively stable decreasing rate since 2000.

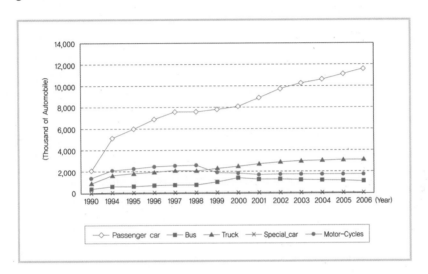

Figure 6.2 **Yearly trends in number of motor vehicles**
(Source : Ministry of Construction and Transportation, 2007, Statistical Yearbook of Ministry of Construction and Transportation [National Statistical Portal : www.kosis.kr]).

CHAPTER 6

C. Trends in passenger and freight traffic

Figures 6.3 and 6.4 show yearly trends of passenger and freight traffic correspondingly. In terms of passenger traffic, the demand for public transit has increased since 1980, representing the largest traffic volume in 2006. Noticeably, the 1997 IMF financial aid played an important role in both passenger and freight traffic. The demand for intra-city buses decreased after 1998 partly due to the IMF. In contrast, the highest demand for freight traffic occurred in 1997. It began to increase particularly after 1997. Among several other modes of public transit, intra-city buses and taxis are the dominating modes. However, traffic by buses and taxis has decreased recently due to the nationwide trend of increased automobile ownership. The traffic by inter-city buses has also gradually decreased in recent years. Meanwhile, freight traffic volume consistently increases over time. Among several types of freight traffic, most is for transporting bulk materials such as oil, cement and grain traffic.

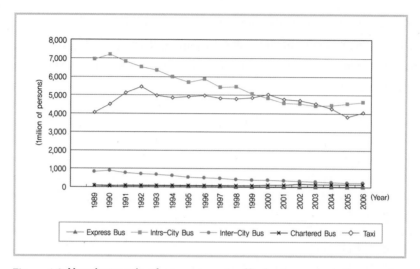

Figure 6.3 **Yearly trends of passenger traffic by transportation modes**
(Source : Ministry of Construction and Transportation, 2007, Statistical Yearbook of Ministry of Construction and Transportation [National Statistical Portal : www.kosis.kr]).

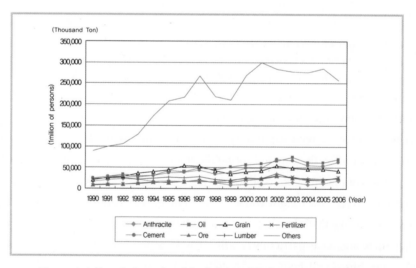

Figure 6.4 **Yearly trends of freight traffic by motor vehicles**
(Source : Ministry of Construction and Transportation, 2007, Statistical Yearbook of Ministry of Construction and Transportation [National Statistical Portal : www.kosis.kr]).

③ Railroad transportation

A. Railroad network development

The length of railways between 1980 and 2006 increased from 3,135 to 3,392 kilometers mainly due to the 2004 extension of the Gyeongbu high-speed electric railroad. During the same period, the volume of railroad passenger traffic increased while the railroad freight traffic decreased. This is partly because much of the railroad freight was replaced by truck freight. In the meantime, the number of train stations has stayed relatively constant (Figure 6.5).

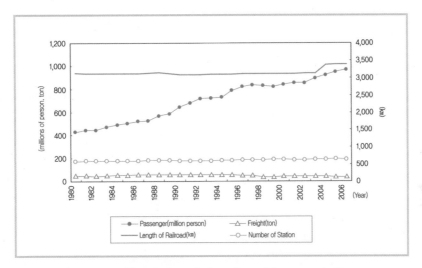

Figure 6.5 **Yearly trends in railroad transportation**
(Source : Ministry of Construction and Transportation, 2007, Statistical Yearbook of Ministry of Construction and Transportation [National Statistical Portal : www.kosis.kr]).

B. Railroad traffic by line

The major railroad lines are used for both passenger and freight traffic. There were a total of 114,331,456 passengers in 2006. In detail, 60.8% of these passengers use the Gyeongbu line, followed by the Honam line (6.5%), Gyeongwon line (6.3%) and Gyeongui line (4.6%). In terms of freight traffic in 2003, the Jungang line delivered the most (23.7%), followed by the Taebaek line (17.1%), Yeongdong line (9.6%), Gyeongbu line (7.9%) and Gaedong line (5.8%). Notice that the freight traffic is high in areas with underground reserves of coal, cement, ore, timber, etc. Among several other commodity types, the volume of cement was largest and other types of commodities have been added to the railroad freight since 2005. The railroad freight as of 2006 consisted of cement (36.5%), coal (17.0%), oil (5.1%), ore (4.1%) and other material (36.9%).

2) Water and air transportation

① Water transportation

The shoreline consists of 12,158 kilometers of mainland (52%) and 6,327 kilometers of islands (48%). As of 2006, there were 52 trading harbors and coastal ports. Among them 28 are classified as trading harbors. With respect to trading harbors, the port of Busan is biggest in terms of berthing capability, as can be seen in Table 6.4. For example, it can accommodate about 150 vessels, including 23 vessels at 50,000 DWT (deadweight), 3 vessels at 30,000 DWT, 12 vessels at 20,000 DWT, 30 vessels at 10,000 DWT, 36 vessels at 5,000-10,000 DWT and 46 vessels at 5,000-10,000 DWT. Ports that hold vessels above 300,000 DWT capacity include Daesan port (1 vessel), Gwangyang port (3 vessels) and Ulsan port (5 vessels). Ports holding vessels between 100,000 and 300,000 DWT capacity include Incheon port (2 vessels), Daesan port (5 vessels), Taean port (2 vessels), Boryeong port (2 vessels), Gwangyang port (7 vessels), Samcheonpo port (2 vessels), Ulsan port (3 vessels) and Pohang port (4 vessels). In terms of ports' berthing capabilities, Busan port is the biggest, followed by Ulsan port (96 vessels), Incheon port (83 vessels), Gwangyang port (78 vessels) and Pohang port (47 vessels). The Okpo port is the smallest, holding only 1 vessel.

Table 6.4. **Port facilities of trading ports (2006)**

Ports	Quay (m)	Break Water (m)	Number of Piers	Warf (m)	Berthing capability (number of vessels)
Busan	26,159	5,769	3	9,604	150
Incheon	11,456	2,233	22	2,059	83
Pyeongtaek & Dangjin	3,120	240	8	330	22
Daesan	600	660	19	362	21
Taean	0	0	2	287	2
Boryeong	0	0	2	90	2
Gunsan	4,806	3,143	13	1,567	31
Janghang	330	0	2	883	3
Mokpo	4,841	0	24	2,961	27
Wando	675	250	5	1,986	4
Yeosu	991	2,176	9	2,548	8
Gwangyang	17,267	0	0	1,558	78
Jeju	2,551	3,346	0	754	18
Seogwipo	630	1,831	0	985	5
Samcheonpo	1,836	2,335	4	2,870	9
Tongyeong	1,337	1,477	12	3,312	7
Gohyeon	122	0	0	192	3
Okpo	100	1,385	0	0	1
Jangseungpo	0	226	3	1,151	0
Masan	5,347	650	7	1,989	31
Jinhae	1,293	122	0	123	9

Ports	Quay (m)	Break Water (m)	Number of Piers	Warf (m)	Berthing capability (number of vessels)
Ulsan	16,422	4,466	0	81	96
Pohang	9,822	12,052	0	2,981	47
Samcheok	776	1,180	0	1,518	7
Donghae	3,412	2,110	1	0	15
Mukho	1,591	1,465	0	925	6
Okgae	940	2,003	1	0	5
Sokcho	1,187	1,398	0	2,007	7
Total	117,611	50,517	137	43,123	697

[Source : Ministry of Land, Transport and Maritime Affairs, 2008, Maritime and Fishery Statistics [http://momaf.go.kr/matrix/momaf/main/index.jsp]].

In terms of voyages by scheduled ocean-going ship routes as of 2006, Southwestern Asia accounted for 46.1% with 119 vessels (2,281,348 tons) followed by the United States (15.5%), China (13.4%) and Europe (2.9%) (Table 6.5).

Table 6.5 **Voyage status of ship routes by scheduled ocean-going vessels (2006)**

Country/Region	Container Vessel		Semi-Container Vessel		Total		
	Number	ton	Number	ton	Number	ton	%
Japan	33	147,367	6	14,338	39	161,705	7.1
China	30	304,703	0	0	30	304,703	13.0
Southeastern Asia	5	108,055	0	0	5	108,055	4.7
Southwestern Asia	18	1,052,708	0	0	18	1,052,708	46.0
Europe	3	64,833	1	1,996	4	66,829	2.9
Russia	18	233,464	0	0	18	233,464	10.0
The United States	5	353,884	0	0	5	353,884	16.0
Total	112	2,265,014	7	16,334	119	2,281,348	100.0

[Source : Ministry of Land, Transport and Maritime Affairs, 2008, Maritime and Fishery Statistics [http://momaf.go.kr/matrix/momaf/main/index.jsp]].

The total number of passengers traveling by water transportation in 2006 was 13,958,467, for which coastal ships and ocean-going ships account for 82.9% and 17.1%, respectively. After the 1997 IMF financial aid, the number decreased, but then increased gradually after 2001. In particular, the number of passengers of ocean-going ships has continuously increased since 2004. There were 11,573,685 coastal ship passengers on 99 routes in 2006. Among them, the Mokpo ship route had 37 routes (39.2%), whereas the Hongdo ship route (12.9%) and Jeju ship route (10.4%) attracted the most passengers. Overall, 69% of the total number of passengers by water transportation traveled by Mokpo (39.2%), Masan (19.5%) and Incheon (10.3%) ship routes, respectively. On the other hand, the freight traffic by water transportation in 2006 was 10,289,024 RT (RT = a unit of volume used for the cargo capacity of a ship defined as 100 cubic feet equivalent to 2.83 cubic meters), for which ocean-going and coastal ships were responsible for 58.7% and 41.3%, respectively. The shipping volume of freight traffic was affected by the IMF over a short-term period but eventually recovered over time. In the meantime, freight traffic volume by coastal ship has maintained its growth, except in 1998. The main ship cargo combining domestic and foreign flags shows regional variations by products. For example, Southwest Asia, Africa, South America and Oceania are mainly responsible for the raw material of industry, whereas Europe, North America and Central America are mainly responsible for machinery industry and textile products. The energy and textile industry are mainly concentrated in Southeast Asia and East Asia, except for Japan. See Table 6.6 for more details.

Table 6.6 **Major international traffic freights by regions (2006)**

Country/Region	Major Traffic Freights
Japan	Product of Petroleum Oils (20.9%), Iron Steel and Articles (20.4%), Textiles and Textile Articles (10.9%), Machinery and Mechanical Appliances (7.5%)
Eastern Asia (excluding Japan)	Textiles and Textile Articles (22.2%), Bituminous Coal (12.8%), Petroleum Oil Products (12.2%), Iron Steel and Articles (10.1%)
Southeastern Asia	Bituminous Coal (21.8%), Petroleum Gases and Other Gases (20.3%), Petroleum Oil Products (12.7%), Textiles and Textile Articles (9.2%)
Southwestern Asia	Crude Oil and Petroleum (62.5%)
Europe	Vehicles and Parts (31.4%), Other (13.8%), Textiles and Textile Articles (10.5%)
Africa	Crude Oil and Petroleum (28.0%), Petroleum Gases and Other Gases (14.6%), Vehicles and Parts (8.7%)
North America	Vehicles and Parts (13.7%), Textiles and Textile Articles (10.6%), Petroleum Oil Products (9.0%), Cereals (8.9%)
Central America	Vehicles and Parts (20.8%), Textiles and Textile Articles (13.8%), Other (9.5%), Iron Steel and Articles (8.3%)
South America	Iron Ore (46.8%), Petroleum Gases and Other Gases (14.0%)
Oceania	Iron Ore (38.2%), Bituminous (33.3%)
Others	Iron Steel and Articles (22.6%), Cereals (24.0%), Fish and Shellfish, Crustacea (19.4%)

(Source : Ministry of Land, Transport and Maritime Affairs, 2008, Maritime and Fishery Statistics [http://momaf.go.kr/matrix/momaf/main/index.jsp]).

② Air Transportation

The private air companies originated with the 1926 establishment of Gyeongseong Aviation Corporation. Since then, several other private air companies have been established, including Korea Aviation Corporation (established in 1930), Korean International Aviation Corporation (in 1946) and Korea National Airlines (KNA) (in 1948). Later the Korean government acquired the KNA and named it Korean Air Lines in 1962. However, Korean Air Lines could not last due to the constant deficit from several problems including the lack of air passenger demand, poor sales conditions caused by poor financial conditions, poor business management and poor service of the public management system. Hanjin Transportation later acquired Korean Air Lines and named it Korean Airlines Co. Ltd. in 1969. The civil aviation industry has achieved remarkable growth since then. The second private airline, Asiana Airlines, accordingly emerged as a mainly domestic supplier and at the same time introduced competition to the domestic air market in 1988. The number of passenger in 2006 grew rapidly to 17,200,000 passengers per year, including both scheduled and non-scheduled flights. The number of domestic air routes has also changed over time. At the beginning of 1970, there were 19 regular routes, which were reduced to 15 in 1974 largely because of the oil shock. The 2006 data showed 22 domestic scheduled routes, including Gimpo International Airport, Incheon International Airport, Jeju International Airport, Gimhae International Airport, Cheongju International Airport, Wonju Airport, Daegu Airport, Gwangju Airport, Sacheon Airport, Yeosu Airport, Pohang Airport, Ulsan Airport, Mokpo Airport and Gunsan Airport. Compared to the domestic routes, the international air routes grew quickly. For example, there were 176 routes by domestic air carriers and 192 routes by foreign air carriers in 2006.

6.1.2 Regional Structure of Information and Communication

1) Regional distribution of mass communication

① Newspapers

A newspaper is defined as a series of publications such as news reports, commentaries, public opinions and information on political, economic, social, cultural and other issues. The types of newspapers include general daily newspapers, daily special newspapers, foreign language daily newspapers, general weekly newspapers and special weekly newspapers. In

Table 6.7 **Numbers of establishments by newspaper type (2006)**

Register Office	General Daily Newspaper	Special Daily Newspaper	Foreign Language Daily Newspaper	Total
Ministry of Culture, Sports and Tourism	46	-	-	46
Greater-city and Province	105	34	8	147
Total	151	34	8	193

(Source : Ministry of Culture, Sports and Tourism, 2007, White Book of Cultural Industry).

summary, 78.2% of newspapers are general daily newspapers and 17.6% are special weekly newspapers (Table 6.7).

Depending on the geographic service area, domestic newspapers are classified as national newspapers for a whole country, local newspapers for a metropolitan area and community newspapers for medium and small cities. Such newspapers are also categorized as daily newspapers, economy newspapers, sports newspapers, foreign language newspapers, technical newspapers, daily living information newspapers and internet newspapers with respect to media characteristics. The total number of newspapers as of April 2008 was 4,580. Among them, 66 daily newspapers are registered by the Ministry of Culture, Sports and Tourism and the rest by each municipality. About 63.2% of the total number of newspapers are printed weekly. The capital metropolitan area supported by Seoul (48.6%) and Gyeonggi-*do* (14.0%) is well represented by the number as a central place of press. Most areas are within the service areas of national newspapers that circulate throughout the whole country (Table 6.8). Internet newspapers play a significant role in newspaper media, accounting for 22.7%. The regional concentration is somehow similar to the traditional newspapers. For instance, Seoul has the most newspapers (297) out of 626, followed by Geyeonggi-*do* (94), Jeollanam-*do* (36), Gyeongsangnam-*do* (34) and Gyeongsangbuk-*do* (33).

Table 6.8 **Numbers of newspaper companies in metropolitan cities and provinces (2008)**

City/Province	Daily Newspaper	Others Daily Newspaper	Weekly Newspaper	Internet Newspaper	Total (%)
Seoul[#]	110	69	1,544	504	2,227 (48.60)
Busan[#]	3	12	77	21	113 (2.50)
Daegu[#]	6	7	64	14	91 (2.00)
Incheon[#]	8	12	125	27	172 (3.70)
Gwangju[#]	16	3	29	16	64 (1.40)
Daejeon[#]	13	3	41	19	76 (1.60)
Ulsan[#]	7	4	25	16	52 (1.10)

City/Province	Daily Newspaper	Others Daily Newspaper	Weekly Newspaper	Internet Newspaper	Total (%)
Gyeonggi - *do*	14	103	374	152	643 (14.00)
Gangwon - *do*	3	26	49	23	101 (2.20)
Chungcheongbuk - *do*	9	8	59	17	93 (2.00)
Chungcheongnam - *do*	1	18	96	35	150 (3.30)
Jeollabuk - *do*	12	14	59	24	109 (2.40)
Jeollanam - *do*	2	10	89	60	161 (3.50)
Gyeongsangbuk - *do*	6	18	104	57	185 (4.00)
Gyeongsangnam - *do*	9	42	127	42	220 (4.80)
Jeju special self-governing province	3	7	34	13	57 (1.20)
Others[*]	66	-	-	-	66 (1.40)
Nation (%)	288 (6.3)	356 (7.8)	2,896 (63.2)	1,040 (22.7)	4,580(100.00)

Metropolitan Area.

* Provided by Ministry of Culture, Sports and Tourism.)

(Source : Ministry of Culture, Sports and Tourism, 2008, Material Ground [http://mcst.go.kr])

② Broadcasting

The 80-year history of Korean broadcasting started in February 1927. More than 1 million TV sets (1,197,808) were sold in 1981 after color television broadcasting became available in December 1980. The Korean Broadcasting System (KBS) was later founded by merging and abolishing both Donga and Dongyang Broadcasting stations by new military authority force in 1980. The establishment of new broadcasting stations as well as the freedom of newspaper publications without permission and controls from the government authorities were not available until the 6.29 Declaration in 1987. Many radio broadcasting systems have been established since then. For example, Pyeonghwa Broadcasting Corporation, Buddha Broadcasting System and Seoul Traffic Broadcasting System started to broadcast FM radio in 1990. The multimedia and multichannel era opened with a launching of new media, such as cable television and satellite broadcasting. Moreover, the Educational Broadcasting System (EBS) also started independent broadcasting in 1990. The Seoul Broadcasting System (SBS) launched radio and television broadcasting in 1991. The multimedia and multichannel era developed further in early 1995 with several new cable television stations and local private broadcasting (DACO D&S, 2007). The total number of independent broadcasting stations was 564, with 29,634 employees as of 2006. There were 46 ground wave companies and 32 terrestrial television broadcasters, including KBS and Munhwa Broadcasting Corporation (MBC). Other examples include 11 radio broadcasters such as Gyeonggi FM and 6 mobile

245

Table 6.9 **Spread of D-TV and DMB**

Year	2003	2004	2005	2006
D-TV spread number (ten thousand persons)	168.0	228.2	314.3	442.2
DMB members (ten thousand persons)*	-	-	48.9	384.4
Sales of ground wave terminal (ten thousand persons)	-	-	12.0	282.6
Members of Satellite DMB (ten thousand persons)	-	-	36.9	101.8

*Satellite DMB started its service in May, 2005. Ground wave DMB adopted European Telecommunications Standards Institute (ETSI) and European Standard in July, 2005. Ground wave and satellite DMB are combined into DMB.
(Source : DACO D and S, 2007, Korea Broadcasting Yearbook).

terrestrial multimedia broadcasting operators such as Yonhap Television News (YTNDMB). The public broadcasters (22) include KBS, EBS, MBC and others. SBS is a good example of the 15 private television broadcasters among otherprivate broadcasters. In addition to public and private broadcasting, there are special broadcasters (9) such as the Christian Broadcasting System (CBS).

There are 2 different types of cable television : a comprehensive wired cable television (cable television) and a relay cable television (cable community antenna television). The 111 cable television operators share 77 service districts, whereas many relay cable operators are merged or closed. As a result, two broadcasters emerged : "Skylife" launched in 2002 and "TU Media" of DMB (Digital Multimedia Broadcasting) multimedia business launched in 2005 (DACO D & S, 2007). In 2006, cable television services had 12,581,819 subscribers and satellite television services had 2,915,550 subscribers. IPTV (Internet Protocol Television), DMB and UCC (User Created Content) are likely to grow in the future thanks to the high demand for blended or new media content in broadcasting and communication. In particular, the production and distribution of the DMB market was promoted by the DMB Expo. The world's first DMB broadcaster for satellite DMB and terrestrial DMB provided services for both in 2005 and 2006, respectively. Accordingly, local DMBs started broadcasting via rural and local service providers in 2006. The number of subscribers to Digital Television (D-TV) and DMB are shown in Table 6.9. Furthermore, carriers of the DMB pilot service such as IPTV, C-Cube, Daum and the UMB Consortium have broadcasted their pilot programs since 2006 (DACO D & S, 2007).

③ Cable television

Cable television broadcasting started with the establishment of the Korean Cable

Television Association in 1993. Two Network Operators (NO) are mainly responsible for operating and broadcasting the cable television channels and programs. In particular, most programs are provided by 33 program providers (PP) and are broadcasted through 44 different channels by 2 system operators (SO). In summary, there were 47 PPs, 99 SOs and 2 NOs in 2008. According to Table 6.10, 94.2% of SO subscribers were served by analog signal in 2007. The number of cable television subscribers generally corresponds to the population distribution : Seoul (21.2%), Gyeonggi-*do* (20.2%), Busan (8.4%), Gyeongsangnam-*do* (7.5%), Gyeongsangbuk-*do* (6.2%), Daegu (5.4%), Incheon (5.1%) and Jeju special self-governing province (1.2%) (Table 6.10).

Geographically there are 77 cable television service districts, which are not always evenly divided in terms of area size or population. For example, Seoul has the most service districts

Table 6.10 **Subscribers to cable television broadcasting by terminal (2007)**

City/Province	Digital Broadcasting	Analog Broadcasting	Total	%
Seoul[#]	424,260	2,701,093	3,125,353	21.0
Busan[#]	73,004	1,174,249	1,247,253	8.4
Daegu[#]	6,283	783,714	789,997	5.4
Incheon[#]	84,786	672,594	757,380	5.1
Gwangju[#]	-	494,032	494,032	3.3
Daejeon[#]	314	465,506	465,820	3.2
Ulsan[#]	3,439	396,251	399,690	2.7
Gyeonggi-*do*	101,512	2,887,375	2,988,887	20.0
Gangwon-*do*	4,969	483,064	488,033	3.3
Chungcheongbuk-*do*	2,028	377,237	379,265	2.6
Chungcheongnam-*do*	2,079	517,484	519,563	3.5
Jeollabuk-*do*	2,406	445,212	447,618	3.0
Jeollanam-*do*	1,295	473,667	474,962	3.2
Gyeongsangbuk-*do*	3,841	905,039	908,880	6.2
Gyeongsangnam-*do*	129,035	971,353	1,100,388	7.5
Jeju special self-governing province	16,320	160,746	177,066	1.2
Nation (%)	855,571 (5.8)	13,908,616 (94.2)	14,764,187	100.0

 # Metropolitan Area.
(Source : Cable Television Broadcasting Society, 2008, Subscriber Status of Cable Television [http://www.kcta.or.kr])

(21), followed by Gyeonggi-*do* (9), Busan (8), Daegu (6) and Incheon (5). It is notable that each service district needs at least 200,000 subscribers to sustain itself. The smallest population is found in the service district of Yongsan-gu cable television in Seoul. For example, it only provides service to 230,000 subscribers. By contrast, a cable television service located in Suwon serves more than 1,470,000, covering Osan and Hwaseong. Similarly, Pyeongtaek cable television serves 1,430,000 including neighboring areas of Yongin, Icheon and Anseong. Ansan cable television provides service to 1,390,000 subscribers in Gwangmyeong and Siheung.

2) Geographical distribution of information and communication

The information and communication industry plays a critical role in promoting the IT (information technology) industry. It is also a key element in implementing information technology in daily life. For example, portable internet services such as WiBro and High Speed Downlink Packet Access (HSDPA) have been provided since June 2006. Since WiBro service has been available in Seoul and its neighboring areas, it has extended its service area to major larger cities. Furthermore, it is expected to grow, owing to the nationwide network service of the HSDPA.

① Trunk communication network

The trunk communication network is classified into cable communication and wireless communication. In 2000, intra-city telephone subscribers were ranked at the top for use of the cable communication network, followed by the high-speed Internet subscribers (14.4%). However, there was a dramatic change in 2005. The use of intra-city telephone service (65.8%) has decreased while use of internet service (32.4%) has increased. On the other hand, the number of wireless mobile subscribers accounted for more than 97% of wireless communication service in 2000 and 2005 (Table 6.11).

Table 6.11 **Number of subscribers by communication service (%, person)**

Year	Cable (Wire) Communication Service								Total
	Telephone			Exclusive Use Circuit	High-Speed Networks			Telegraph and Telegram	
	Intra-city Telephone	Public Telephone	Internet Telephone		High-Speed Internet Service	High-Speed Nation Networks	Others High-Speed Networks		
2000	80.5	1.4	-	3.6	14.4	-	0	0	100.0
									(27,242,397)
2005	65.8	0.4	0.1	1.3	32.4	0.1	-	-	100.0
									(34,844,134)

Year	Wireless Communication Service							
	Mobile Communication	Trunked Radio System	Wireless Data Communication	Wireless Call	Others Mobile Communication	Satellite Communication	Wireless Fixed Communication	Total
2000	97.2	0.4	0.3	2.1	0	-	-	100.0
								(27,596,421)
2005	98.7	0.8	0.3	0.1	-	0	0.1	100.0
								(38,854,074)

(Source : Statistics Korea, 2007, Statistical Yearbook of Korea).

Table 6.12 shows that 83.1% of households have at least 1 mobile phone. In detail, households with more than 2 mobile phones (47.5%) dominate over ones with a single mobile (35.6%). Generally speaking, 153.5 mobile phones are available per every 100 households across the country. The mobile phone registration shows uneven regional distribution primarily concentrated in major cities. For example, Seoul ranked at the top with 179.6 mobile

Table 6.12 **Household mobile phone ownership ratio (2002, %)**

City/Province	Household Ownership Ratio			Holding Household	Not Holding	Total	Numbers per Hundred Household
	1	2	Over 3				
Seoul#	33.3	35.3	22.4	91.0	9.0	100.0	179.6
Busan#	35.9	30.9	19	85.8	14.2	100.0	160.6
Daegu#	34.7	30.6	21.4	86.7	13.3	100.0	166.4
Incheon#	35.1	32.5	21.5	89.2	10.8	100.0	171.7
Gwangju#	37.2	29.8	17.2	84.2	15.8	100.0	154.9
Daejeon#	35.9	31.6	19.3	86.8	13.2	100.0	164.8
Ulsan#	39.2	33.3	17.1	89.6	10.4	100.0	161.5
Gyeonggi-*do*	34.9	35.3	18.3	88.5	11.5	100.0	167.7
Gangwon-*do*	39.4	25.8	11.4	76.6	23.4	100.0	128.4
Chungcheongbuk-*do*	36.6	27.2	11.6	75.5	24.5	100.0	129.8
Chungcheongnam-*do*	36.5	24.6	8.9	70.0	30.0	100.0	114.7
Jeollabuk-*do*	37.4	21.3	11.8	70.5	29.5	100.0	119.4
Jeollanam-*do*	35.4	18.6	8.8	62.8	37.2	100.0	102.2
Gyeongsangbuk-*do*	37.9	22.6	8.3	68.8	31.2	100.0	110.5
Gyeongsangnam-*do*	38.3	24.7	12.1	75.0	25.0	100.0	127.0
Jeju special self-governing province	36.3	29.6	11.1	77.0	23.0	100.0	133.2
Nation	35.6	30.5	17	83.1	16.9	100.0	153.5

 # Metropolitan Area

(Source : Statistics Korea, 2008, National Statistical Portal [www.kosis.kr])

phones per 100 households, followed by Incheon (171.7), Gyeonggi-*do* (167.7), Daegu (166.4), Daejeon (164.8), Ulsan (161.5) and Busan (160.6). Noticeably, Jeollanam-*do* (102.2) has the least number of mobile phones per every 100 households (Table 6.12).

② Computer and internet

Nationwide, 60.1% of the population had computers in 2002. Areas in which computer ownership rates are above the national average include Seoul, Gyeonggi-*do* and other metropolitan cities, while the rest of the nation has ownership rates lower than the national average. The nation average for the number of computers per every 100 households is 67.1. For example, Seoul shows the highest number of computers per every 100 households (81.8), followed by Gyeonggi-*do* (75.6), Ulsan (75.2), Daejeon (71.9) and Incheon (69.7). Other areas of the country have fewer computers per household than the national average. This indicates there is a regional disparity between metropolitan cities and medium-small cities (Table 6.13).

Table 6.13 **Household computer ownership ratio (%)**

City/Province	Household Computer Ownership Rates			None	Total	Numbers of Computersper One Hundred Households
	1	Over 2	Total			
Seoul#	61.5	8.6	70.1	29.9	100.0	81.8
Busan#	57.5	3.4	60.8	39.2	100.0	65.0
Daegu#	58.0	3.7	61.7	38.3	100.0	65.7
Incheon#	62.5	3.5	66.0	34.0	100.0	69.7
Gwangju#	56.6	3.9	60.4	39.6	100.0	65.6
Daejeon#	57.9	6.2	64.1	35.9	100.0	71.9
Ulsan#	63.6	4.8	68.4	31.6	100.0	75.2
Gyeonggi-*do*	59.2	7.2	66.3	33.7	100.0	75.6
Gangwon-*do*	47.5	2.8	50.4	49.6	100.0	54.5
Chungcheongbuk-*do*	46.0	6.1	52.1	47.9	100.0	63.1
Chungcheongnam-*do*	42.5	2.7	45.2	54.8	100.0	48.5
Jeollabuk-*do*	44.9	2.9	47.8	52.2	100.0	51.6
Jeollanam-*do*	38.6	2.1	40.7	59.3	100.0	43.3
Gyeongsangbuk-*do*	43.3	2.2	45.6	54.4	100.0	48.7
Gyeongsangnam-*do*	47.7	2.4	50.1	49.9	100.0	53.5
Jeju special self-governing province	44.2	3.4	47.7	52.3	100.0	51.9
Nation	54.9	5.2	60.1	39.9	100.0	67.1

 # Metropolitan Area

(Source : Statistics Korea, 2008, National Statistical Portal [www.kosis.kr])

Internet domains are fundamental to facilitating the flow of information in Internet operations. The total number of .kr domains in 2007 was 930,485, of which Seoul accounted for 57.1%, followed by Gyeonggi-*do* (17.1%), Busan (4.0%), Daegu (3.5%) and Incheon (3.5%). The configurations of each type of .kr domain are shown in Table 6.14. Types of Internet domains include profit-making, non-profit making, governmental, operational, regional, educational and research domains. The profit-making domain is the most popular one with 57.7% of total usage. In addition to .kr domains, quickdom (23.5%) and Hangul domain (10.1%) are also available.

Table 6.14 **Subscribers to .kr internet domain types (December 2007)**

Domain[#]	co.kr	ac.kr	re.kr	og.kr	go.kr	ne.kr
Number	536,908	12,602	2,099	42,571	2,115	3,027
%	58	1.3	0.2	4.6	0.2	0.3
Domain[#]	pe.kr	quickdom	mil	Hangul	Regional Domain	kr Domain
Number	16,297	218,478	54	94,443	1,891	930,485
%	1.7	23.5	0.0	10.1	0.2	100.0

 # co.kr [profit-making agency], ac.kr [university and graduation school], re.kr [research institute], or.kr [non-profit-making agency], go.kr [government], ne.kr [network operation], pe.kr [individual], mil [defense agency], region [local government domain, ex : seoul.kr].
[Source : National Internet Development Agency of Korea, 2008, Internet Statistics Information Check System [http://isis.nida.or.kr]]

REGIONAL STRUCTURE OF DISTRIBUTION

The number of wholesale and retail industry establishments was 844,695 with 2,422,391 employees in 2006 as can be seen in Table 6.15. The average number of em-ployees per establishment is relatively small (2.9). The average annual revenue is 625,000,000 won per establishment. With respect to the number of establishments by region, Seoul (25.1%) has the most followed by Gyeonggi-*do* (16.5%), Busan (8.8%), Gyeongsangnam-*do* (6.2%), Daegu (5.7%), Gyeongsangbuk-*do* (5.4%), Incheon (4.4%) and Jeju special self-governing province (1.3%). The pattern reflected by the number of employees is similar to that of establishment rankings. For example, Seoul accounts for 30% of employees, followed by Gyeonggi-*do* (17.6%), Busan (8.8%), Gyeongsangnam-*do* (5.4%), Daegu (5.2%), Incheon (4.3%), Gyeongsangbuk-*do* (4.3%) and Jeju special self-governing province (1.3%). Generally speaking, the percentages are related to the area populations, proportionately reflecting the size of the population in each area. Seoul employs the most people per establishment with 3.4 people per establishment, followed by Gyeonggi-*do* (3.1) and Gwangju (3.0). The average number of employees per establishment ranges from 2.2 to 2.9 for the rest of the area. In terms of the sales revenue, establishment in Seoul has the highest average revenue of 1,044,200,000 Won, followed by Gyeonggi-*do* (614,500,000 Won) and Gwangju (604,100,000 Won). Most of the metropolitan areas generate asales revenue of more than 500,000,000 Won while all other regional provinces, except Gyeongsangnam-*do* (411,200,000 Won), have a sales revenue around 300,000,000 Won (Table 6.15).

Table 6.15 **Wholesale and retail industry by city and province (2006)**

City/Province	No. of Establishments	No. of Employees	Sales (million Won)	Employees per Establishment	Sales per Establishment (million Won)
Seoul[#]	212,422	727,836	221,804,278	3.4	1,044.2
Busan[#]	74,637	213,308	44,187,022	2.8	592.0
Daegu[#]	48,046	126,705	24,140,356	2.6	502.4
Incheon[#]	37,410	104,523	19,356,566	2.8	517.4
Gwangju[#]	25,875	76,602	15,632,125	3.0	604.1
Daejeon[#]	24,217	69,864	13,610,297	2.9	562.0
Ulsan[#]	16,151	43,440	8,377,204	2.7	518.7
Gyeonggi-*do*	139,223	426,119	85,549,261	3.1	614.5
Gangwon-*do*	28,698	69,195	9,825,099	2.4	342.4
Chungcheongbuk-*do*	25,131	61,900	9,502,188	2.5	378.1
Chungcheongnam-*do*	33,654	77,953	12,050,191	2.3	358.1
Jeollabuk-*do*	33,352	80,233	11,098,240	2.4	332.8
Jeollanam-*do*	36,055	79,999	10,554,354	2.2	292.7
Gyeongsangbuk-*do*	45,925	103,596	15,530,883	2.3	338.2
Gyeongsangnam-*do*	52,583	130,683	21,619,638	2.5	411.2
Jeju special self-governing province	11,316	30,435	5,086,637	2.7	449.5
Nation	844,695	2,422,391	527,924,339	2.9	625.0

Metropolitan Area
(Source : Statistics Korea, 2008, National Statistical Portal [www.kosis.kr])

Table 6.16 shows sales by retail store types. In regard to sales volume by retail store type, specialty commodity stores accountedfor 54.9% of the total sales amount, followed by large discount stores (11.4%), department stores (8.6%), non-store retail stores (8.3%) and convenience stores (1.8%). The table also supports that non-store retail sales increased and continued their trend of becoming a larger part of total retail sales. Non-store retail sales are all sales that *do* not involve going to a mall or stores. Establishments included in non-store retail stores are mail-order houses, vending machine operators, home delivery sales, door-to-door sales, party plan sales, electronic shopping and sales through portable stalls, street vendors, etc.

Table 6.16 **Sales by retail store type (2007)**

Store Types	Sales (million Won)	%
Department Store	1,968,040	8.6
Large Discount Store	2,632,312	11.4
Supermarket	953,927	4.2
Convenience Store	406,674	1.8
Other General Retail Store	605,210	2.6
Non‑Store Retail Store*	1,902,077	8.3
Cyber Shopping Mall	855,484	3.7
Other Non‑Store Retail Store*	1,046,593	4.5
Specialty Commodity Retail Store	12,615,263	54.9
Total	22,985,580	100.0

The non-store retailers are different from traditional stores and use methods, such as the broadcasting of infomercials, the broadcasting and publishing of direct-response advertising, the publishing of paper and electronic catalogs, door-to-door solicitation, in-home demonstration, selling from portable stalls and distribution through vending machines.
(Source : Statistics Korea, 2008, National Statistical Portal [www.kosis.kr]).

According to the sales data for large stores in December 2007, large retail stores, large discount stores and department stores ranked in the top 3, in that order, as can be seen in Table 6.17. Spatially, large retailers sell the most in Seoul (35.0%), followed by Gyeonggi-*do* (22.4%), Busan (7.1%), Daegu (5.6%), Incheon (5.1%) and Jeju special self-governing province (0.6%). In terms of department store sales, Seoul generates more than half of the national total sales (51.3%), followed by Gyeonggi-*do* (16.3%), Busan (6.6%) and Daegu (6.3%). The spatial concentration of department store sales in Seoul is stronger than that of other large retail stores.

Table 6.17 **Distribution of large retail stores by sales (2007)**

City/Province	Large Retail Stores		Department Stores		Large Discount Stores	
	Sales (million Won)	%	Sales (million Won)	%	Sales (million Won)	%
Seoul#	1,609,503	35.0	961,416	51.3	648,087	24.6
Busan#	324,926	7.1	122,810	6.6	202,116	7.7
Daegu#	257,356	5.6	77,037	6.3	139,079	5.4
Incheon#	235,802	5.1	73,478	4.1	158,765	6.0
Gwangju#	148,206	3.2	67,898	3.9	74,728	2.8
Daejeon#	182,509	4.0	66,890	3.6	114,611	4.3
Ulsan#	132,293	2.9	305,603	3.6	65,403	2.5
Gyeonggi-*do*	1,032,290	22.4	-	-	726,687	27.7
Gangwon-*do*	50,957	1.1	-	-	48,285	1.8
Chungcheongbuk-*do*	64,208	1.4	-	-	55,772	2.1
Chungcheongnam-*do*	76,073	1.7	-	-	50,989	1.9
Jeollabuk-*do*	85,619	1.9	-	-	57,735	2.2
Jeollanam-*do*	61,974	1.3	-	-	55,491	2.1
Gyeongsangbuk-*do*	112,216	2.4	-	-	86,778	3.3
Gyeongsangnam-*do*	199,345	4.3	78,634	4.2	120,711	4.6
Jeju special self-governing province	27,075	0.6	-	-	27,075	1.0
Nation	4,600,352	100.0	1,872,043	100.0	2,632,312	100.0

 # Metropolitan Area.
(Source : Statistics Korea, 2008, National Statistical Portal [www.kosis.kr])

6.2.1 Regional Distribution of Distribution Agencies

There were 683 permanent markets and 366 large-scale stores in Korea as of 2003 as can be seen in Table 6.18. In terms of distribution facilities, regional distribution shows the highest concentration in Seoul (24.5%), followed by Gyeonggi-*do* (13.2%), Busan (9.2%), Daegu (8.8%), Gyeongsangnam-*do* (8.2%), Gyeongsangbuk-*do* (7.3%) and Jeju special self-governing province (1.5%) (Table 6.18).

Table 6.18 **Regional distribution centers by city and province (2003)**

City/Province	Large Stores	Permanent Markets	Agricultural and Aquatic Product Markets	Livestock Periodic Markets	Total	%
Seoul[#]	123	152	7	-	282	24.5
Busan[#]	77	26	3	-	106	9.2
Daegu[#]	-	99	2	-	101	8.8
Incheon[#]	7	33	3	-	43	3.7
Gwangju[#]	1	22	1	-	24	2.1
Daejeon[#]	4	31	2	2	39	3.4
Ulsan[#]	3	26	0	2	31	2.7
Gyeonggi-*do*	86	54	11	1	152	13.2
Gangwon-*do*	6	7	9	-	22	1.9
Chungcheongbuk-*do*	1	23	2	4	30	2.6
Chungcheongnam-*do*	3	26	6	3	38	3.3
Jeollabuk-*do*	12	14	5	2	33	2.9
Jeollanam-*do*	3	37	9	6	55	4.8
Gyeongsangbuk-*do*	10	60	6	8	84	7.3
Gyeongsangnam-*do*	28	60	3	3	94	8.2
Jeju special self-governing province	2	13	2	-	17	1.5
Nation	366	683	71	31	1,151	100.0

Metropolitan Area.
(Source : Statistics Korea, 2004, Statistical Yearbook of Korea)

Table 6.19 indicates that the total number of public wholesale markets in Korea is 32. These markets are well distributed across the country with at least 1 market per each city. Metropolitan areas such as Seoul, Incheon, Busan, Gwangju and Daejeon have multiple markets. Garak-*dong* wholesale market opened for the first time in 1985 selling agricultural products and fishery. The wholesale market of Ojeong-*dong* in Daejeon was opened later in 1987 and then Bukbu wholesale market in the northern part of Daegu and Cheongju wholesale market were opened in 1988. The amount of annual turnover is highest in Seoul, representing 42.3% of the national turnover total at Garak-*dong* wholesale market with 6.5% at Gangseo wholesale market, followed by Guri wholesale market (6%), Bukbu wholesale market in Daegu (5%) and Chuncheon wholesale market (0.2%).

Table 6.19 *Public wholesale markets of agricultural and aquatic products (2006)*

Wholesale Market	Year Opened	Area (㎡)					Turnover (million Won)
		Lot	Building	Auction House	Store	Low Temperature Storage House	
Seoul[#] Garak-*dong*	1985	543,451	281,179	109,393	54,686	9,806	3,420,200
Seoul[#] Gangseo	2004	210,362	114,807	24,408	28,358	12,221	522,981
Busan[#] Eomgung-*dong*	1993	154,190	92,260	21,048	24,496	1,782	318,032
Busan[#] Banyeo-*dong*	2000	151,942	74,773	18,369	8,569	2,908	243,778
Daegu[#] Bukbu	1988	151,654	98,473	34,230	9,071	548	400,768
Incheon[#] Guwol-*dong*	1994	60,810	43,382	14,593	-	888	230,578
Incheon[#] Samsan-*dong*	2001	107,912	56,097	15,961	-	630	203,596
Gwangju[#] Gakhwa-*dong*	1991	56,206	35,532	27,229	1,138	826	270,963
Gwangju[#] Seobu	2004	111,201	58,522	18,399	1,106	3,334	227,265
Daejeon[#] Ojeong-*dong*	1987	71,482	32,454	21,721	-	770	230,079
Daejeon[#] Noeun-*dong*	2001	112,282	45,507	15,797	5,005	1,468	120,887
Ulsan[#]	1990	39,364	18,851	17,027	732	79	117,941
Gyeonggi-*do* Suwon	1993	56,926	21,698	17,705	-	43	137,588
Guri city	1997	186,575	132,990	45,403	18,506	4,764	486,906
Anyang city	1997	84,941	50,202	19,340	3,835	374	131,641
Ansan city	1997	42,499	27,447	9,302	1,950	523	87,178
Gangwon-*do* Chuncheon	1996	31,499	7,489	1,667	1,440	180	15,437
Gangneung city	1999	65,825	15,992	4,312	1,767	986	22,393
Wonju city	2001	44,880	13,995	5,695	1,725	151	38,401
Chungcheongbuk-*do* Cheongju	1988	44,088	20,302	12,189	-	300	91,194
Chungju city	1995	45,756	14,856	5,231	2,224	919	34,702
Chungcheongnam-*do* Cheonan	1995	43,670	14,632	4,707	815	599	94,292
Jeollabuk-*do* Jeonju	1993	59,577	26,754	15,234	-	598	92,363
Iksan city	1998	105,782	23,777	10,540	680	648	63,002
Jeongeup city	2000	70,917	13,886	5,914	3,699	202	24,009
Jeollanam-*do* Suncheon city	2001	74,461	29,930	13,774	3,698	469	65,319
Gyeongsangbuk-*do* Andong	1997	36,279	12,392	9,276	-	-	99,326
Pohang city	2001	84,053	29,872	9,168	-	608	39,853
Gumi city	2001	83,049	23,833	6,604	3,393	536	26,392
Gyeongsangnam-*do* Changwon	1995	56,884	31,788	8,980	3,365	2,191	61,690
Jinju city	1999	77,254	40,065	8,112	3,539	459	86,778
Masan city	2002	77,229	33,601	11,084	2,271	801	69,323
Total		3,143,000	1,537,338	562,412	186,068	50,611	8,074,855

Metropolitan Area.
(Source : Korea Agro-Aquatic Trade Corporation, 2008, Statistical Yearbook of Agro-Aquatics Wholesale Market [http://www.kamis.co.kr])

6.2.2 Regional Distribution of Commodities

1) Agro-livestock products

As can be seen in Table 6.20, farm products are sold through 6 distribution agencies : agricultural cooperative and agriculture corporation, private consumers, government, wholesale market, collection merchant and other. Regionally, Jeju special self-governing province uses only 2 distribution agencies while Gyeongsangbuk-*do* uses 8 different distribution agencies. A high proportion of the farm products in most major cities, including Gyeonggi-*do* and Gangwon-*do*, is sold directly to individual consumers. Statistically the relationship between the number of farmer households and the main sales types is not strong (r = 0.50).

2) Fishery (aquatic products)

Marine fishery is comprised of distant waters fishery, inshore fishery and coastal fishery. It is practiced in almost all the regions except Daejeon and Chungcheongbuk-*do*. Of 99.6% of aquatic products sold in 2005, the sales of live fish and shellfish accounted for 37.4% and 37.3%, respectively. The distribution of aquaculture households shows regional differences. A significant number of aquatic products were produced in Jeollanam-*do* (31.8%), followed by Gyeongsangnam-*do* (18.5%) and Chungcheongnam-*do* (13.2%). In regard to aquatic product sales by type, sales of live fish were relatively high in Gyeongsangnam-*do* and Jeollanam-*do*, whereas those of fresh fish were significant in Jeollanam-*do* and Gyeongsangbuk-*do*. In particular, Jeollanam-*do*, because of its wide tideland, sells the most processed, seasoned products along with seaweed and shellfish in terms of sales volume.

There are several ways to handle aquatic products. Most of the aquatic products are handled by the National Federation of Fisheries Cooperatives (42.8%), followed by gathering wholesale (26.6%) and direct sales to consumers (17.5%). The main distribution agency differs by regions. For example, Gangwon-*do*, Gyeongsangbuk-*do* and Jeju special self-governing province use the single outlet provided by the National Federation of Fisheries Cooperatives. On the other hand, Daegu utilizes 2 distribution agencies while Incheon, Busan, Ulsan, Gyeonggi-*do*, Chungcheongnam-*do*, Jeollabuk-*do* and Gyeongsangnam-*do* use 3. Seoul, Gwangju and Jeollanam-*do* make use of 4 distribution agencies.

Table 6.20 **Major sale methods of agro-livestock products by city and province (2005)**

City/Province	Major Sale Methods	Number of methods
Seoul#	Other, Personal Consumer, Wholesale Market, Collection Merchant	4
Busan#	Personal Consumer, Collection Merchant, Other, Agricultural Cooperative and Agriculture Corporation, Wholesale Market	5
Daegu#	Personal Consumer, Agricultural Cooperative and Agriculture Corporation, Other, Wholesale Market, Collection Merchant, Producing Agricultural Cooperative's Joint Market, Processing Establishment of Agro-Livestock Products	7
Incheon#	Personal Consumer, Agricultural Cooperative and Agriculture Corporation, Collection Merchant, Other	4
Gwangju#	Personal Consumer, Agricultural Cooperative and Agriculture Corporation, Sale for Government, Other	4
Daejeon#	Personal Consumer, Other, Agricultural Cooperative and Agriculture Corporation	3
Ulsan#	Personal Consumer, Other, Agricultural Cooperative and Agriculture Corporation, Sale for Government, Periodic Market	5
Gyeonggi-*do*	Personal Consumer, Agricultural Cooperative and Agriculture Corporation, Other, Collection Merchant, Processing Establishment of Agro-Livestock Products	5
Gangwon-*do*	Personal Consumer, Agricultural cooperative and Agriculture Corporation, Other, Collection Merchant, Processing Establishment of Agro-Livestock Products	5
Chungcheongbuk-*do*	Agricultural Cooperative and Agriculture Corporation, Personal Consumer, Other, Sale for Government, Collection Merchant, Processing Establishment of Agro-Livestock Products	6
Chungcheongnam-*do*	Agricultural Cooperative and Agriculture Corporation, Sale for Government, Collection Merchant, Personal Consumer, Processing Establishment of Agro-Livestock Products, Other	6
Jeollabuk-*do*	Agricultural Cooperative and Agriculture Corporation, Sale for Government, Personal Consumer, Collection Merchant, Processing Establishment of Agro-Livestock Products, Other	6
Jeollanam-*do*	Agricultural Cooperative and Agriculture Corporation, Sale for Government, Collection Merchant, Personal Consumer	4
Gyeongsangbuk-*do*	Agricultural Cooperative and Agriculture Corporation, Collection Merchant, Personal Consumer, Sale for Government, Producing Agricultural Cooperativesí, Joint Market, Other, Wholesale Merchant, Processing Enterprise of Agro-Livestock Products	8
Gyeongsangnam-*do*	Agricultural Cooperative and Agriculture Corporation, Sale for Government, Personal Consumer, Other, Collection Merchant, Wholesale Market	6
Jeju special self-governing province	Collection Merchant, Agricultural Cooperative and Agriculture Corporation	2
Nation	Agricultural Cooperative and Agriculture Corporation, Personal Consumer, Sale for Government, Collection Merchant, Other, Processing Establishment of Agro-Livestock Products	6

Metropolitan Area.

(Source : Statistics Korea, 2008, National Statistical Portal [www.kosis.kr])

CHAPTER 6

3) Distribution of facilities

Physical distribution of facilities is directly related to the region and the spatial structure, which are the main components of the distribution channel. These facilities vary by the locations themselves, the number of locations, their functions and the trade areas. Types of facilities include depot, stock point, physical distribution center, distribution center, and logistics center. The current network of facilities was established to promote intensive collection of agricultural produce and livelihood commodities at a distribution center for livelihood commodities and the Hanaro agricultural cooperative association club and to provide those materials directly to the Hanaro agricultural cooperative association marts. Four physical distribution centers with their respective sizes and trade areas are shown in Table 6.21. The first distribution center, called Giheung, was established in 1997 at Dongtan-myeon, Hwaseong in Gyeonggi-*do*. Other facilities opened in 2000 at 3 different locations : Gwangsan-gu in Gwangju, Gumi Jangchon in Gyeongsangbuk-*do* and Beopsu-myeon, Haman-gun in Gyeongsangnam-*do*. These facilities provide agricultural products and livelihood commodities to different regions. For example, the Giheung physical distribution

Table 6.21 **Locations and supply regions in distribution centers (2008)**

Location	Facilities Scales (Pyeong[*])		Supply Regions	Number of Hanaro Agricultural Cooperative Association Marts	%
	Lot	Building			
Gyeonggi-*do* Hwaseong city Dongtan-*myeon*	10,340	8,110	Seoul Metropolitan Area, Incheon Metropolitan Area, Daejeon Metropolitan Area, Gyeonggi-do, Gangwon-do, Chungcheongbuk-do, Chungcheongnam-do	1,000	43.5
Gwangju Metropolitan Area Gwangsan-*gu*	2,070	1,570	Gwangju Metropolitan Area, Jeollabuk-do, Jeollanam-do, Jeju special self-governing province	550	23.9
Gyeongsangbuk-*do* Gumi city Jangcheon	4,700	2,400	Daegu Metropolitan Area, Gyeongsangbuk-do	350	15.2
Gyeongsangnam-*do* Haman-*gun* Beopsu-*myeon*	1,460	1,886	Busan Metropolitan Area, Ulsan Metropolitan Area, Gyeongsangnam-do	400	17.4

*A pyeong is 3.3058 square meters.
[Source : National Agricultural Cooperative Federation, 2008, Status of National Physical Distribution Centers of Commodities of Life].

center supplies agro-livestock products to 1,000 Hanaro marts while other physical distribution centers provide products to hundreds of Hanaro marts. The main goal of the multipolarization of physical distribution centers dispersed through several different regions is to reduce time and cost of delivery to Hanaro marts.

The Hanaro Club distribution center of National Agricultural Cooperative Federation were established to provide services to both producers and consumers. In its trade area, a center provides consumers with fresh and affordable products by reducing distribution time and at the same time helps producers increase their gains by reducing distribution costs. The centers also provide agro-livestock-fisheries from their own wholesale markets to general retail markets, restaurants and food culture establishments, as well as to Hanaro marts in their districts. As seen in Table 6.22, the distribution centers differ in size by location. Gunwi in Gyeongsangbuk-*do* is the largest center with a lot size of 3,308,408 pyeong. Types of management and investment of physical distribution of Agricultural Cooperative Federation are most branch of the National Agricultural Cooperative Federation, and its funds provided government, local government municipals, and National Agricultural Cooperative Federation.

Each distribution center regulates its delivery areas and times. For example, Yangjae physical distribution center in Seoul delivers twice daily to its delivery areas of Seocho-*gu*, Gangnam-*gu*, Songpa-*gu* and Gwacheon city and once daily to Gangdong-*gu*, Gwanak-*gu*, Dongjak-*gu*, Guro-*gu*, Yeongdeungpo-*gu*, Yangcheon-*gu*, Geumcheon-*gu* and Anyang. Daegu physical distribution center serves most of Gyeongsangbuk-*do* excluding the delivery areas covered by Gunwi physical distribution center. Suwon physical distribution center in Gyeonggi-*do* serves not only all of Suwon, but also several other vicinity areas including Sangrok-*gu* in Ansan, Gunpo, Uiwang, several districts in Hwaseong and a few districts in Anyang. Goyang physical distribution center delivers twice daily to its service areas of Ilsan-*gu* and Deogyang-*gu* and once daily to other cities of Paju, Gimpo, Eunpyung-*gu* and Gangseo-*gu* in Seoul. In these ways, almost all the areas are served by their closest physical distribution centers.

CHAPTER 6

Table 6.22 **Management and investment types of distribution centers (2008)**

Distribution Center	Management Types	Investment Types	Area (Pyeong)	
			Lot	Building
Seoul Yangjae-*gu*	Subsidiary of National Agricultural Cooperative Federation	National Agricultural Cooperative Federation	20,420	17,932
Seoul Chang-*dong*	Subsidiary of Yangjae Corporation	National Agricultural Cooperative Federation	10,290	11,600
Busan	Subsidiary of National Agricultural Cooperative Federation	National Agricultural Cooperative Federation	5,678	13,613
Daegu	Branch of National Agricultural Cooperative Federation	National Funds, Dalseong-gun, National Agricultural Cooperative Federation	10,920	6,606
Daejeon	Subsidiary of National Agricultural Cooperative Federation	Daejeon Metropolitan Area, National Agricultural Cooperative Federation	12,635	5,327
Gyeonggi-*do* Suwon	Branch of National Agricultural Cooperative Federation	National Funds, Suwon City, National Agricultural Cooperative Federation	25,972	5,125
Seongnam	Branch of National Agricultural Cooperative Federation	Seongnam City, National Agricultural Cooperative Federation	25,455	14,370
Goyang	Branch of National Agricultural Cooperative Federation	Goyang City, National Agricultural Cooperative Federation	41,000	16,525
Gangwon-*do* Wonju	Branch of National Agricultural Cooperative Federation	National Agricultural Cooperative Federation	3,205	2,850
Chungcheongbuk-*do* Cheongju	Subsidiary of National Agricultural Cooperative Federation	National Funds, National Agricultural Cooperative Federation, Agricultural Cooperative Association of Members (32 Association)	20,000	5,559
Jeollabuk-*do* Jeonju	Branch of National Agricultural Cooperative Federation	National Funds, National Agricultural Cooperative Federation	10,699	6,143
Jeollanam-*do* Mokpo	Branch of National Agricultural Cooperative Federation	National Agricultural Cooperative Federation	15,562	7,189
Gyeongsangbuk-*do* Gunwi-*gun*	Subsidiary of National Agricultural Cooperative Federation	Agricultural Cooperative of Gunwi-gun, National Agricultural Cooperative Federation, Agricultural Cooperative Association of Members (90 Association)	3,308,408	6,300
Gyeongsangnam-*do* Changwon	Branch of National Agricultural Cooperative Federation	National Agricultural Cooperative Federation	1,300	720

(Source : Interviews Survey of Each Distribution Center).

6.2.3 Internet Commerce

Electronic commerce (e-business) began with the electronic data interchange (EDI) in the 1960s and was developed substantially in the 1990s with the help of the establishment of the World Wide Web (www) in 1991 and the spread of high-speed Internet connections afterward. The fundamental law of electronic transactions and electronic signatures was established and implemented in July 1999 (Ministry of Commerce Industry and Energy Korea Institute for Electronic Commerce, 2006). The implementation of laws concerning e-commerce promoted full development of e-commerce. There are 3 main agencies of e-commerce : business, government and consumer. Among these the business plays a central role in making transactions. The total number of e-transactions has grown for the past 6 years while the proportion of involvement of each agency has grown at different rates. Among the transactions, the business-to-business (B2B) transactions dominate e-commerce, accounting for 91.6% of transactions in 2001 where its e-transactions are relatively high with 88.5%. E-transactions with the other 2 agencies, however, show different temporal trends, which increased from 5.9% to 7.0% for the business-to-government (B2G) transactions and decreased from 5.9% to 2.2% for the business-to-consumer (B2C) transactions from 2001 to 2006 (Figure 6.6).

The amounts of B2B transactions in 2006 differed by industrial type. The transaction amounts were significantly high between manufacturing businesses, accounting for about two-

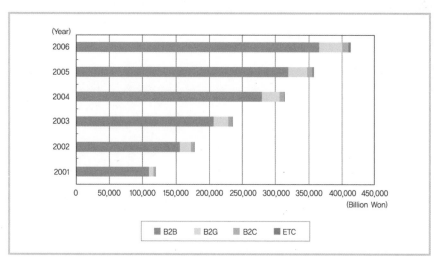

Figure 6.6 **Changes in electronic commerce transactions**
(Source : Ministry of Commerce, Industry and Energy and the Korea Institute for Electronic Commerce ; Statistics Korea, 2007, Statistical Yearbook of Korea).

Table 6.23 **Electronic Commerce Transactions by Industry (2006)**

Industry	Manufacturing Industry	Electric, Gas and Water Service Industry	Construction Industry	Wholesale and Retail Industry	Transportation and Communication Industry	Other Services Industry	Total
Transaction (billion Won)	239,377	8,552	29,335	68,035	11,861	9,033	366,191
%	65.4	2.3	8.0	18.6	3.2	2.5	100.0

(Source : Statistics Korea, 2007, Statistical Yearbook of Korea).

thirds of the total of all B2B transactions. The next highest transaction amount was found between wholesale and retail industries at 18.6%, while the smallest amount was held by electric, gas and water service industries at 2.3% (Table 6.23).

According to the Internet, statistics on commercial transactions in 2002 by product show that cosmetics, clothing, jewelry and accessories were the most popular items in Internet shopping, accounting for 45.6% of total e-transactions, followed by books, CDs, tapes and videos (40.6%), consumer electronics (20.8%) and computer-related products (15.1%). Among the product types, education services were the least popular, accounting for only 4.5% of the total e-transactions. The items purchased show different spatial patterns. For example, cosmetics, clothing, jewelry, accessories, books, CDs, tapes and videos sold well in most cities and provinces while electronics sales were mostly concentrated in Seoul, Incheon and Gyeonggi-*do*.

Chapter 6.3.

ENERGY PRODUCTION AND SUPPLY/DEMAND SYSTEM

6.3.1 Production of Energy Resources

1) Hard coal (anthracite)

Energy resources produced include hard coal, electricity and new renewable energy. The 2008 statistics data estimate that the total stock of hard coal reserves in 2006 was 1,367,030 thousand metric tons (1 metric ton equals 1000 kilograms). Some regions contain more energy resources than other areas. Among several other coalfields, two major coalfields account for

Table 6.24 **Anthracite reserves by coalfield (2006)**

Coalfield	Total Reserves (thousand M/T)	%	Possible Reserves (thousand M/T)		
			Total	Possible Exploitation Reserves	Potential Possible Exploitation Reserves
Samcheok	484,757	35.5	228,983	153,741	75,242
Jeongseon	450,950	33.0	97,968	44,869	53,099
Chungnam	116,293	8.5	53,898	29,902	23,996
Mungyeong	69,928	5.1	43,986	25,406	18,580
Gangneung	63,764	4.7	43,411	20,864	22,547
Danyang	62,067	4.5	30,893	15,839	15,054
Honam	90,548	6.6	54,315	29,348	24,967
Boeun	24,387	1.8	16,525	9,435	7,094
Other	4,336	0.3	2,998	1,659	1,339
Total	1,367,030	100.0	572,981	331,063	241,918

[Source : Korea Energy Economics Institute, 2008, Statistics Data Base].

68.5% of the total as can be seen in Table 6.24. For example, Samcheok coalfield reserves account for 35.5% and Jeongseon coalfield reserves account for 33.0%. Although 41.9% of the total deposit is identified with the potential of possible exploitation, only 24.2% can be exploited economically with current technology (Korea Energy Economics Institute 2008).

The hard coal production in 2005 was 2,832,000 metric tons, which was exploited by private corporations (56.5%) and the Korea Coal Corporation (33.5%). More than half of the total production comes from the two most productive mining stations. A privately owned Gyeongdong mining station produces 37.4% of the coal and a government-affiliated Jangseong mining station produces 21.6%.

2) Petroleum

The amount of imported crude oil increased from 560,560,000 barrels (bbl) in 1993 to 843,200,000 bbls. in 2005. A great amount of the crude oil is imported from Saudi Arabia and the United Arab Emirates. As a result of the policy regarding diversification of importing countries, the crude oil has been imported from many countries since 1996. The component ratio of major exporting countries in 2005 shows that 29.6% of oil is imported from Saudi Arabia, followed by the United Arab Emirates (17.9%), Kuwait (9.5%), Iran (8.4%), Oman (4.6%) and Indonesia (4.5%) (Figure 6.7).

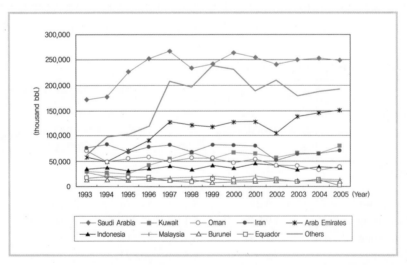

Figure 6.7 **Yearly trends of crude oil import volume by country**
(Source : Statistics Korea, 2008, National Statistical Portal [www.kosis.kr]).

3) Electric power

In 2007, the volume of electric power generation was 403,124,255 megawatt hours. Thermal power generation burning fossil fuel supplies the most electric power (63.2%), followed by nuclear power (35.5%), and hydropower (1.3%). The consumption of electric power varies by geographic regions. The thermal power plants are mainly distributed in the capital region, Chungcheongnam-*do* coastal areas and the Southeast Coastal Industrial Zone. The locations of nuclear power plants and hydropower plants are spatially restricted by the physical conditions. The nuclear power plants consider the distance to the industrial complexes and water bodies for cooling purposes, while the hydropower plants consider the location of large rivers. They especially prefer river basins such as the Han and Seomjin rivers supported mainly by rain rather than other smaller rivers.

4) Natural gas

Natural gas is carried as a compressed liquid form at a temperature of -162°ΔC. Liquefied Natural Gas (LNG) was first introduced from Indonesia in October 1986. The amount of LNG from Indonesia increased until 2000, but decreased to 24,605,000 tons in 2006. As can be seen in Figure 6.8, several other suppliers have been added since 2000. For example, the supply volume has been diversified to include Malaysia, Brunei, Qatar and Oman since 2001 in the

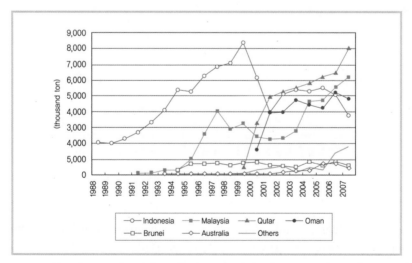

Figure 6.8 **Yearly trends of liquefied natural gas import volume by country**
(Source : Korea Energy Economics Institute, 2009, Statistics Data Base).

267

wake of a building nationwide chain of supply. As of 2006, Qatar supplied the most (27.4%), followed by Malaysia (22.8%), Indonesia (20.5%) and Australia (2.6%).

5) New renewable energy

New renewable energy uses solar heat, solar light, biomass, wind, geothermal, waste and fuel cells. They are recently emerging as new energy sources as substitutes for depleted energy sources. For example, 76.1% of renewable energy is generated from waste, followed by hydropower (16.6%) and biomass (5.3%).

6.3.2 Energy Supply and Demand System

The supply of primary energy has increased constantly with an exception in 1998. Hydropower shows a temporal fluctuation while new renewable energy and others keep increasing after 1993. Total energy consumption continuously increased between 1981 and 2006 except in 1998 (IMF aid). Energy by fuel oil has decreased while energy by bituminous coal, LNG and nuclear power has increased since 1997 (Figure 6.9).

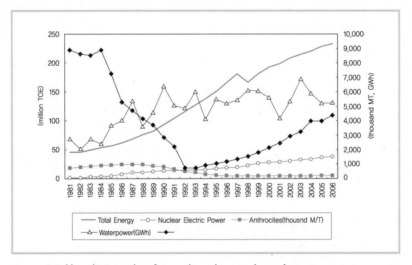

Figure 6.9 **Yearly trends of supply volumes by primary energy source**
(Source : Korea Energy Economics Institute, 2009, Statistics Data Base).

1) Hard coal (anthracite)

The supply of hard coal increased until 1988. After that a continuous rapid decreasing was identified until 1995, with the help of the coal industry rationalization management policy. Although there was a short temporal increase due to the 1997 International Monetary Fund (IMF) financial aid, this temporal fluctuation did little to change the supply trends. In regard to demand, 50% of supplied coal (10,267,000 metric tons) is used for power generation, followed by residential and commercial use (49.3%) and industrial use (0.7%).

2) Petroleum products

Several forms of petroleum by-product are obtained from the crude oil. The amount of its production follows the trend of its demand. According to recent data, the demand for diesel is highest among several other final products. One of the reasons is due to the increasing market share by diesel, especially after 1997. The production of Bunker-C oil (B-C oil), high in demand for residential heating purposes before 1997, decreased in the wake of air pollution recognition (Figure 6.10).

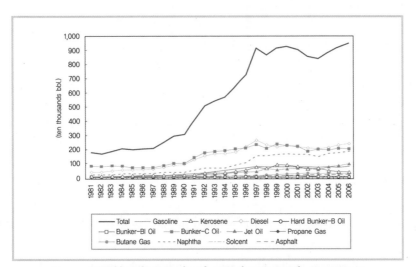

Figure 6.10 **Yearly trends of petroleum product outputs**
(Source : Korea Energy Economics Institute, 2009, Statistics Data Base).

The 765,520,000 barrels of crude oil consumed are used to produce petroleum products. Broken down in detail, naphtha is processed most (37.5%), followed by diesel (18.6%), LPG (12.2%), Bunker-C oil (12.1%), gasoline (7.8%) and others. The consumption of petroleum products shows regional patterns. For example, Ulsan, where a lot of petrochemical plants with a high demand for naphtha for raw material are located, uses 19.2% of petroleum products. On the other hand, Gyeonggi-*do* uses crude oil largely for diesel, B-C oil, LPG and gasoline. In particular, Gyeonggi-*do* and Seoul show high consumption of gasoline with 25.5% and 17.5% of the national total, respectively. Gyeonggi-*do* also consumes a high proportion of crude oil for kerosene (18.3%) and diesel (22%). Due to their geographic locations, Busan and Incheon need more hard Bunker-B oil as a fuel source for ships and vessels. For a similar reason, Jeju special self-governing province and Gyeongsangnam-*do* need more for heavy oil than other areas. Bunker-C oil is also consumed in Gyeonggi-*do* and Ulsan, whereas jet-oil for aircraft fuel is mostly used in Incheon (Figure 6.11).

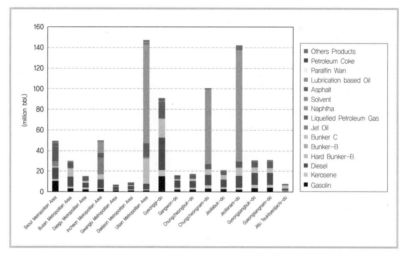

Figure 6.11 **Petroleum product consumption by city and province**
(Source : Korea Petroleum Association, 2008, Yearbook of Korean Petroleum Industry).

3) Electric power

The total volume of electric power consumed in 2007 was 368,605,433 megawatt hours, which is represented by manufacturing (48.0%), service industry (30.6%), residential (14.7%) and others. Regional patterns are highly correlated with population at $r = 0.8611$. For example, the highest sales are found in Gyeonggi-*do* (21.2%) and the lowest sales are found in Jeju special self-governing province (0.8%). Seoul (11.7%), Gyeongsangbuk-*do* (9.8%), Chungcheongnam-*do* (7.6%), Gyeongsangnam-*do* (7.3%) and Ulsan (6.2%) represent the rest.

4) Natural gas

The demand for natural gas increased about 1.8 times between 2000 (14,216,781,000 tons in volume) and 2007 (25,459,931 tons in volume). An additional 2,720.9 kilometers of pipe line (as of April 2008) have also been added to the existing one. In terms of natural gas usage, the highest demand is explained by city gas usage (56.7%), followed by power plants (40.0%), district heating (2.5%) and individual consumption (0.7%). In particular, the number of natural gas suppliers varies by region. Among 33 total suppliers in 2006, 5 of them are located in Seoul.

Gyeongsangbuk-*do* and Gangwon-*do* each have 4 natural gas suppliers. Notice that the number of gas suppliers is not necessarily related to the volume of the gas supply. For example, Seoul (35.5%) provides the highest gas supply, followed by Gyeonggi-*do* (18.5%), Busan (5.9%) and Ulsan (5.7%). In terms of its usage, half of the gas demand is attributed to home usage and 26.2% to industrial usage. Major metropolitan cities (except Seoul and Ulsan), along with Gyeonggi-*do*, Gangwon-*do*, Jeollabuk-*do*, Jeollanam-*do* and Jeju special self-governing province, demand more residential than industrial usage while other provinces and Ulsan, have more industrial demand than residential usage.

Chapter 7.
TOURISM AND LEISURE ACTIVITIES

Korea Bay

East Sea

Sohanman

Donghainman

Gyeonggiman

Yellow Sea

Korea Strait

Jeju Strait

Chapter 7.1.

TRENDS AND CHANGES IN LEISURE AND TOURISM

7.1.1 Evolution of Leisure and Tourism in the Korean Lifestyle

It was not until the 1980s that the concept of leisure and tourism entered people's lives (Table 7.1). Koreans, in general, had been sacrificing their leisure and tourism opportunities to concentrate on work and production for survival, although the concept had been in existence before then and people had participated in leisure and tourism activities sporadically. Leisure and tourism opportunities for the general public began to increase in the late 1980s. By the 1990s, in conjunction with trends in globalization, localization, and informationalization, time and opportunities for leisure and tourism began to expand, and engaging in both became a popular phenomenon in the lives of the general population in all regions of Korea. After 2000, interest in leisure and tourism that emphasizes self-realization and cultural experience became the new leisure trend.

7.1.2 Sociocultural Factors Affecting the Leisure and Tourism Lifestyle

The changes in the leisure and tourism lifestyle through time can be explained by sociocultural changes. These sociocultural changes include 1) diversification in the means by which leisure and tourism activities can be offered and accessed, 2) increase in the amount of time for leisure and tourism activities, 3) expansion of opportunities and resources for leisure and tourism activities, 4) increase in people's ability to participate in leisure and tourism activities, 5) advent of diverse groups of people participating in new leisure and tourism trends, and 6) development of new types of leisure and tourism activities.

Table 7.1 **Trend in leisure and tourism**

Period	Sociocultural Characteristics	Changes in Economic Situation	Administrative Organization and Regulations	Leisure and Tourism Policy	National Leisure Lifestyle
Before 1960s	Tradition of agricultural society, Cold War era	Recovery from the war, economic revival through international aid	Establishment of a modern tourism administration organization	Enforcement of a cultural assets protection policy	Lack of an independent leisure concept
1960s	Urbanization, industrialization	Government-led economic development	Creation of fundamental systems for tourism promotion	Full-scale development of tourism resources	Birth of the concept of leisure
1970s	Pursuit of a humane quality of life	Successful economic development	Establishment of a long-term tourism general plan	Active governmental participation in tourism resource development	Establishment of awareness of leisure activities
1980s	Democratization, unstable national political situation	Acceleration of economic growth after economic crisis	Organizational restructuring, division of tourism operations by regions	Increased basis for leisure life other than tourism	Popularization of leisure after its shrinking
1990s	Unfolding of an era of self-regulation, openness, globalization, localization	Under IMF aid due to the financial crisis, efforts to overcome the hardship	Strengthening of the policy deparment related to leisure life	Awareness of the need for transformation of governmental roles	Realization of unique Korean leisure in the process of globalization
2000s	Introduction of the new 40-hour per week labor system, increase in the desire for self-realization	Introduction of neoliberalism	Expansion of tourism-related departments within the Ministries and self-governing bodies	Improvement of the national quality of life, balanced development of the nation	Effective time utilization and management for leisure

(Sources : Korea Culture and Tourism Institute, 2007, 2007 White Paper of Leisure).

Advancement in transportation technology and the development of information and communication technology highly diversified the means by which people can engage in leisure and tourism activities. There has been a major increase in car ownership since the late 1980s, which is often referred to as the "My Car Era," and the high-speed train network (KTX) has been available since 2004, which enhanced people's mobility for leisure and travel. The spread of internet use and opening up of cable and satellite broadcasting markets since the 1990s, and the widespread use of mobile phones and development of digital convergence since 2000, have also influenced this diversification, both on and off line. Specifically, Korea shows strength in the field of information and technology (IT, hereafter) as it ranks at the top of the Digital Opportunity Index, which makes new travel patterns that utilize IT, such as information and communication tourism or ubiquitous tourism, possible.

The increase in people's time for leisure and tourism activities is the result of an increase in the night and weekend hours available for leisure and a decrease in labor hours. In 1982, the curfew that existed for thirty-seven years after liberation from Japan was removed. Labor hour reduction and acceleration of democratization after the labor struggle in 1987 also made it possible for more diversification in people's leisure and tourism activities and their lifestyles. Late night business restrictions were abolished after 1998, and a 5-day (40-hour) work-week system was established in 2002. These new policies enabled rapid growth in night tourism or leisure activities that took advantage of the weekend.

Expansion of space, opportunity, and resources for leisure and tourism activities is due to both globalization and an increase in leisure and tourism facilities and destinations. As private sector international trade and exchange began with the Asian Games in 1986 and the summer Olympics in 1988, overseas travel restrictions were all cleared in 1989. With this in the 1990s came the popularity of backpacking among college students, and the internationalization of leisure and tourism spaces. The pace of this expansion was quickened by progress in globalization aided by the development of internet and transportation accessibility, an increase in the amount of travel, and international cultural exchange. The expansion of leisure and tourism spaces is also explained by many state-led policies such as the designation of the National Park System in 1967, expansion of diverse commercial recreation facilities since 1989 (including 24-hour convenience stores), designation of Special Tourist Zones in 1994, and designation of cultural tourism festivals in 1996.

The increase in people's ability to participate in leisure and tourism activities resulted from growth in the economic ability of people and low level of growth in many economic indices. As national income is increasing consistently and economic indices such as the consumer price rate, unemployment rate, and Gross Domestic Product are growing at a minimum level,

CHAPTER 7

people's ability and opportunities to participate in leisure and tourism activities are augmented.

Aging, a low birthrate and the advent of new generations explain the fifth phenomenon affecting the leisure and tourism lifestyle. In 2000, those who were 65 years old or over accounted for 7% of the entire population. With an aging society, the demand for a new type of tourism, such as silver tourism that caters to senior leisure and tourism activities, is gradually increasing. As the number of children per household decreases and the number of double-income, no-kids couples (DINKS) and one-child families increases, the "Little Emperor" culture and the demand for experiential and family-oriented, well-being types of tourism increases. To meet the needs of new generations, innovations in the leisure and tourism industry have been achieved by utilizing media, cyber space, and festivals and events.

Lastly, the development of new types of leisure and tourism activities results from changes in people's consumption patterns and the popularity of well-being culture. Experience-based consumption is the emerging pattern, which includes 1) consumption of high-end luxury goods, custom-made or value-added products, and personalized leisure and entertainment, 2) participation in festivals and event tourism, and 3) increased interest in the issues related to care facilities, health, longevity, environmental and ecological protection, cyber leisure activities, and outdoor recreation. Because interest in the well-being culture and LOHAS (Lifestyles of Health and Sustainability) has grown rapidly since 2000, new types of leisure and tourism activities are being developed that meet the needs and wants brought about by these trends.

7.1.3 Trends in the Leisure and Tourism Lifestyle

Due to the above-mentioned changes, the following new leisure and tourism trends have been emerging as popular in Korea : increase in overseas travel, family-oriented tourism, senior leisure and tourism, experiential- and well-being-oriented leisure and tourism, cyber leisure and tourism, leisure associated with the various PC bang opportunities (e.g., high-speed internet cafés), and serious leisure (see Figure 7.1).

After overseas travel restrictions were removed, the number of international departures increased significantly. It reached 1 million in 1989, 2 million in 1991, 5 million in 2002, and 13 million in 2007. Family-oriented leisure and travel also increased due to 2 main reasons. First, the change to a decreased, 5-day work-week system increased time people spend with their family. Second, many households now have only one child, which increases the fervor,

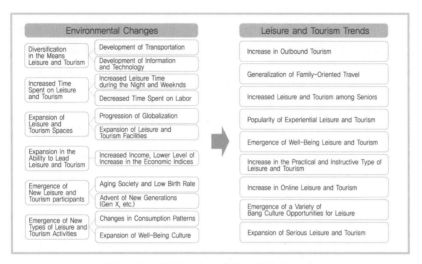

Figure 7.1 **Leisure and tourism trends**
(Source : Ko, 2006)

associated with the "Little Emperor" culture, to provide a quality education for their child. Both factors increased the relative popularity of family-oriented leisure and thus, the development of new family-oriented tourism products.

Changing perceptions on seniorleisure and travel, influenced by an aging society, ignited the drastic increase in senior leisure and tourism activities. Spending lesson tangible goods, the senior population now tends to spend more on travel, leisure, and liberal arts, the products that enable them to self-realize. In fact, demand for leisure and travel as well as expenditure on these products is strongest among the senior population compared to other age groups, which increases the demand for silver tourism products.

Direct experiential leisure activities, rather than activities that rely mostly on indirect experiences, are becoming popular. These include driving on a scenic route, travel, and outdoor adventures-places and things that people can visit or experience by themselves. As direct visits and participatory activities become the new cultural trends, leisure and travel products that provide genuine "experience" instead of "functional" benefits are becoming popular.

An increase in the average household income and growing interest in health-related issues lead to the rise of well-being leisure and tourism activities. As people become interested in their quality of life and prefer high-end products, the leisure and tourism products in this category are developed, targeting the middle to upper class who have interests in environmental and health issues and leisure.

The leisure lifestyle has been evolving from a cocoon type to an activity type, and to an instructive type after the work-week system changed. The cocoon type was more popular at the initial stage of the system change because of a decrease in household income, a lack of information, and a lack of experience in time management. As the 5-day work-week system became the standard, predominant mode of living in society, people's leisure activities became more active, and instructive products aimed at self re-investment are now becoming popular.

People now increasingly utilize internet or mobile products as a means to leisure and travel. Specifically, the younger generation uses internet or mobile products to search for and receive information on travel, to plan trips, and to experience destinations and trips virtually. Therefore, the internet leisure culture is being nurtured by the younger generation and thus, so too is the emergence of new products such as ubiquitous or IT tourism.

Bang (room) culture is a unique leisure culture of Korea. Norae-bang (Karaoke room) was first introduced in the mid-1990s, followed by the video-bang, game-bang, PC-bang, and bath-bang. Use of these various bangs, which portrays traditional, collective Korean leisure culture both on and off line, now comprises a fairly high percentage of people's leisure lifestyle.

Finally, very specialized serious leisure enthusiasts such as Otakus in Japan are another rapidly growing group. As time that can be spent on leisure or specific hobbies increases, so too do expert leisure or specialized hobby groups. To meet this demand, the availability of a variety of travel or field trip clubs as well as group tours is increasing.

7.1.4 Future Outlook on Leisure and Tourism

1) Increase in the demand for futuristic tourism products

The demand for futuristic tourism products is increasing due to a change in tourists' perceptions of how leisure time should be used and their desire to enhance their quality of life through tourism. Futuristic tourism products include those types of tourism that are quality-rather than quantity-oriented, fun tourism products that are enjoyed by both host community residents and the tourists, network tourism that enhances balanced development of communities, and tourism that focuses on culture and life experience. This means that the demand for new or alternative tourism options is increasing.

The main national tourism policy is to attract as many tourists as possible, and it still focuses on mass tourism development where quantity is prioritized over the quality of tourism. It raises many socioeconomic and environmental concerns, such as detachment of the tourists from the local hosts, disruption of local culture and environment in the name of economic development, and loss of unique traditional characteristics of the area due to diffusion of standardized package tours.

To develop desirable futuristic tourism, it is advised that alternative types of tourism products that emphasize quality mutual understanding of all, involving the communities at stake, and that stress the enhancement of distinctive local culture, should be developed steadily. Recently, emerging types of tourism such as heritage tourism, art tourism, lifestyle tourism, voluntourism, and dark tourism are highlighted as new tourism resources. Emergence of these options shows increased opportunity as well as the need for development of a creative, alternative tourism planning strategy that combines place, identity, and future trends.

2) Multi-convergence of the tourism industry

It is recommended that the structure of the industry be reinforced to adjust to the new tourism paradigm changes. As boundaries between the industries break down and multi-convergence commonly occurs, the tourism industry appears not only in the primary industry (e.g., rural tourism intersects both primary and secondary industries), but also in the secondary and tertiary industries (e.g., medical tourism, industrial tourism, sports tourism, event tourism, cinema tourism, food tourism, well-being tourism, health tourism, ubiquitous tourism). For example, medical tourism, a new type of tourism that combines the concepts of medical service, recuperation, leisure, and cultural activities, is expected to increase as 21st century interest in well-being and a health-oriented lifestyle increases.

3) Increase in cultural welfare, social leisure, and social tourism

Future leisure and tourism will require a new paradigm that combines culture and welfare. In fact, a demand for cultural welfare, social leisure, and social tourism is steadily increasing. With economic growth, people began to desire social relationships and self-realization not only within their social life, but also in their leisure lifestyles. This is expected to influence the development of a more collective type of leisure and tourism that emphasizes social welfare.

Cultural welfare leisure is trying to reach the goal of guaranteeing the right to lead a cultural life (including the right to cultural enjoyment and cultural creation) for the neglected and isolated population. In addition to pursuing self-satisfaction as a way to attain intrinsic rewards through social leisure, people also participate in social leisure activities as a way to contribute to society and to make their lives more meaningful and worthwhile. That is, social leisure activities such as voluntainment are altruistic and contribute meaningfully to society. While participating in those activities, the participants are also indirectly and internally compensated through self-enlightenment (acquisition of leisure skills), self-purification (psychological satisfaction), and self-expression (manifested in social relationships) (Yoon, 2007).

Social tourism refers to tourism opportunities given by the government and many organizations to individuals or groups who do not have access to leisure travel because of lower income and other deficiencies. The goal is to realize social integration by mitigating discord among people across all levels of society. Social tourism is now one of the major welfare policies in the tourism field. It enriches people's lives by enabling them to have access to a variety of cultural activities, which is directly connected to self-realization, rights to happiness, and survival (Cho, 2005).

TOURISTS AND TOURISM INCOME/EXPENDITURE

7.2.1 National and International Tourists

1) Changes in the number of inbound and outbound tourists

The changing trends in the number of inbound and outbound tourists can be divided into 4 distinctive stages by time (Figure 7.2 and Table 7.2).

① The first stage : The recognition period (1961~1977)

This period starts when the government began to keep tourism statistics. In 1961, the number of inbound tourists was first counted, and the Tourism Promotion Act was effected, which came a little before the first 5-year Plan for Economic Development (1962). The

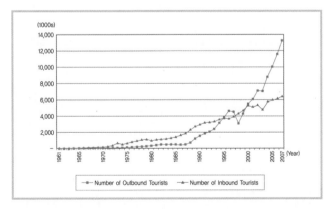

Figure 7.2 **Number of inbound and outbound tourists per year**
(units : 1000s, Year, Number of Outbound Tourists, Number of Inbound Tourists)
(Source : Korea Tourism Organization, 2007, Korean Tourism Statistics : Number of Inbound and Outbound Tourists and Tourism Balance per Year).

Table 7.2 **Yearly tourism statistics (1961-2007)**

	Number of Inbound Tourists		Number of Outbound Tourists		Tourism Income		Tourism Expenditure		Tourism Balance
	Number	%Growth	Number	%Growth	Number	%Growth	Number	%Growth	
1961	11,109	28.1	11,245	43.1	1,353	210.3	2,374	-48.3	-1,021
1962	15,184	36.7	10,242	-8.9	4,632	242.4	2,166	-8.8	2,466
1963	22,061	45.3	11,860	15.8	5,212	12.5	2,276	5.1	2,936
1964	24,953	13.1	20,486	72.7	15,704	201.3	2,381	4.6	13,323
1965	33,464	34.1	19,796	-3.4	20,798	32.4	1,662	-30.2	19,136
1966	67,955	103.1	35,095	77.3	32,494	56.2	3,193	92.1	29,301
1967	84,216	23.9	40,374	15	33,817	4.1	8,395	16.3	25,421
1968	102,748	22	67,381	66.9	35,454	4.8	10,487	24.9	24,967
1969	126,686	23.3	72,311	7.3	32,809	-7.5	10,964	4.5	21,845
1970	173,335	36.8	73,569	1.7	46,772	42.6	12,424	13.3	34,348
1971	232,795	34.3	76,701	4.3	52,383	12	14,808	19.2	37,575
1972	370,656	59.2	84,245	9.8	83,011	58.5	12,570	-15.1	70,441
1973	679,221	83.2	101,295	20.2	269,434	224.6	16,984	35.1	252,450
1974	517,590	-23.8	121,573	20	158,571	-41.1	27,618	62.6	130,953
1975	632,846	22.3	129,378	6.4	140,627	-11.3	30,709	11.2	109,918
1976	834,239	31.8	164,727	27.3	275,011	95.6	46,234	50.6	228,777
1977	949,666	13.8	209,698	27.3	370,030	34.6	102,714	122.2	267,316
1978	1,079,396	13.7	259,578	23.8	408,106	10.3	208,019	102.5	200,087
1979	1,126,100	4.3	295,546	13.9	326,006	-20.1	405,284	94.8	-79,278
1980	976,415	-13.3	338,840	14.6	369,265	13.3	349,557	-13.8	19,708
1981	1,093,214	12	436,025	28.7	447,640	21.2	439,029	25.6	8,611
1982	1,145,044	4.7	499,707	14.6	502,318	12.2	632,177	44	-129,859
1983	1,194,551	4.3	493,461	-1.2	596,245	18.7	555,401	-12.1	40,844
1984	1,297,318	8.6	493,108	-0.1	673,355	12.9	576,250	3.8	97,105
1985	1,426,045	9.9	484,155	-1.8	784,312	16.5	605,973	5.2	178,339
1986	1,659,972	16.4	454,974	-6	1,547,502	97.3	612,969	1.2	934,533
1987	1,874,501	12.9	510,538	12.1	2,299,156	48.6	704,201	14.9	1594,955
1988	2,340,462	24.9	725,176	4.2	3,265,232	42	1,353,891	92.3	1911,341
1989	2,728,054	16.6	1,213,112	67.3	3,556,279	8.9	2,601,532	92.2	954,747
1990	2,958,839	8.5	1,560,923	28.7	3,558,666	0.1	3,165,623	21.7	393,043
1991	3,196,340	8	1,856,018	18.9	3,426,416	-3.7	3,784,304	19.5	-357,888
1992	3,231,081	1.1	2,043,299	10.1	3,271,524	-4.5	3,794,409	0.3	-522,885
1993	3,331,226	3.1	2,419,930	18.4	3,474,640	6.2	3,258,907	-14.1	215,733
1994	3,580,024	7.5	3,154,326	30.3	3,806,051	9.5	4,088,081	25.4	-282,030
1995	3,753,197	4.8	3,818,740	21.1	5,586,536	46.8	5,902,693	44.4	-316,157
1996	3,683,779	-1.8	4,649,251	21.7	5,430,210	-2.8	6,962,847	18	-1,532,637
1997	3,908,140	6.1	4,542,159	-2.3	5,115,963	-5.8	6,261,539	-10.1	-1,145,576
1998	4,250,216	8.8	3,066,926	-32.5	6,865,400	34.2	2,640,300	-57.8	4,225,100
1999	4,659,785	9.6	4,341,546	41.6	6,801,900	-0.9	3,975,400	50.6	2,826,500
2000	5,321,792	14.2	5,508,242	26.9	6,811,300	0.1	6,174,000	55.3	637,300
2001	5,147,204	-3.3	6,084,476	10.5	6,373,200	-6.4	6,547,000	6	-173,800
2002	5,347,468	3.9	7,123,407	17.1	5,918,800	-7.1	9,037,900	38	-3,119,100
2003	4,752,762	-11.1	7,086,133	-0.5	5,343,400	-9.7	8,248,100	-8.7	-2,904,700
2004	5,818,138	22.4	8,825,585	24.5	6,053,100	13.3	9,856,400	19.5	-3,803,300
2005	6,022,752	3.5	10,080,143	14.2	5,793,000	-4.3	12,025,000	22	-6,232,000
2006	6,155,047	2.2	11,609,878	15.2	5,759,800	-0.6	14,337,900	19.2	-8,578,100
2007	6,448,240	4.8	13,324,977	14.8	5,750,100	-0.2	15,879,500	10.8	-10,129,400

(Source : Korea Tourism Organization, 2007, Korean Tourism Statistics)

government started to operate Tourism Promotion and Development Funds to expand tourism facilities, and arranged tourism-related legislation. In 1975, a public opinion survey on inbound tourists was performed, and the development of Gyeongju Bomun Tourist Resorts began. Except for the year 1974 when an oil crisis occurred, the annual growth rate for the number of inbound tourists was recorded between 13% and 103% for the period of 1961 to 1977. Although the number of inbound tourists was lower than 1 million, international tourism revenue increased consistently each year from $10.3 million in 1961 to $370 million in 1977.

② The second stage : The development of inbound tourism (1978-1987)

This is when the number of inbound tourists exceeded 1 million. In 1977, Korea achieved $10 billion in exports, and began active measures such as overseas promotion to prepare for the mass tourism era that began in 1978. The number showed a growth trend overall except for a slight decrease in 1980 (less than 1 million in international arrivals), right after the second oil crisis (1979). In 1987, the number of inbound tourists was 1.8 million, and international tourism revenue was almost $2.3 billion.

③ The third stage : The growth of inbound tourism (1988-1999)

The 12-year period from 1988 to 1999 represents the growth stage for Korean tourism. The number of inbound tourists to Korea reached 2 million for the first time in 1988 when the Summer Olympics was held, exceeded 3 million after 3 years, and 4 million by 1998. In 1999 both the number of inbound tourists and international revenue exceeded twice that of 12 years before. Many things happened in this period internally and externally. Overseas travel restrictions were all removed right after the Olympics on January 1, 1989, and since then all citizens have been able to travel abroad for leisure. The number of outbound tourists first exceeded 1 million and expenditure also exceeded $2.6 billion in 1999. It was truly the growth stage for both inbound and outbound tourism. New consumption patterns such as backpacking and study abroad (focusing on language study) that combined travel, education, experience, leisure, and novelty-seeking became very popular and widespread among college students and youth. By 1995, the number of outbound tourists exceeded that of inbound tourists, and tourism expenditure reached $5.9 billion, which resulted in a tourism deficit. The number of inbound tourists reached 3-4 million by 1991, but a tourism deficit has been recorded since then and it continued consistently except for the 3 years during the financial crisis (IMF Crisis) that began in 1997. Like the rest of the world, Korea had been experiencing great economic growth (achieving a national income per capita of $10,000 in 1996) before the

CHAPTER 7

285

financial crisis. With the series of Asian financial crises, Korea fell into an economic recession and had to receive financial aid from the International Monetary Fund. Because of this, expenditure by outbound tourists abroad dropped almost 50%, which made the tourism revenue generated versus spent abroad higher in 1998 and 1999.

④ The fourth stage : Rapid growth of outbound tourism (2000-2007)

Since 2000, the number of inbound tourists recorded has been over 5 million per year and it exceeded 6 million after 2005. The FIFA World Cup was held in Korea in 2002, but it did not increase inbound tourists in the same way as the 1986 Asian Games or 1988 Olympics did. On the other hand, there were 5 million outbound tourists in 2000 and the number exceeded 13 million in 2007, reflecting a double-digit growth rate every year. It seems that 9/11 in 2001 did not have too much effect on outbound tourism. Because the number of inbound tourists increased but international tourism revenue did not show a growth trend, this period can be called neither a growth nor a stagnant period. In fact, Korea experienced a tourism deficit again in this period because of an increased number of outbound tourists and tourism expenditure for overseas travel.

The fact that international tourism revenue decreased even with the increase in the number of inbound tourists shows that the period of accelerated Korean tourism growth has ended. Many things could have been done to reverse the tourism deficit. Some of the efforts included finding ways to increase the number of first-time and returning inbound tourists.

2) Inbound tourists by continent and type

The majority of the inbound tourists (98%) are from Asia (especially Japan), and only a small percentage of them are from other continents ; about 1% of them are from North America (the majority of these are Americans), followed by unknown, Oceania, Europe, and very rarely, Africa and South America. In 1981, 66% of inbound tourists were Asians (46% Japanese), and about 13% were from North America. After about 20 years, in the 2000s, Asians accounted for 98% of all the inbound tourists (92% from Japan), and most of them were student groups on school excursions and Hanllyu tourists who came through travel agencies. Revisitation by Japanese is common due to the geographical proximity between the 2 countries.

Asian inbound tourists account for the largest percentage of group tourists. Their main visiting purpose is shopping, followed by cultural experience. Concerning cultural tourists who are interested in things such as arts, pottery, temple, and academia, 46% of inbound tourists from Asia are cultural tourists, 56% from North America, 41% from Oceania, and 41% from Europe. These percentages reflect group tourists only ; considering that there are more individual tourists than group tourists, it is reasonable to say that cultural tourism resource development should be further encouraged utilizing traditional Korean resources.

Recent statistics show an increase in the number of Chinese tourists. Of the 6.44 million inbound tourists to Korea (2007), 73% were from Asia. Of them, 35% (2.23 million) were from Japan and 17% (1.07 million) were from China. This is equivalent to the total number of inbound tourists from all of North America and Europe. About 19% of inbound tourists (1.2 million) were in their 30s, and the majority (53%) was 30-50 years old.

International conferences are held all over the world, and convention tourism is receiving increased attention as a way to increase the number of inbound tourists. In 1988, 216 international conferences were held, which increased to 428 in 1997 and 825 in 2006. Although it is gradually increasing, this is not a high number considering the scale of the economy of Korea. Convention tourism can result in a major industrial and cultural multiplier effect and is rising as a field worth developing to attract more inbound tourists.

7.2.2 Scale of Tourism Balance and its Characteristics

1) International tourism revenue and tourism expenditure

Tourism income and expenditure parallels the economic situation, and is very closely related to the previously mentioned changes in the number of inbound tourists. During the first stage (the recognition period : 1961-1977), Korean tourism experienced steady growth and a tourism surplus. The highest tourism surplus ($260 million) was recorded in 1977 (Figure 7.3).

The second stage (the development period : 1978-1987) showed twice the growth rate of the previous stage due to the second oil crisis and hosting of the 1986 Asian Games. In 1986, tourism income reached $1.5 billion, and by 1987, it had reached $2.29 billion, which resulted in a tourism surplus of $1.59 billion. During this stage, the total tourism surplus was $2.8 billion.

The third stage (the growth period : 1988-1999) showed an increase in the number of outbound tourists. Compared to the previous stages, it seems that differences were not so dramatic between the total number of inbound and outbound tourists or tourism income and expenditure. Overall, though, more than $6.3 billion in income was earned during this stage.

A net loss in tourism income versus expenditure was recorded as Korean tourism began the fourth stage (the period of rapid growth of outbound tourism : 2000-present). There are

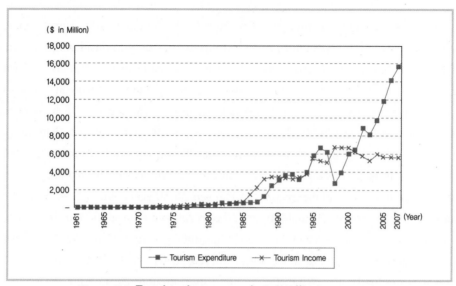

Figure 7.3 **Tourism income and expenditure per year**
(Units : $ in million, Year, Tourism Expenditure, Tourism Income)
(Source : Created based on Korean Tourism Organization, 2007).

more and more people traveling abroad and the amount of expenditure per person is also increasing. Although the number of inbound tourists is increasing, tourist expenditure within Korea is not increasing. Compared to 2001, the tourism surplus decreased even in 2002 when the FIFA World Cup was held. Many factors can explain this decrease, such as co-hosting of the games with Japan, but it is an unfortunate outcome when compared to the high growth rate recorded in 1986 or 1988 after the Asian Games or the Olympics. Korea has been experiencing an even worse situation in terms of a tourism balance since 2002. In 2007, there were twice as many outbound tourists as inbound tourists, and the outbound tourists spent 3 times more during their travel than the inbound tourists did in Korea. This resulted in a tourism deficit of more than $10 billion in 2007 for the first time in the history of Korea's tourism. Over the last 8 years, inbound tourists have spent $47.8 billion in Korea, whereas outbound tourists spent $82.1 billion during their overseas travel, making a tourism deficit of $34.3 billion.

2) Number of inbound/outbound tourists and tourism import/ export

The number of inbound tourists is gradually increasing and tourism income was the highest in the third stage (the growth period) (Figure 7.4). As seen in the figure, the tourism income level reflects a horizontal line, and it does not show any increase for a while since that period. Outbound tourism and tourism expenditure increased rapidly in a short period of time

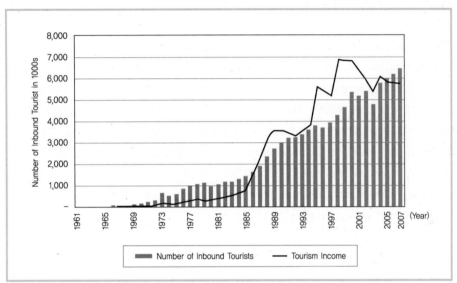

Figure 7.4 **Number of inbound tourist and tourism Income**
(Units : Number of Inbound Tourist in 1000s, Year, Number of Inbound Tourists, tourism Income)
(Source : Created based on Korean Tourism Organization, 2007)

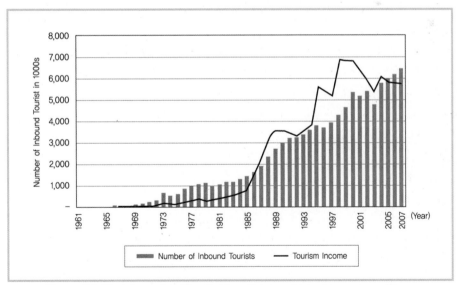

Figure 7.5 **Number of outbound tourists and tourism expenditure**
(Units : Number of Outbound Tourist in 1000s, Year, Number of Outbound Tourists, Tourism Expenditure)
(Source : Created based on Korean Tourism Organization, 2007)

CHAPTER 7

(Figure 7.5). This figure shows that the number of outbound tourists and tourism expenditure kept increasing during the growth period in the 1990s, although it slowed down during the financial crisis, then accelerated again afterwards.

③ Average tourism expenditure per capita

Outbound tourists' average expenditure per capita was significantly higher than that of the inbound tourists' during the development and growth stages except for the period during the financial crisis in the late 1990s. During the IMF crisis, outbound tourists spent less than the inbound tourists. In addition, expenditure associated with study abroad or any travel expenses for educational purposes have been excluded from tourism expenditure data since 1993, which made the tourism expenditure line descend. Were these data included, it is expected that the average tourism expenditure per capita line would be higher from 1993 to 2007.

Chapter 7.3.

LEISURE AND TOURISM SPACE AND RESOURCES

7.3.1 Changes in the Amount of Leisure Space

Leisure space refers to all types of space where leisure activities take place, where people can relax and participate in leisure-related activities comfortably and happily without any life constraints (Yoon et. al, 2002). There are a variety of types of leisure spaces depending on the extent of space, number of units per facility, participant activities, and resource characteristics. Recent trends in leisure space development include increased mixed-use and educational facilities, diversification of outdoor leisure spaces, and the appearance of a 3rd space (social surroundings separate from the 2 usual social environments of home and work).

The demand for complex types of leisure facilities is rapidly growing for several reasons. As Korean society experiences rapid social change, the value systems of the general public, their consumption patterns, and their participation in leisure activities are also changing. To satisfy this rapidly changing demand, the need for mixed-use types of leisure spaces is also rapidly increasing. Examples include Seoul Arts Center or the National Museum of Contemporary Art where green space and rest areas are provided simultaneously with cultural leisure spaces. Others include a variety of themed spaces such as KOEX Mall in Samseong-dong or I Park Mall around Yongsan station where shopping and entertainment opportunities are provided. These days, high-rise residential-commercial complexes include shopping, socialization, hobby, and other leisure-related facilities in the building so that the users can experience the urban lifestyle of one-stop living.

The increase in cultural and educational facilities surrounding the everyday life zone is another phenomenon as the leisure environments in residential areas change. Public libraries, public museums, and local art centers not only hold exhibitions or lend books, but also develop a variety of educational programs to provide the local residents with leisure opportunities. Cultural centers run by outlet malls or department stores also provide a variety of specialized cultural and educational programs at a reasonable cost so that local residents can use them more often.

The demand for resource-oriented leisure spaces such as natural parks, recretional forests, and tourism attractions, as well as facility-oriented outdoor spaces including sporting and exhibition areas or urban parks, is also increasing. In addition, the demand for recreational forest areas is steadily increasing as there is increased demand for family-oriented lodging facilities in the recreational forests, club-oriented adventure and experiential sports, and ecotourism. Recently, leisure spaces for the urban population are emerging as unused spaces around the urban areas are redeveloped. Idle lands such as waterfront and railroad bridge areas, pedestrian overpasses, roadsides, and abandoned school buildings are renovated to provide a pleasant atmosphere and are used as new leisure spaces by the local residents.

In addition to residence and work spaces, the emergence of a 3rd space as a leisure space is a relatively new trend. This place acts as a shelter where people can step out of their busy daily lives, socialize regularly, and generate new ideas. Cafés, bars, bookstores, conference rooms, and restrooms fall into this category.

7.3.2 Tourism Attractions

Every year, about 200 new sites are designated and maintained by the state as tourism attractions. There were 194 in 2000, which increased to 222 by 2007. As of August 2007, there are 40 state-designated tourism attractions in Gangwon-*do*, followed by 28 in Gyeongsangbuk-*do*, 25 in Chungcheongnam-*do*, 24 in Jeollanam-*do*, 23 in Jeollabuk-*do*, 22 in Gyeongsangnam-*do*, 21 in Chungcheongbuk-*do*, 19 in Jeju Special Self-Governing Province, 14 in Gyeonggi-*do*, 4 in Busan, and 2 in Incheon. In addition to these, there have been a variety of development projects linked with different policies, such as the designated cultural zone, special tourist zone, and livable community.

Tourist areas have been going through specialty development processes since the 1990s. The designated cultural zone was introduced in 1993 by the state, and they started to support development of specific areas such as historic and cultural resources, tourism resources, scenic resources, specialty industries, and special areas. The result was the designation and promotion of regions including Baekje Cultural Zone (1993), Naepo Cultural Zone (2004), and Yeongsan River Cultural Zone (2005).

The special tourist zone system was introduced in 1994 to attract tourists. The concept of this system was generated from the concept of the Free Trade District where economic activities are allowed without any constraints within a certain region. Special tourist zones are allowed to have unrestricted tourism businesses within the designated area. In 1994, Seoraksan, Yuseong, Gyeongju, Haeundae, and Jeju Island were designated as special tourist zones, and 14 other zones including Itaewon, Dongducheon, Suanbo Hot Springs, Boryeong Beach, Mujugucheondong, and Bugok Hot Springs were designated in 1997. As of 2006, 5 other areas such as Myeong-dong, Wolmi-*do*, and Danyang were added to the list, and there were 24 special tourist zones.

Tourist attractions are also developed as a way to make an area a habitable or livable community This new idea was introduced in 2006 to make neighborhoods more likely to be visited by tourists and invested in by corporations through renovation of the neighborhood communities to make these neighborhoods preferable places to live. This project, connected with the destination marketing strategies of the local government, is focusing on developing region-specific tourism brands and products. As of 2007, there are 30 designated livable cities and guns around the country.

7.3.3 Tourism Resources and Programs

Tourism resources can be roughly categorized into cultural, natural, and ecological attractions and facility resources. As of 2007, there are about 47,000 tourism resources around the country, of which 60% are cultural resources followed by 30% tourism attractions and facility resources, and 10% natural and ecological resources (Table 7.3). About 14% of them (6,500) are located in Jeollanam-*do*, followed by Gyeongsangbuk-*do*, Gyeongsangnam-*do*, Gyeonggi-*do*, Gangwon-*do*, Chungcheongnam-*do*, Chungcheongbuk-*do*, Seoul, Jeollabuk-*do*, Jeju Special Self-Governing Province, Incheon, Daegu, Daejeon, Gwangju, and Ulsan, in descending order. Regionally, about 31% are located in the Yeongnamregion, followed by 21% in the capital region, 20% in the Honam region, 17% in the Chungcheong region, 8% in the Gangwon-*do*, and 3% in the Jeju Self-Governing Province.

New types of tourism products and programs are also constantly being developed. One of them is film tourism, which connects the film industry with tourism by making film studios and filming locations into tourism attractions. Film studios or locations then become famous tourism attractions, or the region itself becomes the center of media culture by holding film

Table 7.3 **National tourism resources by type (2007)**

(Unit : Frequency).

		Seoul	Pusan	Dagu	Incheon	Gwangju	Daejeon	Ulsan	Gyeonggi-do	Gangwon-do	Chungcheongbuk-do	Chungcheongnam-do	Jeollabuk-do	Jeollanam-do	Gyeongsangbuk-do	Gyeongsangnam-do	Jeju Self-Governing Province	Total
Cultural Resources	Person	385	147	97	95	52	120	15	955	253	505	403	187	492	576	490	30	4,802
	Festival/Ceremony	90	109	26	31	10	46	19	207	202	86	230	92	329	137	214	58	1,886
	Tradition/Custom	196	124	88	79	77	75	57	484	809	475	790	155	649	701	1,299	74	6,132
	Village	15	2	4	1	0	0	0	6	3	10	3	2	5	28	7	0	86
	Archeological / Historic Site	212	61	61	85	28	27	33	386	195	245	327	149	1,452	374	469	282	4,386
	Architecture	412	248	229	173	103	132	61	693	393	760	683	484	1,121	1,774	1,242	95	8,603
	Sculpture	77	30	56	31	18	23	18	240	169	202	250	133	395	400	211	44	2,297
	Paintings/Calligraphy	39	14	10	30	5	6	1	36	22	20	21	17	86	54	28	0	389
	Book/Type/Equipment	55	11	9	7	12	21	2	46	27	3	46	27	160	95	105	3	629
	Crafts/Ceramics	62	11	5	9	5	6	4	29	12	5	26	27	26	42	30	5	304
	Subtotal	1,543	757	585	541	310	456	210	3,082	2,085	2,311	2,779	1,273	4,715	4,181	4,095	594	29,514
Environmental and Ecological Resources	Flora/Fauna	16	13	6	8	2	0	1	42	53	22	25	40	87	59	81	55	510
	Protected Area	4	3	0	0	0	0	2	2	6	0	2	4	5	1	4	7	40
	Mountain/Plain	173	101	39	39	17	12	45	368	279	185	154	115	229	232	285	137	2,410
	Waterfront/ Coastal Resource	27	53	15	60	11	9	15	189	129	71	81	76	244	181	143	42	1,346
	Scenic Spot	14	21	3	9	1	3	2	20	42	24	52	53	76	22	32	20	394
	Subtotal	234	191	63	116	31	24	65	621	509	302	314	288	641	495	545	261	4,700
Tourism Attractions and Facilities	Special Tourist Zone	3	3	0	9	0	1	0	17	45	25	26	21	23	35	27	21	256
	Park	74	23	21	11	11	14	5	61	29	21	11	37	44	40	79	15	496
	Exhibition/Exposition Facility	334	137	51	63	50	81	19	301	178	107	129	122	167	181	191	59	2,170
	Sports/Physical Activities Facility	125	36	29	53	10	22	18	406	182	94	112	51	110	123	140	76	1,587
	Accommodation/ Restaurants	521	265	57	126	114	46	38	632	364	160	194	120	346	431	242	83	3,739
	Shopping	138	119	52	41	32	31	12	169	105	89	70	116	143	237	191	30	1,575
	Transportation	113	73	31	28	6	12	21	162	127	53	65	61	105	157	110	24	1,155
	Amusement/Recreation/ Training Facilities	36	49	31	69	13	18	14	182	365	105	143	114	229	204	192	84	1,842
	Supplementary Facilities	83	42	18	20	11	13	10	56	27	19	21	25	42	40	29	7	463
	Subtotal	1,427	747	290	420	247	238	137	1986	1422	679	771	667	1,203	1,449	1,201	399	13,283
Grand Total		3,204	1,695	938	1,077	588	718	412	5,689	4,016	3,292	3,864	2,228	6,559	6,125	5,841	1,251	47,497

(Source : www.tour.go.kr)

festivals or sites related to the film industry (Ko, 2004). Local governments' and travel agencies' interest in the development of film tourism resources is increasing as Korean films and TV series are receiving public interest in many different countries.

New tourism products connected with the transportation industry are also developing. Examples include train travel products associated with KTX and the Citytour Bus Program. KTX service has been provided since 2004, and KORAIL has developed a variety of themed train travel packages since then. These include travel to cities, islands, beaches, mountains, valleys, rivers, tea gardens, traditional market places, festivals, hot springs, and trips to watch snow blossoms in Taebaeksan or the sunrise in Jeongdongjin. They recently started to operate trains around a new concept called the ladybird train, where passengers can enjoy a variety of events and group activities while moving on the train.

More recently, tourism belts have been created around the eastern, western, and southern coastal regions, and Yeosu Expo is going to be held in 2012, which is the first oceanic expo. These belts and events have brought about the development of a variety of coastal tourism products such as cruise and island tours. In addition, lifestyle tourism has been gaining attention with the perception that "livable communities are good tourist attractions." Regions known for natural disasters are also being developed as dark tourism attractions. Truly, it seems that the blue-ocean era of tourism products is on the rise.

7.3.4 Local Festivals

Except for some old traditional festivals, the majority of Korean festivals have begun since the 1950s. The number of festivals grew gradually until the 1980s, and it has doubled every 5 years since the 1990s. Sixty-four percent of the total festivals were created between 1996 and 2005, and the number of local festivals grew at an enormous rate in the last decade because of the implementation of local self-governing systems since the middle of 1990. The local governments began to use festivals as a way to enhance their destination image and to promote the area to attract tourists. Since state-designation of cultural tourism festivals began in 1996, the development of event tourism resources has also grown and been reinforced. The distinctive periods for the development of cultural tourism festivals can be divided into the introduction (1996-1998), growth (1999-2002), and mature stages (2003-present).

In 1995, the per capita income exceeded USD 10,000, and there were exploratory attempts to market the Icheon Ceramic Festival and the Great Battle of Hansan Festival as tourism products. As the Icheon Ceramic Festival experienced great success, they realized that the destination image could be enhanced and the local economy could be revitalized through local festivals. Impressed with the result, the government decided to formally support cultural festivals for tourism beginning in 1996. The Ministry of Culture, Sports, and Tourism chose a total of eight festivals as cultural tourism festivals. Among them, the Icheon Ceramic Festival, Andong Mask Dance Festival, and Gangjin Celadon Festival were selected and later on were awarded "the greatest" festivals title in 1997. In 1998, many famous festivals such as the Boryeong Mud Festival, Nangye Traditional Korean Music Festival, Hansanmosi Cultural Festival, and Yangyang Songi Mushroom Festival appeared in the tourism market. In 1999, the government began systematic evaluation of festivals to guarantee desirable development of cultural festivals as a tourism resource, make fair the selection process, and induce well-intentioned competitiveness among the festivals.

The growth period was led by the Icheon Ceramic Festival. With initial success in attracting attendees, it grew into the World Ceramic Exposition in 2001 (co-hosted with Yeoju and Gwangju), and then into the World Ceramic Biennale. This was the first example of co-hosting a festival through community collaboration. Other fast growing festivals include the Geumsan Insam Festival and Andong Mask Dance Festival. These festivals show cased cultural and economic success, and also made people realize that cultural festivals work as a great means to revitalize a stagnant local economy. Therefore, to industrialize festivals, the government increased designation of festivals every year from 8 in 1996 to 21 in 1999, 25 in 2000, 30 in 2001, and 29 in 2002. A few examples include the Gimje Jipyeongseon Festival, Muju Firefly Festival, Cheongdo Bullfighting Festival, Hadong Wild Tea Cultural Festival, Chuncheon International Mime Festival, and Ganggyeong Fermented Seafood Festival.

Unconventional and innovative festivals were beginning to be developed during the mature period. These include the Silla Cultural Festival and Baekje Cultural Festival. In addition to these, the Jinju Gaecheon Art Festival, which is one of the 3 largest cultural festivals in Korea, changed its name to the Namgang Yudeung Festival and expanded its historic lantern theme to make it a genuine cultural tourism festival. This earned it the title of "the greatest" festival by the Ministry of Culture, Sports, and Tourism in 2006, though it was merely a "preliminary" festival in 2003. Sancheoneo Ice Festival, held in Hwacheon-*gun*, Gangwon-*do*, was also a small-scale Nangcheon Ice Festival that was enjoyed by only the specific market of interested parties. It has now evolved into a successful tourism festival, and there have been more than 1 million attendees with more than $40 billion in economic impact generated in the area since 2005 when it was selected as a "preliminary" festival. During the mature period, government officials in charge of festival planning were highly encouraged to take field trips to other famous festivals all over the world and to participate in workshops to which expert festival

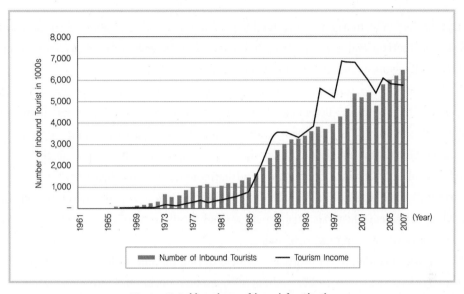

Figure 7.6 **Number of local festivals**
(Units : %, Number of Festivals)
(Source : Ministry of Culture and Tourism, 2007, Changes in and Accomplishments of Cultural Tourism Festivals).

executives were invited. This helped them to gather new ideas to innovate and substantiate their own festivals. Since the middle of 2000, government support policies also changed from a quantity expansion strategy to a quality improvement strategy by ranking the cultural festivals as "preliminary," "promising," "great," or "greatest" festivals, and financially supporting them according to their title. In 2008, they developed distinctive evaluation indices for each type of festival, and established the Korean "signature" festival category. The Andong Mask Dance Festival and Boryeong Mud Festival were the first 2 festivals selected as "signature" festivals, through which they strive to globalize Korean festivals. As of 2008, there were a total of 56 cultural festivals designated by the Ministry of Culture, Sports, and Tourism. These include 2 "signature," 7 "greatest," 9 "great," 18 "promising," and 20 "preliminary" festivals.

As of 2006, there are a total of 1,176 local festivals in Korea (Korea Culture and Tourism Policy Institute, 2006). Of them, 152 festivals are held in Gyeonggi-*do* (12.9%), followed by 124 in Gangwon-*do* (10.5%), 109 in Gyeongsangnam-*do* (9.3%), 105 in Jeollanam-*do* (8.9%), 88 in Chungcheongnam-*do* (7.5%), 87 in Seoul (7.4%), and 83 in Busan (7.1%). There are only 19 festivals in Ulsan (1.3%) and 15 in Daejeon (1.3%) (Figure 7.6).

Depending on the theme, the largest number of festivals fall into the category of arts and cultural festivals (21.9%), followed by traditional folk festivals (17.2%), cultural tourism festivals(10.5%), and tourism and specialty products festivals (17.4%). If cultural tourism festivals and tourism and specialty products festivals are combined, the category comprises 27.9% of all festivals, which makes it the largest category of all.

In terms of the structure of the programs, most of them are experience-, exhibition-, performance-, and other supplementary activities-oriented programs. The goals are to enhance the sense of community among local residents, foster unity, harmony, and cooperation, and enhance the destination image to cultivate local tourism and industry development. Typically, the major goal is to enhance cooperation and harmony among the residents for the festivals that are small scale and have a high level of local residents' voluntary participation. On the other hand, large-scale festivals that are subsidized by the government tend to focus on the development of tourism and the local area.

The majority (41.4%) of the festivals are held during the fall, followed by spring (28.2%), summer (20.1%), and winter (9.7%). About 70% are held during the spring and fall, with 28% of them held in October, followed by April (12.5%), May (11.5%), and September (11%).

LEISURE AND TOURISM POLICY

7.4.1 Changes in the Leisure Policy

The leisure policy in Korea was starting to be established in the 1960s, and focused on tourism resource development. As excavation, maintenance, and management of cultural assets began in 1963, the National Museum of Korea, Gyeongju National Museum, the National Folk Museum of Korea, and the Folklore and Natural History Museum were built to preserve excavated assets. The Parks Law was proclaimed in 1967, and Jirisan was designated as the first national park in Korea, followed by Gyeongju and Gyeryongsan. Discussions were held on leisure and recreation facilities development as a way to enhance national welfare, and interest in the development of recreation areas for family and youth increased. Through the first and second Economic Development Plan, arrangements were made to develop libraries, broadcasting facilities, youth hostels, and tourism hotels.

There has been active government participation in the development of tourism resources since the 1970s. Large-scale tourism and recreation areas have been developed since 1974 to augment the citizens' right to lead a leisure lifestyle. The first of these areas include Gyeongju Bomun Lake Resort Complex (1974) and Jeju Jungmun Tourism Complex (1978). By 1971, the number of national parks increased to 7, and then to 14 by 1981. Since 1977, sites associated with national security have been developed for tourism. By 1981, 16 sites including Imjingak, Panmunjeom, and the first Infiltration Tunnel were developed as national security tourism sites. After 1982, 8 more national security sites including Kim Ilsung Cottage and Dora Observation Station were opened to the public. A comprehensive and long-term tourism development plan was established in 1978 focused on the development of day visit attractions surrounding urban areas, and many tourism-related programs were enforced, including simplification of the tourism hotels classification system and the opening of Tourist Complaint

Centers. Sex tourism and other pleasure-seeking types of tourism also prospered in association with international tourism. Since the late 1970s, damage to nature has accelerated with the development of tourism resources and rapid increase in the number of tourists and excursionists. Addressing the issue, the Nature Protection Charter was proclaimed in 1978, which triggered general interest in the natural resources and green spaces preservation movement.

The 1980s was the period when the focus was on the expansion of the fundamentals of the overall leisure lifestyle. The Ministry of Sports was inaugurated to enhance national awareness of leisure, and it totally revised the National Sports Advancement Law (1982). People's leisure activities further diversified with the removal of control measures for overseas travel in 1989. The focus of the leisure policy associated with the Second Comprehensive Land Development Plan (enforced since 1982) included expanded state designation of natural resources, development of recreation and entertainment areas and facilities, extended development of urban parks, and clarification and maintenance of cultural and historic tourism resources. In addition to these, the International Tourism Corporation was renamed the Korea National Tourism Corporation in 1982, and the National Comprehensive Long-term Tourism Development Plan was established in 1983, with a target to accomplish its goals by 2001. This plan emphasizes increased domestic tourism, active encouragement of participation in recreation activities, an increase in the number of tourists using scenic drives, quality improvement of lodging facilities, an increase in indoor leisure activities and long-term travel, diversification of honeymoon trips, and the development of leisure facilities for the increased number of overseas travelers. Leisure facilities development progressed with a focus on the development of nature parks, urban parks, and rural cities around the peripheries of urban areas. It was hoped that this could meet the increased demand for leisure spaces. The National Comprehensive Long-term Tourism Development Plan of 1989 presents a developmental scheme for tourism and entertainment facilities and resources to be accomplished by 2001. This involves guidelines for tourism development in the 1990s, including 1) establishment of development plans that take into consideration the area's function and unique characteristics, 2) establishment of development plans linked to nationwide development, 3) expansion of tourism infrastructure, 4) diversification of tourism resources and creation of new tourism products, 5) reinforcement of a support system for tourism attraction development and promotion, and 6) introduction of an effective maintenance and operation system.

It was necessary for the government to change its role in the 1990s to adapt to the new era of self-regulation, openness, globalization, and localization. The government established a long-term tourism promotion plan in 1992 (1992-2001) and set goals to accomplish richness in the leisure lifestyle and social equilibrium, and to promote Korea as a global tourism destination. To achieve this, they took a leading role in setting the direction of the tourism advancement policy as 1) re-establishment of perceptions on tourism, 2) active correspondence with the new trends of globalization, 3) localization and autonomy, 4) active accommodation of changes in the tourists' wants, 5) acceleration of international tourism promotion and reinforcement of international cooperation, 6) fostering of national tourism as a way to enhance welfare, and 7) enhancement of competitiveness of the tourism industry associated with market development. The tourism resorts development project that was first started in the 1970s to expand leisure and tourism resources was further expanded in the 1990s, and they introduced the special tourist zone system in 1993 to accelerate the attraction of tourists. Daejeon Expo was held in 1993 to attract 14 million native and foreign tourists, and a "Visit Korea" year was announced in 1994 to promote traditional culture and to launch a new stage in Korean tourism to prepare for globalization. In addition to these efforts, a global tourism promotional plan was established to prepare for the 21st century and to join advanced tourism countries through cultural development. To this end, they have set as their initial strategies unique Korean cultural tourism product development, international level convention industry development, balanced development and expansion of accommodation facilities, and local tourism resource development. In the first half of 1995, they also developed signature tourism itineraries as a part of a cultural tourism itinerary development project.

In the 2000s, a leisure policy was established focusing on the enhancement of quality of life of the citizens and balanced local development. As the tourism deficit increased, efforts were made to increase the number of domestic and inbound tourists. For this, Korea has included tourism as the major policy of local self-governing bodies, followed by initiation of Geumgangsan tourism (1998) based on the political and economic cooperation between South and North Korea after 2000. It was designated as the Geumgangsan Tourism Special District in 2002, and a land route to Geumgangsan was developed in 2003. South and North Korean tourism programs were beginning to be developed as discussions started on the development of a land route for tourism in Gaeseong and the opening of Pyeongyang to general group tourists. Lastly, a leisure policy for the population in need was stimulated as it is now considered crucial to the enhancement of the nation's quality of life.

7.4.2 Changes in the Tourism Policy

A tourism policy was first introduced between the 1950s and 1960s in Korea. The central government-led tourism development policy was developed in 1954 when the Department of Tourism was established within the Ministry of Transportation. It was not until the 1960s when full-scale tourism-related laws, ordinances, and organizations were composed in Korea. Tourism infrastructure was beginning to be developed to earn foreign exchange, and organizations such as the International Tourism Corporation (currently the Korea Tourism Organization), the Korea Tourism Association, the Tourism Policy Review Committee, and the Korean Air Company were established as the Tourism Promotion Act was enacted in 1961. The national parks system began in 1967, and Korean Air was privatized in 1969. These efforts during the 1960s, however, were not executed systematically based on the policy.

The goal of the 1970s was promotion of international tourism and acquisition of foreign exchange. Tourism was included in the Economic Development Plan and was promoted as the nation's major strategic industry. A legal system was also set regarding tourism development. For example, 10major tourism regions were selected as the first Comprehensive Land Development Plan (1972) started, and the General Law on Tourism was enacted in 1975. The concept of a tourism region that was different from the existing administrative regions (comprised of 8 extensive regions and 24 smaller development regions) was introduced in 1978, and the number of inbound tourists hit 1 million. Tax support for tourist hotels ignited a hotel construction boom around the country.

The 1980s were characterized as the period of reduction in the existing tourism organizations with the establishment of the 5th Republican government that was indifferent to tourism. Nonetheless, tourism attractions were re-organized, intangible cultural assets were developed as tourism products, and interest in and plans for tourism was reflected in the second Comprehensive Land Development Plan (1982). Enhancement of people's quality of life was perceived as the goal of tourism development in this period, and potential for successful tourism industry development was confirmed with the fruitful holding of the Asian Games (1986) and the Olympic Games (1988). With overseas travel restrictions gone (1989), openness to the global tourism market and the enhancement of people's quality of life became the major goals of the tourism policy.

All tourism-related tasks were transferred to the Ministry of Culture and Sports in 1994. The General Tourism Development Plan and the Region Specific Tourism Development Plan were established as official governmental plans, and restrictions on the tourism industry were relaxed. With this came the inclusion of the casino industry (1944) and the amusement facilities industry (1998) in the tourism business realm. Environmental protection and local resident participation rose as important issues of tourism development in the latter part of the 1990s, which changed the existing tourism development policy. Later in 1998, the Ministry was renamed the Ministry of Culture and Tourism, and many other Ministries also actively supported different types of tourism businesses such as ecotourism (Ministry of Environment), rural tourism (Ministry of Food, Agriculture, Forestry, and Fisheries), and coastal tourism (Ministry of Land, Transport, and Maritime Affairs).

With the start of a new Administration that puts importance on citizen participation (2003), the contents of tourism policies diversified with the focus on balanced regional development. With the start of President Lee's Administration(2008), policies became rather practical to achieve competitiveness through advancement of the tourism industry.

These changes show that the goals of the tourism policy are changing from promotion of international tourism for foreign exchange earning to the balanced development of international and domestic tourism. The main body that led this development changed from the central government to private parties, showing the decentralization process. Facilities development had been focused on the quantity expansion, integration, and complex concept, but changed to an emphasis on quality improvement, specialization, diversification, and localization. Resource development had been centered around a point-based development and hardware emphasis, but changed to a networking and software emphasis.

7.4.3 Major Tourism Plans and Strategies After 2000

1) 10-year plan for tourism promotion (1996-2005)

The goals of this 10-year plan was to reach an overall national tourism volume of 530 million, including 8 million inbound tourists and 7.5 million outbound tourists, and tourism income of $20 billion ($5 billion of tourism surplus) by 2005. The plan also aimed to reflect globalization, localization, privatization, and information orientation in its tourism promotion strategies. The Korean government generated measures to accomplish these objectives, which include creating a tourism environment to improve quality of life, strengthening international competitiveness of the tourism industry, creating a substantial tourism industry, and prompting South and North Korean tourism exchange.

CHAPTER 7

2) Tourism Vision 21 (1999-2003)

Tourism Vision 21 was developed to establish Korea as the major tourism country of the world. The vision of this policy is to make Korea the nucleus of Northeastern Asian tourism, adestination that has high potential for receiving outside investment, a cultural tourism destination through national cooperation, a place where free and creative competition are enabled, and a destination that actively encourages private investment. The goal of this policy is to increase inbound tourists to 7 million, decrease outbound tourists to 4.5 million, and increase tourism income to $12 billion ($7 billion of tourism surplus). The government also kept the existing 10-year tourism promotion plan to develop a new plan to adapt to the social changes such as the IMF financial crisis. To this end, they came up with 8strategies to overcome economic hardships through tourism promotion. These include 1) development of international level traditional Korean tourism resources, 2) development of unique tourism products, 3) establishment of a competitive tourism infrastructure, 4) development of systematic tourism promotional activities, 5) advancement of a tourism reception system, 6) successful holding of millennium tourism events, 7) realization of a national lifestyle tourism, and finally, 8) international cooperation and expansion of South and North Korean tourism exchange.

3) The second tourism development general plan (2002-2011)

The goal of this plan is to "develop Korea as the focal point of world tourism that leads the 21st century." The agenda centers around the concept of "Tourism Korea," which aims to be attractive to stand up to competition, sustainable to realize harmony between development and preservation, information-based to augment the value of tourism resources, citizen participation-oriented to contribute to the improvement of the overall quality of life, and wide open to open up a peaceful era on the Korean Peninsula. Specifically, it aims to reach 8.78 million inbound tourists, with a policy goal of reaching 10.5 million by 2011. To reach this goal, they have adopted along-term plan that presents future tourism development, a tourism development general plan that covers the entire country, and a detailed general plan that can guide regional tourism development. In addition to this, they have also developed 7 separate strategies : 1) encouragement of tourism facilities' development to improve international competitiveness, 2) development of tourism through localization and regional networking, 3) systematic development of cultural resources for tourism, 4) sustainable development and a strengthened maintenance scheme for tourism resources, 5) development of information-based tourism and its management system, 6) development of tourism for the enhancement of people's tourism lifestyle, and 7) formation of a tourism cooperation system between South and North Korea, and among Northeastern Asian countries.

4) 5-year plan for tourism promotion (2004-2008)

This plan is enforced to make a creative and attractive "Tourism Korea." It was planned with a goal of reaching an inbound tourist demand of 6.44 million people, a policy goal demand of 10 million people, an overall domestic tourism volume of 650 million people, and a tourism income goal of $10 billion by 2008. Four strategies were set to increase policy synergy by linking culture and tourism, including 1) tourism that is absorbed into the everyday life, 2) tourism development that is harmonized with local development, 3) a solid tourism industry that is valuable, and 4) a "Tourism Korea" that attracts the global population.

5) Cultural vision : Strategic nurturing of the tourism industry (2004-2009)

This plan accompanies the 5-year Plan for Tourism Promotion to transform Korea into an attractive and creative tourism destination. The main points of this plan are to increase the number of inbound tourists, substantiate the tourism industry, and encourage national tourism. Six policy goals and 16 detailed strategies were set to strengthen the basis of domestic tourism, to balance and diversify different regions, to improve the quality of tourism, and to support self-empowerment. These goals include 1) securing competitiveness through quality improvement of tourism resources and tourism products, 2) innovating improvement of tourism business investment conditions, 3) inducing active local development through tourism, 4) intensifying the tourism industry as a new growth industry, 5) strengthening the foundations to amplify competitiveness of the tourism industry, and 6) advancing tourism policies through the empowerment of related bodies.

6)Policy for balanced local development : The happy city, the enterprise city, the innocity, and the hub city of culture

This was the main regional policy that President Roh's Administration stressed beginning in 2003. It is still in progress and has been a great force that affects tourism. Some of the major projects include the happy city (multifunctional administrative city), the enterprise city,

CHAPTER 7

the innocity (innovation city), and the hub city of culture.

The happy city project is led by the government to create multifunctional and self-sufficient cities. The focus of the city is its administrative function, but educational, cultural, and welfare functions are also stressed. Gongju-si and Yeongi-*gun* in Chungcheongnam-*do* was selected as the first candidate city and is now being developed as such.

The enterprise city project is led by the private sector to host multifunctional and self-sufficient cities that have economic (industry, research, and tourism) as well as residential (housing, medical, educational, and cultural) functions. There are 4 types of enterprise cities, including knowledge-based (Wonju, Cheongju), tourism/leisure-based (Yeongam, Haenam, Muju, Taean), industry/trade-based (Muan), and innovative hub-based.

The innocity (innovation city) is a public-sector-led project that began with the moving of 175 public institutions from the capital area to the provinces. The aim of the project is to create futuristic cities through the cooperation of industry, academia, research institutes, and the government to generate new growth power. There are 10 innocities selected so far.

The hub city of culture originated with President Roh's 2002 pledge to make Gwangju a cultural capital. Following the designation of Gwangju as the Hub City of Asian Culture in 2002, the Hub City of Media Culture (Busan), the Hub City of History and Culture (Gyeongju), and the Hub City of Traditional Culture (Jeonju) are expected to be designated in the future. The Gwangju Asian Culture Hub City project will continue development until 2023, and its major goals are to construct and operate the Asia Culture Complex, to create an urban cultural environment, to promote arts, culture, and the tourism industry, and to strengthen its capacity as a city of cultural exchange.

7) Policy for highly imaginative and creative cultural tourism

The Creative Cultural Tourism Policy, which aims to strengthen competitiveness through advancement of the tourism industry, was developed with the beginning of President Lee's Administration in 2008. It is based on practicality (industrialization, integration, and connectivity) and creativity. The Policy includes tax reduction and the easing of regulations, the building of a high-profit industry structure through the development of specialized cultural products, enforcement of strategic marketing practices, tourism development in metropolitan cities, creation of custom-made tourism, encouragement of domestic tourism, and establishment of public-private sector partnerships.

Tax reduction and the easing of tax regulations is associated with the relaxation of regulations related to the tourism industry and the provision of tax support. Major goals include 1) elevation of price competitiveness and encouragement of investment by supporting the tourism industry, 2) easing of restrictions on tourism development such as relaxation of regulations for siting of large scale tourism facilities, 3) simplification of the administrative process for tourism development, 4) extension and encouragement of private sector investments in the tourism industry, and 5) extended allowance of multiple-entry visas for Chinese tourists.

A high-profit industry structure can be achieved through the development of specialized cultural tourism products. The structure includes 1) development of the MICE (Meeting, Incentive, Convention, Exhibit) industry, 2) development of tourism products that incorporate traditional Korean values and culture (tourism products that highlight characteristics of the nation's psychological culture, such as unique taste, enthusiasm, and passion ; products that utilize traditional culture, regional characteristics, and cultural characteristics), 3) high-end tourism product development that has strong Korean characteristics (the Cheonri-gil project, which is a cultural eco-adventure with a story), and 4) development of new high-value added products such as theme parks and coastal leisure and sports.

Enforcement of strategic marketing practices focuses on marketing towards target markets. Specifically, such marketing aims to reach Chinese (attracting 3 million tourists by 2012) and Japanese (attracting 2 million tourists by 2012) markets. For the Chinese market, the goal is to develop new rural tourism (by developing specialized products for the middle class, a dining menu they prefer, and expansion of specialized restaurants), medical tourism, and food tourism. For the Japanese market, the goal is to develop cultural tourism (through specialized products that draw on culture, the 4 seasons, and tastes, specifically targeting the Dankai generation), urban tourism, nature tourism, and food tourism.

Tourism development in metropolitan cities is focused on stimulating linked regional development, which aims to raise the competitiveness of the metropolitan economy through tourism development of metropolitan areas such as the Eastern, Western, and Southern coastal regions, and Jirisan region. Specifically, the tourism belt located on the southern coast (the Sun Belt) is going to be developed as an international level tourism cluster through the Yeosu World Expo, and private-sector-led tourism development, such as the development of leisure- and tourism-based business cities, is being encouraged.

The core of the custom-made tourism strategy is building attitudes that meet specific needs of foreign tourists. The strategies include 1) providing heightened hospitality towards foreign tourists for their entire travel in Korea, including the entry/exit process, things to see and eat, accommodations, transportation, information centers, and other services, 2) expansion of low-cost and diverse tourism accommodation facilities (a designation system for hotels,

CHAPTER 7

development of mid- to low-cost accommodation brands, expansion of mid- to low-cost hotels utilizing old commercial buildings), 3) construction of advanced information systems (such as establishment of a tourism information and communication system [I-net], production of walking tour maps, standardization of tourism information signage, and introduction of advanced technology in information service), 4) improvement in airline connectivity and food services, and 5) expansion of large-scale tourism resources that are family-, overnight stay-, and general recreation-oriented.

The main focus for encouragement of domestic tourism is on developing programs to convert the demand for overseas tourism to a domestic tourism demand. Some of the major strategic development projects include the Guseokguseok Campaign to actively promote the hidden treasures of Korea, improvement of the tourism culture through avacation dispersion system, expansion of welfare tourism (social tourism) for those in need, and the recently emerging high-value-added tourism-related industries (medical tourism, convention tourism, cruise tourism, golf tourism, and theme parks).

Finally, the private-public partnership focuses on the development of an effective partnership system. It aims to convert the current government-led tourism promotional system to a private-sector-led system. They expect to establish local self-governing bodies and neighborhood-level Pulbburi CVBs (Convention and Visitors' Bureaus), and to encourage public participation in the decision-making process for tourism promotion and the distribution of development funds.

7.4.4 Future Directions for a Leisure and Tourism Policy

Leisure trends are constantly changing. Some of these changes include pursuit of a balanced life (with balance between work and leisure), evolution of the media environment, increased opportunities for diverse leisure experiences, increase in social leisure activities, the leisure isolation phenomenon between social classes and the emergence of the leisure postponement phenomenon, and education- and socialization-oriented leisure throughout people's lifespan. These will lead the society into the mature stage of a mass leisure society : a one-leisure activity per person society, an era of national leisure and tourism, and a society where experiential leisure is considered important. Therefore, a future leisure policy should be directed toward constructing a policy system that corresponds to the movement toward a mass leisure society, and toward constructing the basis for the society to enter a happy leisure society. To this end, it should strive to 1) improve leisure policy organizations and develop a systematic support scheme, 2) promote a leisure industry development policy, 3) develop leisure spaces and facilities programs, 4) train experts and provide quality information, and 5) enhance social perceptions on leisure (Kim and Yoon, 2007).

There have been many challenges and problems with the tourism policy, including 1) duplications in tourism development projects and lack of control by the government, 2) lack of differentiation in tourism resource development and insufficient tourism opportunities and resources, 3) lack of discussions about and unpreparedness for negative impacts from large-scale tourism development, and 4) lack of understanding of sustainable tourism development and lack of expertise and experience in it. Therefore, future tourism policies should focus on taking a mid-term to long-term approach, developing pluralistic creative tourism that adjusts to the new paradigm shift, establishing a neo-tourism policy system, improving conditions for domestic tourism, strengthening the policy for silver tourism, reinforcing the tourism policy and its administration, and developing a tourism policy between both Koreas for their future peaceful unification (Baek, 2007).

Chapter 8.
EDUCATION, WELFARE AND POLITICS

EDUCATION

8.1.1 Educational Environment and Facilities

1) Educational environment

Since the industrialization of the 20th century, Korean education and student population have grown explosively. As a result of the increased population, major city areas, including Seoul and Busan, led almost all of the quantitative growth. It is remarkable that most of the rural areas experienced decreased numbers of students and school staff and the degradation of education quality, while urban schools struggled with a lack of teaching staff and classroom congestion due to the population explosion among elementary and middle school students. This contrast was caused by accelerating urbanization.

The most conspicuous feature in Korean education since the 1980s has been the concentration of school-age children in the capital region. In 2005, the capital region had 44.5% of the country's preschoolers, 47.7% of its elementary students, 47.9% of its middle school students, and 46.7% of its high school students. The population in higher education has been increasing as well. In 2005, the capital region had 38.9% of the country's 4-year colleges and 38.0% of its college students. The concentration of student populations paralleled the total population of Korea. In 1985, the population of the capital region was 39.1% of the entire population ; in 1990, it was 42.8% ; in 1995, 45.3% ; in 2000, 46.3% ; and in 2005, 48.2%.

During the 1990s, there was a significant change in the range and total number of students in the capital region (Table 8.1 and Table 8.2). While the number of students, schools, and school staff continuously increased in the entire area, the number of elementary schools decreased in Seoul, the core city of the capital region. As a result, Gyeonggi-*do* leads the country in student population growth in the 2000s. The change around the capital region was correlated with the stages of urbanization in Korea since the 1990s. Seoul was so populated at that time because it was in the last stage of urbanization. This situation induced dispersed urbanization and suburbanization in the capital region, such as U-turn migration (the return of people who once left the area) or J-turn migration (the outflow of people from one area of a country and inflow of people to another area of the country). This change of population distribution in the capital region resulting from the dispersions of population and employment also influenced the distribution of the education-related population.

The average monthly educational expenditure per household was 200,000 to 600,000 won in most Korean cities or provinces in 2005. The average monthly educational expenditure per student was 309,000 won in the same year, and the city of Seoul recorded the highest educational expenditure with 378,000 won per student. The bigger the population of a growth pole city in the non-the capital region is, the more expensive the educational expenditure per student per month.

The enrollment rate for each school level in Korea has grown at a rapid pace-a rarity in other countries (Figure 8.1). Throughout half a century of Korea's education history, the

Table 8.1 **Total and student population density in the Seoul National Capital Area (the capital region)** *(Unit : people, percentage)*

	Region	1985	1990	1995	2000	2005
Population	Nation	40,448,486 (100.0)	43,410,899 (100.0)	44,608,726 (100.0)	46,136,101 (100.0)	47,278,951 (100.0)
	Seoul	9,639,110 (23.8)	10,612,577 (24.4)	10,231,217 (22.9)	9,895,217 (21.4)	9,820,171 (20.8)
	Incheon	1,386,911 (3.4)	1,817,919 (4.2)	2,308,188 (5.2)	2,475,139 (5.4)	2,531,280 (5.4)
	Gyeonggi-*do*	4,794,135 (11.9)	6,155,632 (14.2)	7,649,741 (17.1)	8,984,134 (19.5)	10,415,399 (22.0)
	Capital Region	15,820,156 (39.1)	18,586,128 (42.8)	20,189,146 (45.3)	21,354,490 (46.3)	22,766,850 (48.2)
Student Population	Nation	11,038,303 (100.0)	10,882,775 (100.0)	10,261,891 (100.0)	10,162,659 (100.0)	10,197,643 (100.0)
	Seoul	2,581,570 (23.4)	2,653,329 (24.4)	2,346,881 (22.9)	2,105,400 (20.7)	1,975,248 (19.4)
	Incheon	333,245 (3.0)	412,840 (3.8)	491,857 (4.8)	521,094 (5.1)	514,628 (5.0)
	Gyeonggi-*do*	1,070,658 (9.7)	1,304,353 (12.0)	1,578,781 (15.4)	1,899,426 (18.7)	2,165,152 (21.2)
	Capital Region	3,985,473 (36.1)	4,370,522 (40.2)	4,417,519 (43.0)	4,525,920 (44.5)	4,655,028 (45.6)

(Source : National Geographic Information Institute)

Table 8.2 **Trends in the numbers of preschool students, schools, and teachers**

(Unit : people, schools)

	1985			1990			1995		
	Student	School	Teacher	Student	School	Teacher	Student	School	Teacher
The Capital Region	106,125	1,840	4,297	176,004	2,770	7715	231,550	3,104	10,514
Seoul	58,677	919	2,807	94,005	1,398	4,751	104,810	1,370	5,389
Incheon	8,172	100	321	17,373	206	585	28,520	317	1,058
Gyeonggi-*do*	39,276	821	1,169	64,626	1,166	2,379	98,220	1,417	4,067

	2000			2005		
	Student	School	Teacher	Student	School	Teacher
The Capital Region	234,975	3,088	11,487	240,969	2,997	13,155
Seoul	94,690	1,160	4,933	85,302	923	5,033
Incheon	26,811	324	1,201	26,136	313	1,369
Gyeonggi-*do*	113,474	1,604	5,353	129,531	1,761	6,753

(Source : Statistics Korea, Korean Statistical yearbook)

enrollment rate has been almost 100% for those who progress from elementary to the high school level. The elementary school enrollment rate was already higher than 90% in the 1980s. In 2005, the elementary, middle, and high school enrollment rate was almost 100% and the college enrollment rate reached 80%.

There was no regional or gender difference in the school enrollment rate. Gender equality

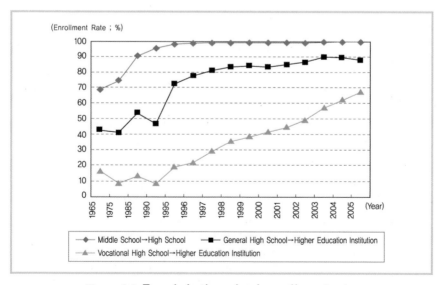

Figure 8.1 **Trends in the school enrollment rate.**

(Source : Korean education yearbook, 2006)

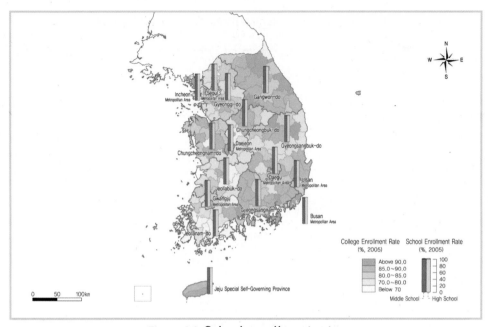

Figure 8.2 **School enrollment rate.**

(Source : The National Atlas of Korea. http://atlas.ngii.go.kr)

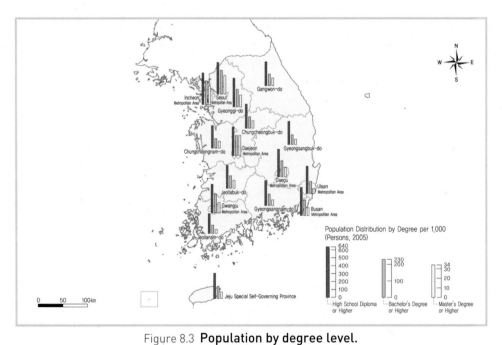

Figure 8.3 **Population by degree level.**

(Source : The National Atlas of Korea. http://atlas.ngii.go.kr)

in education was accomplished by 2005. Also, school enrollment rates showed equal distribution among major cities and provinces and between urban and rural areas within a province (Figure 8.2).

Population by degree level is one of the educational indices. Figure 8.3 shows a relatively even distribution of the population with high school diplomas across the country.

Generally, urban areas have slightly higher ratios of the population with a bachelor's degree than rural areas. Seoul records the highest ratio, which was 227.41 people per thousand. Meanwhile, Daejeon metropolitan area has the largest population with a master's degree or higher-34.12 people per thousand, followed by the city of Seoul with 31.33 people per thousand, with these 2 areas predominating over other areas in Korea.

2) Educational facilities

In the 2000s the Korean classroom environment and conditions of education significantly improved due to the Educational Environment Improvement Project, which included modernization of school facilities and the amendment of school and health regulations such as ventilation improvements inside school buildings.

The school space per student of K-12th grade in Seoul, other metropolitan cities, or urban areas of a province was smaller than in rural areas (Figure 8.4). The counties or cities that

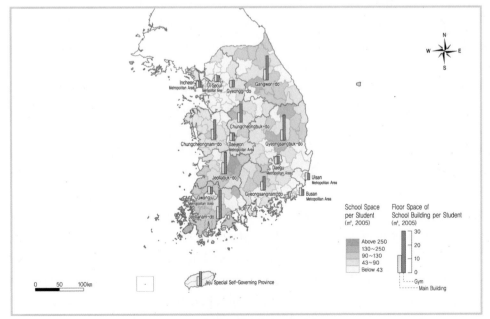

Figure 8.4 **Educational facilities** Ⅰ.
(Source : The National Atlas of Korea. http://atlas.ngii.go.kr)

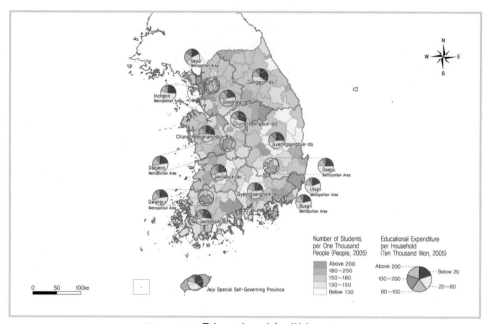

Figure 8.5 **Educational facilities** Ⅱ.
(Source : The National Atlas of Korea. http://atlas.ngii.go.kr)

were incorporated by 1995 and after had larger school space per student ; those not incorporated had smaller space. In summary, the school space per student showed a sharp contrast between urban and rural areas. This contrast was connected to the continuous decrease in numbers of students caused by low birth rates and an aging population in rural areas. The floor space of school buildings per student showed a similar pattern, in that urban schools were more crowded than rural schools.

The size of the library collection is often an indicator of educational support and environment. On average, there were 8.3 books per student in Korean elementary, middle, and high schools : elementary schools (9.6 books), middle schools (7.7 books), general high schools (8.3 books), and vocational high schools (9.1 books). The fact that these ratios were higher in counties than in metropolitan areas or cities was related to the recent reduction in the number of students in rural areas.

The number of computers per student, a critical index for instructional technology (IT) advancement in education, has reached global standards with rapid growth of the IT industry in Korea and the recent considerable investment in such technologies. The number of students per computer has been drastically reduced within a short period of time. In 1991, the number of elementary students per computer was 54.8, but it became 7.2 in 2005. In the same period, the number of middle school students per computer changed from 65.7 to 6.1, and the number of high school students per computer changed from103.5 to 5.6. But this number fell by 2.1 for vocational high school students (Figure 8.5).

8.1.2 Regional Characteristics

1) Regional tendency of education-related indicators

There are a variety of indices used to understand the characteristics of regional education. The ones most frequently referred to are the number of students per thousand people, the number of students per teacher, the number of students per class, and the number of public educational officers per thousand people.

First, in 2005, the number of students per one thousand people was 44.1 : the number of preschoolers per one thousand was 11.5, primary school students per one thousand was 85.1, and middle and high school students per one thousand was 42.5 and 37.3, respectively. The regional distribution of the student population is shown in Figure 8.6. The regions having more than 200 students per one thousand people were Seoul, the metropolitans of Daegu, Gwangju, Daejeon, and Ulsan, and the cities of Suwon, Anyang, Ansan, Goyang, Gwacheon, and Guri in

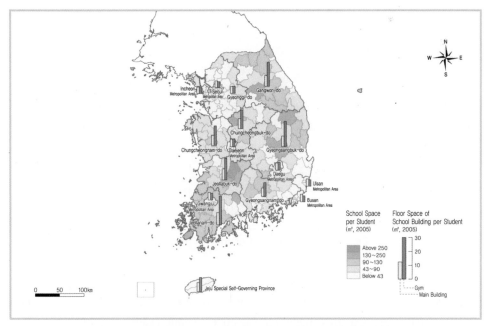

Figure 8.6 **Number of students per one thousand people and educational expenditure per household.**
(*Source : The National Atlas of Korea. http://atlas.ngii.go.kr*)

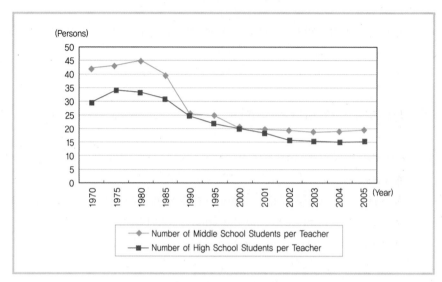

Figure 8.7 **Trends in number of students per teacher**

(Source : Korea education yearbook, 2006)

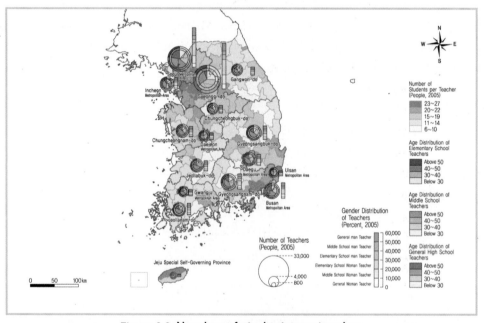

Figure 8.8 **Number of students per teacher**

(Source : The National Atlas of Korea. http://atlas.ngii.go.kr)

Gyeonggi-*do*. Figure 8.6 indicates the student population was concentrated in the capital region and other major metropolitan areas including Daegu, Gwangju, Daejeon, and Ulsan.

Second, the number of students per teacher was very high in the 1980s, but decreased rapidly during the 1990s. In particular, the number of high school students per teacher decreased continuously and the quality of education improved. In 2005, the number drastically decreased to 17.5 students per teacher in preschools, 25.1 in elementary schools, 19.4 in middle schools, and 15.1 in high schools. This decreasing pattern is not only because of the decrease in student population by low birth rate in the 2000s, but also because of the Educational Environment Improvement Project, which including increasing the number of teachers, thereby resolving classroom congestion (Figure 8.7).

The regional distribution of the number of students per teacher in Figure 8.8 shows similar patterns between general and student population distribution. In the major cities except Busan, in which student emigration was frequent, the number of students per teacher was around 20 (Figure 8.8). The number was specifically high in the capital region, while the local cities in Chungcheongnam-*do*, Jeollabuk-*do*, Jeollanam-*do*, Gyeongsangbuk-*do*, and mountainous regions decreased. The significant decrease of student population in those regions was due to the multiple factors of an aging population, low birth rate, and emigration from rural areas to cities.

Meanwhile, student migration, both immigration and emigration, was overwhelming in the city of Seoul and its surrounding area. The metropolitan cities of Busan and Ulsan had huge student emigration and Incheon and Gwangju had more emigration than immigration, whereas Daejeon and Daegu had patterns similar to those of Seoul (Figure 8.9). Education in Korea was still concentrated in Seoul, which explains the huge immigration of the student population

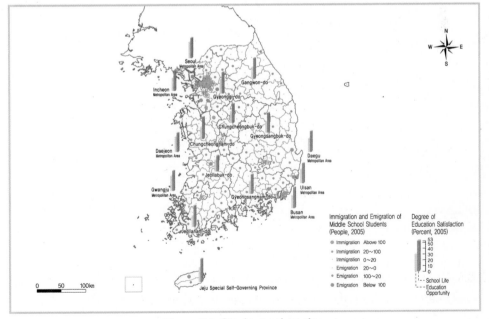

Figure 8.9 **Student migration.**
(Source : The National Atlas of Korea. http://atlas.ngii.go.kr)

to Seoul. For the same reason, some metropolitan cities have more emigration than immigration in their student population. Metropolitan Incheon lost students because of its proximity to Seoul. The excessive emigration from metropolitan Ulsan was explained by its relatively poor quality of educational conditions.

Third, the number of students per class showed a similar pattern to the number of students per teacher. In particular, in 2002, which was the first year of implementation of the 7th revised national curriculum, the 9th grade classrooms were required to have fewer than 35 students (Table 8.3). The range of the number of students per class in elementary schools was 24 to 37 ; in middle schools, 29to 40 ; and in high schools, 28 to 34.

Lastly, the number of government officers in education per thousand students, which shows the degree of support for education services, was generally lower in large cities than in counties (Figure 8.10). Even within a province, urban areas had fewer government officers in education per thousand students than in rural areas. It could be assumed that the government officers in urban areas have a heavier workload than in rural areas. Gangwon-*do*, Jeollanam-*do*, Jeollabuk-*do*, and Gyeongsangnam-*do* had an equal distribution of government officers,

Table 8.3 **Trends in number of students per class**

	1985				1990				1995				2000				2005			
	Kindergarten	Primary	middle school	High school	Kindergarten	Primary	middle school	High school	Kindergarten	Primary	middle school	High school	Kindergarten	Primary	middle school	High school	Kindergarten	Primary	middle school	High school
Country	34.5	44.7	61.8	56.9	28.6	41.4	50.3	52.8	28.5	36.4	48.3	47.9	26.3	35.8	37.8	42.7	24.2	31.8	35.3	32.7
Seoul	34.4	56.2	66.1	58.9	31.6	51.2	52.8	55.6	30.6	40.9	50.1	50.5	26.6	37.3	34.6	45.4	24.3	32.8	35.0	33.6
Pusan	36.4	53.9	63.9	58.7	33.6	47.9	53.0	53.6	32.1	39.1	52.3	49.1	28.7	36.5	36.8	42.9	27.3	30.2	34.7	33.1
Dagu	37.5	55.1	64.6	58.9	34.2	49.3	54.5	54.6	34.2	41.6	51.7	50.4	1.5	40.5	40.0	44.7	29.5	33.8	36.8	34.5
Incheon	36.8	56.2	64.3	57.5	34.1	53.0	53.5	53.4	31.3	42.0	50.6	51.0	28.1	41.3	40.3	43.2	26.4	33.0	40.3	34.5
Gwangju	-	-	-	-	32.5	47.5	52.6	53.2	30.8	39.4	51.9	47.6	27.9	40.1	39.5	43.0	25.9	35.3	37.9	33.9
Daejeon	-	-	-	-	32.0	47.5	52.3	53.8	30.2	40.9	49.4	49.7	28.2	38.5	38.9	43.0	25.6	34.6	36.1	33.6
Ulsan	-	-	-	-	-	-	-	-	-	-	-	-	29.5	39.7	43.4	46.9	25.8	33.4	37.9	34.6
Gyeonggi-*do*	34.8	46.1	62.9	56.5	30.0	44.3	50.2	52.0	30.7	42.0	51.0	47.7	27.2	40.6	43.1	45.2	25.9	37.3	38.7	34.8
Gangwon-*do*	34.7	34.9	58.1	54.8	26.8	30.6	46.6	50.6	26.8	27.8	44.5	44.8	24.8	28.0	34.9	38.7	20.8	26.1	32.2	29.5
Chungcheongbuk-*do*	35.0	37.9	58.3	56.1	27.2	34.7	48.4	51.8	26.1	31.8	45.0	46.5	25.6	32.0	39.9	42.0	21.8	29.6	32.2	32.4
Chungcheongnam-*do*	33.8	41.4	58.5	55.3	24.8	33.2	46.8	51.6	23.6	29.1	44.0	45.6	22.5	29.2	35.6	38.4	20.3	26.8	30.7	30.1
Jeollabuk-*do*	33.9	39.3	58.7	56.1	22.8	34.3	48.5	51.8	22.6	30.3	44.1	45.2	20.4	30.2	33.5	35.9	17.9	27.3	31.6	28.1
Jeollanam-*do*	33.6	38.3	61.7	55.6	23.3	30.5	45.6	49.7	22.3	25.9	40.9	43.7	22.8	26.2	32.6	36.5	19.5	24.4	29.1	28.3
Gyeongsangbuk-*do*	33.7	36.5	57.9	54.8	25.2	32.2	48.8	50.2	25.2	29.0	43.3	44.8	24.7	29.6	37.8	39.6	22.4	27.0	30.6	29.8
Gyeongsangnam-*do*	34.2	39.9	59.4	57.2	26.5	37.8	48.6	51.4	26.8	34.4	47.6	47.5	25.6	34.2	39.0	41.7	23.7	30.1	34.7	31.4
Jeju Self-Governing Province	36.8	41.9	59.2	55.7	31.2	37.5	49.3	51.3	29.8	31.3	44.9	44.7	28.7	32.2	33.0	39.2	23.9	30.1	35.3	30.2

[Source : Natioan Statistical Office, Korea education yearbook]

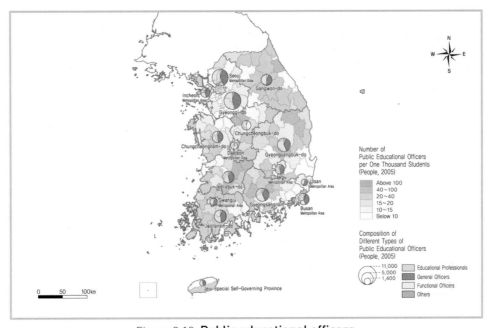

Figure 8.10 **Public educational officers.**
(Source : The National Atlas of Korea. http://atlas.ngii.go.kr)

but other major cities and provinces had a big gap between urban and rural areas.

2) Regional characteristics by grade level

In this section, the regional characteristics of Korean education by grade levels are discussed. For the preschool level, there were 8,275 preschools in 2005. There were 4,412 public preschools-more than the private counterpart at 3,863. Although there were more public preschools, private preschools actually had a higher number of teachers and students. The number of preschoolers per a thousand people reflected the population in a region. Within a province, the number was generally higher in urban than in rural areas. Meanwhile, the number of teachers per preschool was higher in Seoul and other metropolitan areas at 4-6 teachers per school, with 2-3 teachers per school in provinces. The number of students per preschool in Seoul or other metropolitan areas was much higher than in provinces. There was usually no difference in the number of students per class between most metropolitan areas and provinces, except higher population cities like Seoul and some major metropolitan cities had more students per class (Figure 8.11).

In elementary education, the number of students had decreased due to the continued population growth control policies, improved social status of women, and change in values

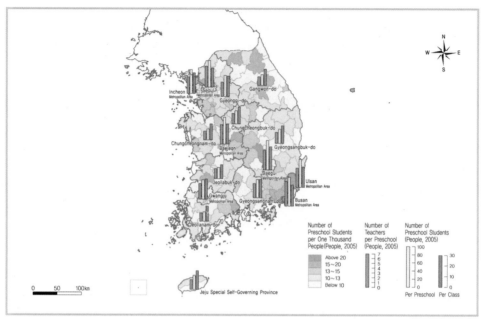

Figure 8.11 **Regional tendency of preschool education indices.**
(Source : The National Atlas of Korea. http://atlas.ngii.go.kr)

with respect to having children. In the 1970s there were about 6 million elementary students, but the number dropped to 4.02 million in 2005.

Along with the decrease inpopulation, the number of elementary schools also decreased since the mid 1980s. However, with the continued investment in education through the Education Environment Improvement Project, which decreased the number of students per class, the number of elementary schools has started to increase since 2000 ; in 1980, it was 6,487 ; in 2000, 5,276 ; and in 2005, 5,646.

The number of elementary students per a thousand people was relatively low in Seoul and in rural areas of provinces (Figure 8.12). The number of elementary students per a thousand people in Seoul was particularly lower than its surrounding areas because the families with elementary students lived in the surrounding areas but tended to move to Seoul as their children became middle school students. In rural areas the number of schools substantially decreased due to the consolidation of small schools, along with the decreased population. However, there was a rapid growth in the cities of Ansan, Goyang, Gwacheon, Siheung, in the surrounding area of Seoul, and in the cities of Changwon, Gumi, Gimhae, Gwangyang, Suncheon, and Goryeong in other provinces. Those cities had more than 100 elementary students per one thousand people, which was a higher number than other areas.

The number of teachers per elementary school was highest in Seoul, followed by

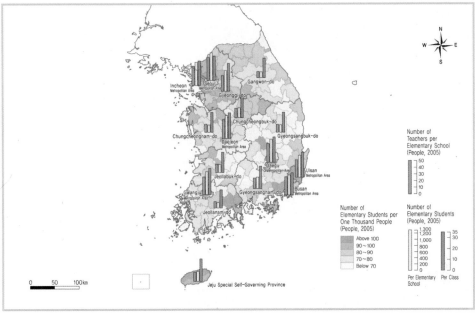

Figure 8.12 **Regional tendency of elementary education indices.**
(Source : The National Atlas of Korea. http://atlas.ngii.go.kr)

metropolitan cities and the surrounding cities of Seoul, indicating elementary teachers were concentrated in the capital region , and in the 6 metropolitan cities. The number of students per elementary school followed a similar pattern.

As for middle school education, the number of students had increased since the 1960s, but decreased after the apex, 2,782,173 students in 1985. However, the number began gradually rising again after 2003. The number of middle school students per one thousand people was high in metropolitan cities, relatively low in Seoul, and the lowest in counties of all provinces except Gyeonggi-*do*. Within a large city such as Seoul, there was unequal distribution. Within a province, urban areas had more students than rural areas (Figure 8.13).

There were more public middle schools than private ones, but the percentage of private elementary schools was relatively higher than public ones at 25%. Private schools once accounted for more than 50% of middle schools, but due to compulsory middle schooling in the mid-1980s, a large part of the private middle school enrollment moved to national and public schools.

The numbers of teachers and students per school in middle schools showed almost the same pattern as in elementary schools urban areas had higher numbers than rural areas. There was no regional difference in the number of students per class, due to the continuous nationwide movement of decreasing the number of students per class.

CHAPTER 8

325

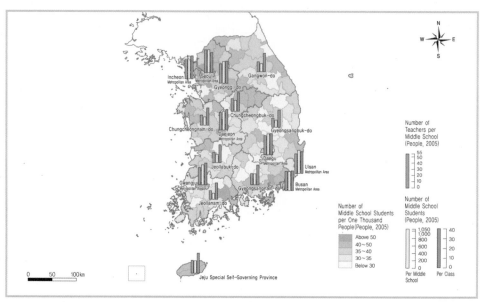

Figure 8.13 **Regional tendency of middle school education indices.**
(Source : The National Atlas of Korea. http://atlas.ngii.go.kr)

As for high school education, the number of schools steadily increased. The proportion of general to vocational high school students was 69 to 31 in 2003 and 71.5 to 28.5 in 2005, showing a growing preference for general high schools. The number of general high school students was fluctuating in the 1990s, but remained steady at 1.2 million in the 2000s, while the number of vocational high school students has tended to decrease since 1995. The number of high school students per a thousand people was higher in Seoul and metropolitan areas than in provinces, but the gap was not very noticeable. Rather, the gap within a large city was bigger than among regions. In Seoul or metropolitan areas, certain areas around specific high schools drew an increased student population (Figure 8.14).

The numbers of teachers and students per high school were higher the capital region than in other areas. This could be explained by the population concentration in the capital region, which has better educational resources. However, there was no regional difference in the number of students per class, which was 28-34 per class.

The numbers of 2-year colleges and students have also grown by leaps and bounds since the 1980s, reflecting the need for higher education. The college admission rate of vocational high school graduates has continuously increased. These 2-year colleges are the alternatives for the accumulated number of repeaters for the college entrance exams, which has been one of the major problems in Korean education.

There was a huge expansion of higher education in Korea due to the explosive student population growth during the last half century. The college enrollment rate was 81% in 2005. This was significantly high compared to 63% in the U.S. and 49% in Japan. The number of higher education institutions in cities, counties (*gun*), and districts/wards (*gu*) nationwide was 358, which means that each of the 234 cities, counties, and districts/wards nationwide has an average of 1.5 higher education institutions. In 2005, there were 226 higher education institutions with 10,189 departments and 1,859,639 students, and 175 of them were 4-year universities. The number of full-time faculty members also continuously increased to 60,418 in 2005. In 2005, the number of college students per faculty member was 25.6 and the number of students per faculty in national and public universities was 22.98 (the number of faculty members of national and public universities was 15,601).

The regional distribution of higher education showed significant concentration in the capital region. Particularly, 4-year universities are concentrated in Seoul and 2-year colleges are concentrated in Gyeonggi-*do*. The number of students per college was high-more than 10,000,in Daegu, Busan, Ulsan, Seoul, and Chungcheong-*do*-showing large-scale colleges were concentrated in those areas. The number of departments per college was highest in Busan (87.8), followed by Daejeon (66.4), Jeju Special Self-Governing Province (61.6), and Chungcheong-do (60.2), indicating that many colleges are too comprehensive and that there is a lack of specialized colleges (Figure 8.15).

Regarding graduate school education, the number of graduate students has grown steeply

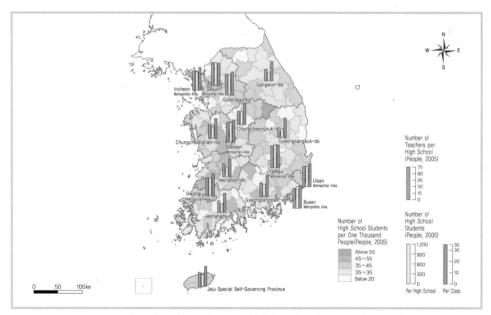

Figure 8.14 **Regional tendency of high school education indices.**
(Source : The National Atlas of Korea. http://atlas.ngii.go.kr)

327

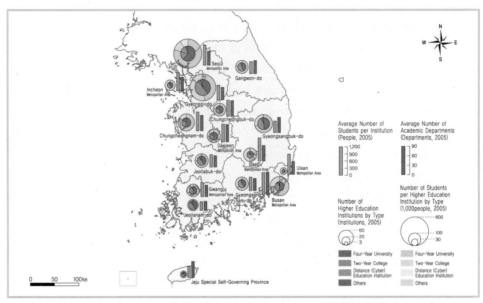

Figure 8.15 **Regional tendency of higher education indices.**
(Source : The National Atlas of Korea. http://atlas.ngii.go.kr)

since the 1990s and reached 86,074 in 2005. The growth could be explained by the loose standards for creating a college, and increased needs of college graduates who could not get a job with a bachelor's degree. There was significant unequal distribution of the number of graduate students across the country ; Seoul had the most graduate students (133,325 students, or 46.0%). That is, high-skilled labor was concentrated and unbalanced, resulting in severe regional imbalances.

Chapter 8.2.

QUALITY OF LIFE AND SOCIAL WELFARE

8.2.1 Economic Development and Quality of Life

South Korea embarked on its capitalist economic development in the 1960s, and experienced a major change in domestic and global situations by the late 1980s. Seen from the domestic point of view, having recorded a considerable trade surplus due to the low price of oil and low international interest rate, the South Korean economy turned its efforts to developing its own domestic market, which was made possible through increasing real incomes of workers ; hence the Fordist regime of accumulation reached its maturity, completing a cycle of mass production and mass consumption, and consequently the relatively peripheral characteristics of Fordism were eliminated. At the same time, the democracy movement in June 1987 forced a turning point in South Korea's political and social development from a military and authoritarian state to a relatively more democratic and neoliberal state.

On the global level, the globalization processes of capitalism, which have promoted mechanisms of free market and free trade, and which enhanced a global integration of economic space, began to have a decisive influence on local societies, facilitating the opening of local markets and the inflow of international capital throughout the world, including South Korea. What is more, this globalization process proceeded hand in hand with the disintegration of the Cold War political system at the end of the 1980s, which led to a strategic transformation from political and military opposition to economic competition and cooperation between countries (Choi, 2007a).

Under these kinds of changing economic and political conditions on the domestic and global level, South Korea experienced a rapid increase in its general domestic production ; its income per capita rose from $254 in 1970 to $6,147 in 1990, and reached over $10,000 in

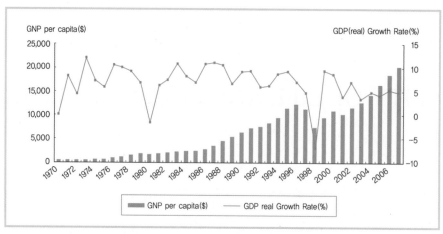

Figure 8.16 **Trends in GNP per capita and GDP real growth rate.**
(Source : Statistics Korea. http://www.kostat.go.kr)

1995. Even though it decreased seriously after the economic crisis in 1997, the income per capita again exceeded $10,000 in 2000, and amounted to about $20,000 in 2007 (Figure 8.16).

The economic growth and increasing income per capita has extended consumption expenditure and improved considerably the material aspect of the quality of life of South Korean people, as shown in Table 8.4. As the composition of individual consumption expenditure has changed, the Engel's coefficient, that is, the percentage of expenditure for food and beverages, decreased from 40.8% in 1982 to 25.1% in 2007, while that for meals outside of the home increased from 2.4% to 11.8% in the same period. Expenditure for other items such as housing, fuel? electricity and water, clothing and footwear, and medical care has decreased, but expenditure for education (especially for private education), transportation, and communication, with the widespread use of cars, personal computers, mobile phones, and so on, and for culture and recreation, has increased remarkably.

However, the general growth of the economy, combined with the increasing income per capita and individual consumption expenditure in South Korea, does not mean the improvement of quality of life in terms of personal satisfaction with income and living. For example, as shown in a national survey on subjective income satisfaction (Table 8.5), people with low and very low satisfaction with their income comprised 47.9% of the population in 1999 just after the economic crisis in 1997, yet the percentage of people with dissatisfaction with their income has not decreased since then, but rather increased to 53.5% in 2007. The individual income in urban areas is higher than in rural areas, but the level of income satisfaction is reversed, though with a slight difference.

The fact that income satisfaction has decreased in spite of the general economic growth

Table 8.4 **Average monthly consumption expenditure of urban households**

(unit : 1,000 won, %)

Year	Total consumption expenditure	Food & beverages	Meals out-side the home	Housing	Fuel electricity and water expenses	Furniture & utensils	Clothing & foot wear	Clothing & foot wear	Medical care (Fee for medical consultation)	Education	Culture & recreation	Transportation & communication	Personal transportation	Communication	Other consumption expenditure	Miscellaneous
1982	249	40.8	2.4	4.4	8.1	4.4	8.0	6.0	3.0	7.2	3.7	6.6	0.2	1.6	10.8	6.9
1990	686	32.2	6.5	4.7	4.5	5.6	8.2	5.1	2.4	8.4	4.7	8.5	3.6	1.9	18.2	14.1
2000	1,632	27.4	10.8	3.5	5.3	3.6	5.6	4.3	2.7	11.2	5.2	16.0	8.2	4.7	17.8	13.5
2007	2,349	25.1	11.8	3.4	4.8	4.4	5.3	5.2	3.5	12.0	5.0	17.2	8.5	6.0	17.5	13.4

(Source : Statistics Korea, KOSIS [KOrean Statistical Information Service]).

Table 8.5 **Income satisfaction**

Year	Region	Very High	High	Moderate	Low	Very Low	Unknown
	Total	0.4	9.6	40.9	37.1	10.8	1.1
1999	Urban	0.5	9.5	40.9	37.1	11.0	1.1
	Rural	0.3	10.2	40.8	37.2	10.1	1.5
	Total	1.1	8.9	36.5	35.7	17.8	-
2007	Urban	1.1	8.9	36.2	35.7	18.2	-
	Rural	1.3	8.9	37.8	35.9	16.1	-

(Source : Statistics Korea, e-national indicators).
Note : The respondents participating in this survey were 15-years old or older, except people without an income.

CHAPTER 8

and increase in the absolute amount of individual income seems to be due to not only personal dissatisfaction with income itself but also unfair distribution of income on the national level. Indeed, even though it can be said that the income disparity in South Korea decreased as the economy grew, after the 1997 crisis, the income disparity became worse gradually and continued until recently. That is, in the trend of wage income polarization, the Gini-coefficient, bottoming out at 0.272 in 1994, increased to 0.320 in 2003, and the ratio of the upper 10% to lower 10% increased from 3.64 in 1994 to 4.35 in 2003 (Figure 8.17).

In addition to wage income polarization, property inequality has also worsened the

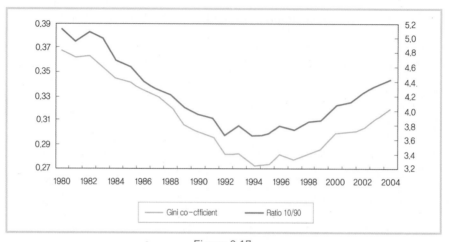

Figure 8.17
(Source : Ministry of Labor, Kim. 2005a)

distribution of household income. In particular, inequality of land property ownership has led to a seriously distorted distribution of property gains generated by periodic booms in land price. The possession of land in South Korea is so highly biased that the upper 5% of land owners in 1989 possessed 65.2% of the national privately-owned land area, and the upper 25% possessed 90.8%. This polarization of land property ownership continues today with little change.

Based on these inequalities of income and property, the question can be posed of whether or not the rapid economic growth for several decades has really improved the quality of life of South Korean people. In the OECD Statistical Year Book in 2008, among micro-economic indicators, South Korea's GDP per capita and the growth rate of real GDP in 2006 ranked 23rd ($23,038) and 7th (5.0%), respectively. But the annual working hours recorded 2,357 hours, which is 3 hours longer than the previous year, and is longest among OECD members, greatly exceeding the average hours (1,777 hours). The individual expenditure for medical care and for culture and recreation also ranked low at 26th and 27th, respectively.

Another problem for the quality of life in South Korea is its regional disparity. A study on 7 services to support the quality of life for people (medical care, housing, environment, education, welfare, culture, and basic infrastructure) shows considerable regional inequality. Seen from the general level of these services, which aggregates the points of each of these indicators, Nowon-*gu* in Seoul had the highest score, and most regions with relatively high points were within or near large cities, while Sinan-*gun* in Jeollanam-*do* had the lowest score. Most regions with relatively low points are peripheral rural areas (Figure 8.18).

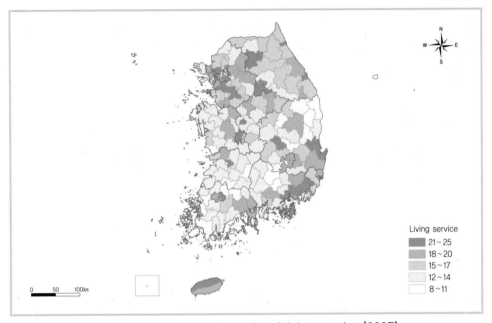

Figure 8.18 **Regional disparity of living service (2007)**
(Source : Weekly Donga, 2008, National Indicator of Living Service [Cover Story]).

8.2.2 Major Aspects of Quality of Life

1) Housing

Housing is not only one of the major factors in quality of life but also one of the biggest problems in South Korea. As the construction of houses has been promoted by construction capital and the government in order to resolve the housing shortage in large cities, the national housing stock increased from 5.3 million in 1980 to 13.5 million in 2005, and the national ratio of housing supply increased from 71.2% in 1980 to 96.2% in 2000, exceeding 100% to reach 107.1% in 2005 (Figure 8.19). The rapid increase in housing stock since the end of the 1980s was possible due mainly to construction of large apartment complexes, which were widespread especially through government construction policies for large new towns mainly in the capital region (Figure 8.20).

The supply of housing, mainly through construction of large apartment complexes, has a close relationship with the instability or volatility of land prices and with general business fluctuations. Housing prices were stable during the 1990s, and even fell with the burst of the property bubble just after the economic crisis of 1997. But prices have tended to increase

CHAPTER 8

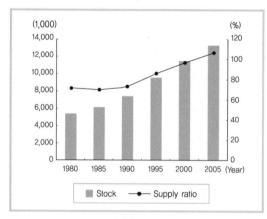 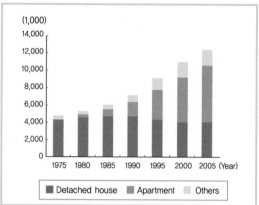

Figure 8.19 **Trend of increasing house stock and supply ratio.**   Figure 8.20 **Trend of increasing housing stock by type.**

(Source : Statistics Korea. http://www.kostat.go.kr, http://www.kosis.kr)

rapidly in the 2000s, a phenomenon led by Seoul, especially in the Gangnam region, a densely populated region with luxury housing. Yet, the housing prices of most cities and rural regions outside of the capital region have been stagnant or have decreased, so that the difference in housing prices between the capital region and other regions has become wider than before.

Apart from the rapidly increasing disparity in housing prices and the ever-widening regional differences, another serious housing problem is little improvement of the ratio of housing ownership in spite of a vast housing supply. Even though the national rate of housing supply increased from 72.4% in 1990 to 96.2% in 2000, and reached 107.1% in 2005, the ratio of housing ownership was recorded at 53.3% in 1995, 54.2% in 2000, and 55.6% in 2005. The tendency for a low ratio of housing ownership has been most serious in Seoul, with 44.6% in 2005, and the capital region and 7 major cities, with 50.2% and 51.0%, respectively (Table 8.6). This inequality in housing ownership, with soaring housing prices, which led to a much distorted distribution of enormous property gains, is a major factor that has made the housing problem ever more serious.

Both the inequality in housing ownership and the uneven rise in housing prices seem to be reflected in dwellers' satisfaction with housing. The rate of satisfaction with housing is especially low in large cities and the capital region, including Seoul, Busan, Incheon, and Gyeonggi-*do*, while it is considerably high in rural regions such as Gangwon-*do* and Jeju Special Self-Governing Province (Figure 8.21).

Table 8.6 **Ratio of housing ownership in regions**

Region	1995	2000	2005	Region	1995	2000	2005
Total	53.3	54.2	55.6	Gyeonggi - *do*	51.0	52.1	53.2
7 major cities	44.3	47.5	51.0	Gangwon - *do*	63.0	59.2	57.9
Seoul	39.7	40.9	44.6	Chungcheongbuk - *do*	65.1	61.6	60.2
Busan	44.2	52.0	56.7	Chungcheongnam - *do*	72.5	66.1	62.9
Daegu	43.9	49.7	53.9	Jeollabuk - *do*	69.0	65.6	65.7
Incheon	57.4	59.1	60.6	Jeollanam - *do*	74.5	70.7	69.5
Gwangju	48.1	51.2	53.6	Cyeongsangbuk - *do*	68.7	67.1	66.6
Daejeon	50.6	51.2	52.0	Gyeongsangnam - *do*	62.9	62.9	62.6
Ulsan	49.9	54.3	58.8	Jeju special self-governing province	57.9	55.4	54.8
Others	62.1	60.2	59.6	The Capital Region	46.0	47.6	50.2

(Source : Statistics Korea, e-national indicators).

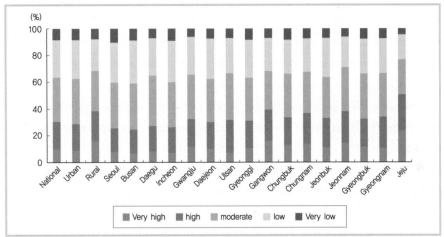

Figure 8.21 **Satisfaction with house by region (2004)**
(Source : Statistics Korea, KOSIS [http://www.kostat.go.kr])

2) Medical care

Another major aspect of quality of life is medical care, which reveals awakened public interest in disease prevention as well as in general health care as individual income has increased with economic growth. The delivery system of medical care in South Korea depends in principle on market mechanisms, and hence high quality medical care facilities are concentrated in large cities, especially in the high-income districts within them. As the Medical Care Assistance Act has been carried out since 2001, medical aid funds financed with

335

subsidies from both central and local governments have supported some part of the medical expenses of the poor in large cities, but those who live in low-income regions or rural areas are still outside of the delivery system of medical care (Lee, 2007).

There were 75,106 medical facilities in 2006, including general hospitals, hospitals, midwifery units, public health centers, and pharmacies. These facilities are concentrated within or near the capital region and large cities. As shown in Figure 8.22, the distribution of these facilities is very uneven, especially considering that medical facilities in rural areas are usually quite small. The recent rate of increase in medical beds is also higher in the capital region and Busan than in other regions.

The rate of patients and death among people in regions is another important indicator of medical care. The number of outpatients per 100,000 people is relatively small in the capital region and large cities such as Daegu and Daejeon, while the number is higher in rural regions such as Jeollanam-*do*, Jeollabuk-*do*, and Jeju Special Self-Governing Province. This is mainly because the percentage of seniors in these regions,who need more medical care, is higher than in other regions. This is very similar to the distribution seen with the crude death rate, which is relatively low in the capital region and large cities including Daejeon and Ulsan, while relatively high in rural regions such as Jeollanam-*do* and Gyeongsangbuk-*do*. In particular, this can be identified in the extremely high crude death rate in rural regions distant from the capital region and the large cities. The infant mortality rate shows quite a similar pattern in its spatial distribution.

The centralization of medical facilities in the capital region and large cities and relatively low rate of patients and death do not mean that these regions have ahigher satisfaction level among their populations than other regions. The level of satisfaction with medical care in 2006 had increased considerably compared to that of 1999. But what is peculiar is that the satisfaction rate in rural areas with a lack of medical care is higher than that in urban areas with densely concentrated medical facilities, as shown in Figure 8.23. In a regional comparison, Seoul, Busan, and Incheon show relatively low rates of satisfaction, while Gangwon-*do* and Jeollanam-do show relatively high rates.

8.2.3 Social Welfare for Major Groups

It was expected that the growth of the national economy and the improvement of material living standards in South Korea would promote the security of social welfare for those who have been excluded or alienated from the distribution of social wealth. But, the Korean

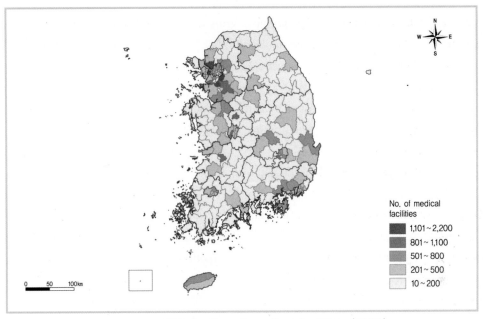

Figure 8.22 **Distribution of medical facilities (2006)**
(Source : Statistics Korea, KOSIS [http://www.kostat.go.kr])

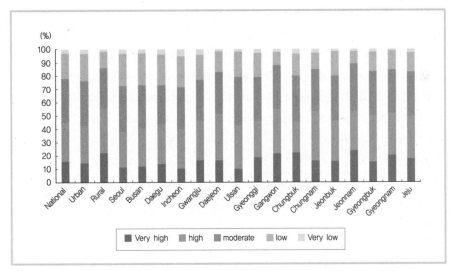

Figure 8.23 **Satisfaction with medical care by region (2006)**
(Source : Statistics Korea, KOSIS [http://www.kostat.go.kr])

337

government, which has prioritized economic growth in general, could not institutionalize social welfare systems to support the poor and other peripheral groups. In particular, as the polarization, which deepened after the economic crisis in 1997, continues and becomes more serious in spite of the government's increasing investment in social welfare, the expansion of social welfare policies is urgent for increasing the social well-being of the under-classes or alienated groups such as the poor, the disabled, and seniors.

1) Social welfare for the poor

The poverty rate, which decreased gradually in the 1990s, has risen rapidly since the economic crisis in 1997 (Table 8.7). That is, 13.4% of national households in 1993 were classified in the poverty population, a number that reduced to 7.3% in 1997, even though the poverty rate in rural areas was much higher than that in urban areas. But after the economic crisis in 1997, the poverty rate rose to 13.1%in 1998. This level of poverty has continued and especially after 2003, the national poverty situation became worse than before (Lee, and Lee, 2001 ; Kim, 2006).

In order to secure a basic living standard for the poor classes, the Korean government enacted the National Minimum Livelihood Security Law for an anti-poverty program in 1999, substituted for the previous Livelihood Aid Law, and has provided cash benefits to the absolute poverty class earning under the minimum cost of living. In 2001, the number of people who receive cash benefits from the government was 1.42 million, which amounted to a distribution of about 2 trillion won. The number of poor people receiving cash benefits in 2006 increased to 1.53 million, and the distribution amount increased to3.2 trillion won. This

Table 8.7 **Changing trend of poverty rate**

a) Percent of households under the minimum cost of living (national, 1993-1998)   (unit : %).

	1993	1994	1995	1996	1997	1998
national	13.37	13.89	10.01	8.71	7.33	13.13
large cities	9.72	9.49	6.41	5.57	4.59	11.76
Small - & medium - sized cities	11.33	14.43	9.43	8.34	7.82	11.91
rural areas	44.61	35.57	31.88	24.13	18.04	22.91

b) Absolute and relative poverty rates (urban, 1998-2003)   (unit : %).

	1998	1999	2000	2001	2002	2003
absolute poverty rate	7.68	8.51	6.68	5.63	4.44	5.79
relative poverty rate	10.88	10.89	10.11	10.04	9.88	10.93

(Source : a) Lee, and Lee, (2001) ; b) Kim, (2006)).

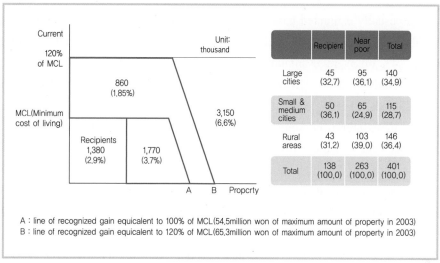

	Recipient	Near poor	Total
Large cities	45 (32.7)	95 (36.1)	140 (34.9)
Small & medium cities	50 (36.1)	65 (24.9)	115 (28.7)
Rural areas	43 (31.2)	103 (39.0)	146 (36.4)
Total	138 (100.0)	263 (100.0)	401 (100.0)

A : line of recognized gain equicalent to 100% of MCL(54.5million won of maximum amount of property in 2003)
B : line of recognized gain equicalent to 120% of MCL(65.3million won of maximum amount of property in 2003)

Figure 8.24 **Targets of social welfare policy for the poor in consideration of income and property**

(Source : Korea Institute for Health and Social Affairs, 2008, Survey on the near poor).

trend of increasing basic livelihood security recipients and the amount of the cash benefit they receive means not only that households in absolute poverty have increased, but also that the government loosened its selection criteria and increased the total amount of the cash benefits distributed.

But with deepening polarization and problems with recipient selection, there have been blind spots that were excluded from this program, and there are some households in relative poverty, even though they are not in absolute poverty. In particular, after the economic crisis, the so-called "working poor" emerged. These are people who are working but cannot escape from poverty because of low income and instability of employment. In order to solve this problem, the government introduced the concept of "near poor" people living within 100?120% of the minimum cost of living, and tried to extend social welfare security to them. Considering both current income and property, the near poor who need direct government support numbered 2.63 million (Figure 8.24). The extension of the government's welfare policy to the near poor would help especially those who live in rural areas and have some agricultural land, but are suffering from a low and unstable income.

2) Social welfare for persons with disabilities

It is not easy to count the exact number of persons with disabilities because they include various types with different degrees of disability, and some of them are not registered. Hence, the number is usually estimated based on a sample survey. The number of households with persons with disabilities was estimated to be 950,000 in 1995, and this number has increased at a rate of 7.4% on average annually, reaching 1.3 million (8.9% of the total number of national households) in 2000. The number reached 1.94 million (9.8% of the total number of national households) in 2005, with an annual increasing rate of 9.8% after 2000 (Table 8.8 a). The number of registered persons with disabilities also has rapidly increased, with the increasing percentage of the estimated number of persons with disabilities rising from 36.8% in 1995 to 84.6% in 2005, which means that social prejudice against persons with disabilities has been alleviated considerably in recent years.

Based on regional rates of emergence of persons with disabilities, both the estimated number of households with persons with disabilities and estimated number of persons with disabilities are much higher in rural areas than urban areas. The rate of emergence of persons with disabilities in 2005 was 6.88% in rural areas, while it was 4.13% in Seoul, 4.0% in the 6 metropolitan cities, and 3.84 in small- and medium-sized cities (Table 8.8 b). The high rate of emergence of persons with disabilities in rural areas is mainly caused by the high number of seniors with disabilities due to dementia in rural areas.

Persons with disabilities require various facilities and services suitable for types and degrees of disability. In 1995, of 233 facilities for persons with disabilities in the nation, 50 and 27 facilities were located in Seoul and Gyeonggi-*do*, respectively ; in 2003, of 225 facilities, Seoul and Gyeonggi-*do* had 28 and 44 facilities, respectively. Social welfare for persons with disabilities has recently transformed from the provision of facilities to the provision of welfare services. Based on a questionnaire survey on social welfare for persons with disabilities in 2007, the greatest needis for expansion of programs for employment promotion and vocational rehabilitation of persons with disabilities (48.9%), and the second greatest need is for medical support for persons with disabilities (41.3%).

The Korean government has endeavored to reflect the requirements of persons with disabilities in its social welfare policies. The payment of disability allowance, stated in the National Basic Livelihood Security Act (NBLSA), and the number of recipients of this payment, has increased from 1997 : the recipients of the disability allowance payment numbered about 55,000 in 1998, and increased to 404,000 in 2008. The government budget for these paymentshas increased from 15.7 million won in 1998 to 327.9 million won in 2008. In the regional distribution of disability allowance payments, Seoul and Gyeonggi-*do* receive the most in terms of amount allocated, while Jeollanam-*do* and Jeollabuk-*do* receive the mostin proportion to the total population of these provinces.

Table 8.8 **trend in the number of persons with disabilities**
a) National   *(unit : person, %)*

Year	Estimated households with persons with disabilities			Estimated number of persons with disabilities	No. of registered persons with disabilities (Percentage)
	No. of Households	Rate of emergence	Increasing rate in annual average		
1995	952,720	7.4	-	1,028,837	378,323 (36.77)
2000	1,304,710	8.9	7.4	1,449,494	958,196 (66.11)
2005	1,944,791	12.3	9.8	2,101,057	1,777,400 (84.60)

b) Regional

Rate of emergence	Total	Seoul	Metropolitan cities	Small and medium cities	Rural areas
Estimated number of persons with disabilities	2,101,057 (4.50)	398,074 (4.13)	495,808 (4.00)	618,738 (3.84)	588,437 (6.88)
Number of persons with disabilities 65 years and older	681,889 (15.10)	113,280 (13.91)	145,538 (16.42)	180,965 (14.46)	242,106 (15.50)

(Source : Korea Institute for Health and Social Affairs, 2000, 2005, Survey on persons with disabilities.)

3) Social welfare for seniors

As the percentage of the senior (over 65 years old) population has rapidly increased over the past few decades, social welfare for them has become a new and very important issue in South Korea. The percentage of seniors was 3.1% in 1970, and 3.8% in 1980, but since then it increased rapidly to 5.1% in 1990, 7.2% in 2000, and 9.5% in 2006. Korean society, which became an aging society in 2000, is expected to be an aged society by 2018, with the senior population expected to comprise 14.3% of the total population, and to be a super-aged society in 2026, with the senior population expected to comprise 20.8% of the total population.

While the number of seniors and its ratio in the total population has increased rapidly, the birth rate has gradually decreased, and hence the index of aging has been rising dramatically. In particular, the index of aging has become very high in rural regions, revealing a big disparity with urban regions (Table 8.9). That is, the index of aging for Ulsan, which has been developed and still is prosperous as an industrial city, was 28.8% in 2007, the lowest ratio in South Korea, while that of Jeollanam-*do* was recorded at 105.9%, the highest, and those of

Table 8.9 **Index of aging in regions** *(unit : %)*

Region	1990	2000	2007	Region	1990	2000	2007
Seoul	14.2	28.8	51.4	Gangwon-*do*	26.4	48.7	79.3
Busan	13.7	32.2	62.5	Chungcheongbuk-*do*	28.6	45.6	69.8
Daegu	15.6	28.0	49.1	Chungcheongnam-*do*	32.6	59.1	82.6
Incheon	14.7	23.3	40.8	Jeollabuk-*do*	28.8	54.2	84.0
Gwangju	15.1	23.8	37.9	Jeollanam-*do*	30.5	67.0	105.9
Daejeon	15.5	24.1	39.4	Gyeongsangbuk-*do*	35.0	58.0	91.1
Ulsan	10.5	15.8	28.8	Gyeongsangnam-*do*	25.0	40.6	60.0
Gyeonggi-*do*	16.6	23.7	38.5	Jeju Special Self-Governing Province	23.4	36.1	53.1

(Source : Statistics Korea, e-national indicators).

other rural regions, such as Gangwon-*do*, Chungcheongbuk-*do*, Jeollabuk-*do*, and Gyeongsangbuk-*do*, reached more than 80%. This is mainly because the youth and the middle-aged population have moved in a mass selective migration to large cities, and hence the number of seniors in rural areas has increased, while the number of infants and young people has decreased because of a very low birth rate.

With an increasing senior population, provisions of facilities and services able to support and care for them have gone beyond the ability of individual families, and become the responsibility of public social welfare. As the demand for such facilities and services has increased, public facilities for living and welfare for seniors have increased from 146 in 1995 to 351 in 2003, and seniors staying in such facilities have increased from 8,396 in 1995 to 19,848 in 2003. These welfare facilities for seniors are mainly distributed in large cities such as Seoul, Busan, and Daegu, and in Gyeonggi-*do*, with a rapidly increasing population, but recently they have dispersed to rural regions such as Jeollabuk-*do* and Gyeongsangbuk-*do*.

As some problems with welfare policies for seniors specifically concerning facility provisions (for example, collective and bureaucratic control of seniors staying in facilities, inability to provide services to meet their individual needs, no consideration of the independence of seniors to live) have been pointed out, the primary concern of welfare policies for seniors has transformed to services for seniors at home. This type of welfare service for seniors was recognized in the mid-1980s and has been implemented since the end of the 1980s : for example, by enacting rules for organization and management of community social welfare centers in 1989, welfare services for seniors at home, such as services for bath and meal time, began to be provided by home-care aides.

With a transformation in welfare policies for seniors at home, welfare facilities for seniors at home have increased greatly in 2007 there were 1,408 facilities with 5,859 workers, but there were only 72,563 seniors who received such welfare services at home, which was less than 2% of seniors in the national total. These welfare service facilities for seniors at home are located mainly in Gyeonggi-*do* and other rural regions, especially Jeollanam-*do* and Jeollabuk-*do*, with a relatively high ratio compared to the population, and hence there were relatively more seniors in these regions who received welfare services from such facilities.

8.2.4 Prospects for Social Welfare Policy

Even though social welfare or social well-being in a broad sense means quality of life, considered so far in a more restricted sense, it means social security for disadvantaged or alienated groups who have been excluded from the distribution of social wealth or social power, including the poor, persons with disabilities, seniors, and other minority groups such as the recently growing group of foreign immigrants. Members of these groups need various government support structures, such as welfare policies, to assure that they lead lives worthy of human beings. But social welfare policies in South Korea remain at a relatively low level compared to its level of economic development. In particular, after the economic crisis in 1997, socio-spatial polarizations become more serious, and there has emerged a new poverty class who, despite their working, cannot escape from the state of poverty because of low wages and instability of employment.

In order to resolve these problems of the disadvantaged classes, and improve quality of life issues, the South Korean government has tended to expand the budget for social welfare : the amount of expenditure for social welfare was 29 trillion won (6.5% of the GDP) in 1997, increased to 48 trillion won (10.0% of the GDP) in the following year, and to 57 trillion won in 2003. Its percent of the GDP tends to decrease slightly over time (Figure 8.25). In such a situation, proposing a vision for the future of Korean society, the government in 2006 expected that the GDP per capita in 2030 would amount to the level of Switzerland in 2005, and that the ratio of welfare expenditure to the GDP would reach the average level of the OECD in 2001 (Figure 8.26) (The Korean Government, 2006 ; see also The Presidential Commission on Policy Planning, 2006).

Based on this vision, the future of social welfare in South Korea appears not so hopeful, for it would take about 25 years for South Korea to catch up to the present level of social welfare represented by the average for the OECD. In order to overcome this problem, the expenditure for social welfare should be expanded more positively, and the welfare delivery

CHAPTER 8

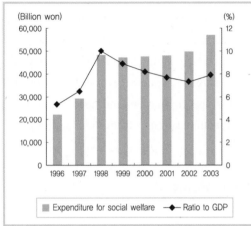

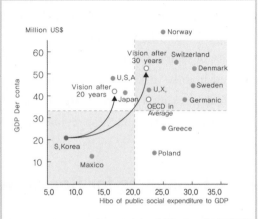

Figure 8.25 **Trends of expenditure for social welfare**
(Source : Korea Institute for Health and Social Affairs, 2008, Survey on the near poor).

Figure 8.26 **International comparison of public social expenditure**
(Source : Korean Government, 2006, Vision 2030). note : GDP per capita (2005 ; IMF, Wrld Economic Outlook ('06.4) Public Social Expenditure (2001 ; OECO, Social Indicators, '05)

system should be improved for both its efficiency and equity. Within a limited budget, the governments (both central and local) also need to consider what kinds of facilities and services are more helpful for the disadvantaged groups, and where facilities more accessible to them are located.

Thus, for example, in order to improve the accessibility of day care centers for seniors, the number and capacity of the centers needs to be increased, especially in regions with lower levels of services provided (Sohn, J-Y. and Oh, S-K., 2007). Indeed, the concept of social welfare already has implications for both the realization of social justice by prioritizing disadvantaged groups (Bae, M-A., 2007), and the reconstruction of community by enhancing the quality of life (Choi, B-D., 2000).

Chapter 8.3.

REGIONAL CONSCIOUSNESS AND POLITICS

8.3.1 Regional Satisfaction and Regional Pride

In contemporary Korea, regional consciousness and identity are weak mainly due to a formation of functional socio-spatial relationships as well as frequent geographical movements. Moreover, regional consciousness and identity, which were formed naturally through regional satisfaction and pride on the basis of place of residence, are now artificially modified and manipulated for special interests. They are natural and endogenous in origin, but are perverted externally to an exclusive regionalism, even taking the form of regional prejudice or antagonism, which often has been mobilized by political agitations, as evidenced by the serious socio-spatial problem in South Korea.

In this sense, recent situations and changes in regional satisfaction must be considered first. The percent of respondents in 1997 who were very or somewhat satisfied with where they lived was 28.7%, which is almost the same as those who felt very or somewhat dissatisfied with where they lived (28.6%). The state of regional satisfaction was slightly improved in 2004 : the percent of respondents who were very or somewhat satisfied with where they lived increased to 34.3%, while those who felt very or somewhat dissatisfied with where they lived decreased to 26.7%. The degree of satisfaction was higher in rural regions than urban regions : the percent of respondents who were very or somewhat satisfied in rural regions was 36.1% in 1997 and 40.3% in 2004, which was considerably higher than that of urban regions (26.8% and 32.9%, respectively).

The main reasons for dissatisfaction with one's place of residence in 1998 were "poor surrounding environment" and "poor traffic conditions" (both at approximately 22%), followed by "lack of convenience facilities" and "lack of parking facilities" (Table 8.10). There were considerable differences between urban regions and rural regions. For example, the percent of dissatisfaction with "poor surrounding environments" was 24.6% in urban regions, while only 12.0% in rural regions. The reported levels of dissatisfaction with "lack of convenience facilities," "poor traffic conditions," and "poor education conditions" were higher in rural regions than in urban regions.

Measures of satisfaction with the place or region in which one lives may result more generally from projections of pride onto the region. Surveys indicate that the degree of pride based on city of residence varies. The percent of citizens with very high or high city pride was 60.1% in Daejeon, the highest among large cities in the survey, while that of Daegu was 43.4%, the lowest among the cities (Table 8.11). Based on this data, there seems to be no direct relationship between regional pride and exclusive regionalism, especially in a political sense.

Table 8.10 **Reasons for Dissatisfaction with Place of Residence** *(unit : %)*

Year	Region	Poor education conditions	Poor traffic conditions	Poor surrounding environment	Pollution problems	Lack of convenience facilities	Lack of occurrence of crime	Frequent occurrence of crime	Lack of parking facilities	High price of commodities	Other	Unfavorable neighborhood
1998	Total	6.4	22.2	22,5	9.8	16.2	2.6	15.0	4.5	0.9	-
	Urban	5.0	18.7	24.6	11.1	14.4	3.0	17.5	4.8	0.9	-
	Rural	13.3	39.8	12.0	2.7	25.2	0.4	2.4	2.7	1.3	-
2007	Total	6.6	23.6	13.5	13.3	14.9	1.4	18.5	2.9	1.5	3.8
	Urban	5.9	22.7	14.6	14.4	12.2	1.5	20.9	3.1	1.3	3.5
	Rural	10.6	28.9	6.9	6.9	30.5	0.6	4.7	2.2	3.1	5.5

(Source : Statistics Korea, e-national indicators).

Table 8.11 **Regional Pride (2003)** *(unit : %)*

	Cases	Very High Pride	High Pride	Moderate Pride	Low Pride	Very Low Pride
Total	996	13.5	36.5	34.2	12.3	3.4
Seoul	228	12.3	35.5	34.2	14.5	3.5
Daejeon	266	18.4	41.7	26.7	9.0	4.1
Daegu	265	13.2	30.2	37.4	14.0	5.3
Gwangju	237	9.3	38.8	39.2	12.2	0.4
Busan[*]	1,000	10.2	39.1	40.0	7.8	2.9

(Source : on Busan, Kang, et al., 2004 ; on others, Choi, et al., 2004).
Note : Busan is excluded from the total

8.3.2 Exclusive Regionalism and Regional Conflict

The type of regional consciousness which, as mentioned above, can be seen from a positive and productive view is distinct from that of a regional consciousness that is negative and irrational, or what can be called exclusive regionalism. The former naturally occurs and can be thought of as a pure type of regionalism that can promote the internal integration and development of a region, as well as mutual recognition and cooperation between regions. The latter, however, has been intentionally promoted or manipulated, easily mobilized by special political purposes, and hence promotes internally irrational solidarity and antagonism to members of other regions (Jung, 2005).

Exclusive regionalism in people of one region can be measured or expressed in terms of their preference for vs. unfavoritism toward, or social distance from, those who come from other regions. A study on this phenomenon in the late 1980s revealed some characteristics of this kind of unfavoritism (Table 8.12). First, people prefer those from the same region. Second, people from Chungcheong region (Chungcheongnam-*do* and Chungcheongbuk-*do*) were preferred by all people, while people from Honam region were unfavored by all people except those from the same region. Third, while there was mutual aversion between people from Gyeongsang region (Gyeongsangnam-*do* and Gyeongsangbuk-*do*) and those from Honam region, the degree of unfavoritism was stronger in the former than the latter. Fourth, unfavoritism toward people from North Korea was primarily explained by un attractiveness, but at a lesser degree of un attractiveness than those from Honam region.

In a survey conducted in 2003, it was suggested that regionalism as expressed through people's preference for or unfavoritism toward people from different regions has continued until recently (Chung, K-S., 2005). That is, there were few changes in the ordering of people's preferences for regional groups between 1988 and 2003 : people from Chungcheong region were liked the most and people from Honam region were liked the least. But it is noteworthy that people's tendency toward in-region favoritism, in particular people from Honam region, was somewhat reduced. Furthermore, the degree of unfavoritisim that people of Jeollanam-*do* showed toward those of Youngnam region decreased in this time period.

As major reasons for this kind of regionalism and regional conflicts, respondents in 1988 pointed out "the economic development policy" (28.6%), "people's prejudices" (24.6%), and "politicians' election campaigns" (22.6%). However, there were considerable differences between regional groups. Honam people particularly pointed out that external factors such as "the economic development policy of the government" (about 50%) and "political and administrative factors" (16.0%) were more serious than internal factors such as "people's

Table 8.12 **unfavoritism toward people from other regions**

			Region of People with Unfavoritism, Evaluated by the Five-point Scale											
			Seoul	Gyeonggi-*do*	Gangwon-*do*	Chungcheongbuk-*do*	Chungcheongnam-*do*	Gyeongsangbuk-*do*	Gyeongsangnam-*do*	Jeollabuk-*do*	Jeollanam-*do*	Jeju Self-Governing Province	North Korea	Cases
Region of People Doing the Evaluation	1 9 8 8	Seoul	2.42	2.56	2.67	2.64	2.64	2.72	2.70	3.13	3.22	2.81	-	153
		Gyeonggi-*do*	2.63	2.20	2.60	2.69	2.68	2.75	2.75	3.16	3.18	2.76	-	233
		Gangwon-*do*	2.76	2.75	1.86	2.53	2.59	2.69	2.75	3.24	3.32	2.69	-	106
		Chungcheongbuk-*do*	2.69	2.72	2.74	1.90	2.24	2.81	2.86	3.34	3.40	2.81	-	125
		Chungcheongnam-*do*	2.79	2.71	2.65	2.43	2.08	2.79	2.80	3.21	3.24	2.82	-	222
		Gyeongsangbuk-*do*	2.79	2.80	2.70	2.65	2.69	2.06	2.39	3.33	3.32	2.77	-	327
		Gyeongsangnam-*do*	2.88	2.87	2.75	2.71	2.73	2.52	2.17	3.34	3.36	2.77	-	296
		Jeollabuk-*do*	2.77	2.77	2.82	2.74	2.69	3.15	3.16	1.90	2.42	2.85	-	177
		Jeollanam-*do*	2.83	2.91	2.93	2.88	2.83	3.16	3.15	2.40	1.89	2.85	-	289
		Jeju Self-Governing Province	2.91	2.89	2.91	2.80	2.84	2.82	2.80	3.31	3.56	1.33	-	45
		Average	2.75	2.72	2.69	2.63	2.61	2.70	2.71	3.01	3.01	2.76	-	-
		Cases	2001	1999	1997	1995	1995	1994	1993	1999	2000	1990	-	-
			Seoul	Gyeonggi-*do*	Gangwon-*do*	Chungcheongbuk-*do*	Chungcheongnam-*do*	Gyeongsangbuk-*do*	Gyeongsangnam-*do*	Jeollabuk-*do*	Jeollanam-*do*	Jeju Self-Governing Province	North Korea	Cases
	2 0 0 3	Seoul	2.32	2.53	2.55	2.65	2.62	2.89	2.90	3.08	3.02	2.70	2.82	133
		Gyeonggi-*do*	2.61	2.33	2.46	2.61	2.60	2.88	2.88	3.12	3.07	2.73	2.92	86
		Gangwon-*do*	2.76	2.83	2.34	2.63	2.59	2.73	2.76	3.15	3.15	2.76	2.83	43
		Chungcheongbuk-*do*	2.72	2.90	2.79	2.38	2.41	2.76	2.86	3.14	3.14	2.72	2.92	30
		Chungcheongnam-*do*	2.68	2.63	2.63	2.39	2.23	2.60	2.63	3.26	3.16	2.62	3.14	81
		Gyeongsangbuk-*do*	2.72	2.73	2.61	2.66	2.70	2.36	2.48	3.37	3.32	2.68	3.25	148
		Gyeongsangnam-*do*	2.99	2.93	2.85	2.82	2.77	2.54	2.35	3.27	3.20	2.88	3.11	128
		Jeollabuk-*do*	2.66	2.77	2.73	2.75	2.74	3.03	3.03	2.59	3.24	2.66	2.93	63
		Jeollanam-*do*	2.62	2.65	2.82	2.71	2.74	2.97	2.87	2.16	2.32	2.57	3.21	94
		Jeju Self-Governing Province	2.57	2.43	2.57	2.43	2.36	2.50	2.50	2.07	3.07	2.43	2.50	15
		Average	2.66	2.67	2.65	2.65	2.63	2.71	2.70	2.99	3.04	2.70	3.03	-
		Cases	814	809	802	808	803	812	808	808	810	789	753	833

(Sources : Na, G-C., 1991 ; Chung, K-S., 2005).

Note : 1) Preference/unfavoritism evaluation scores are meaningful statistically at the 0.05 level of significance.

2) There is little difference in score between two regions' evaluations of each other.

348

regional prejudices." People's recognition of reasons for regionalism changed somewhat from 1988 to 2003 : while most people in 1988 tended to attribute regionalism to regional differences in economic development, people in 2003 saw the major reasons for regionalism as people's prejudices against regional groups and politicians' election campaigns.

Seen from these survey studies, regional favoritism is not merely ideological but actually exists in reality, and regionalism antagonism between people from Honam region and those from Youngnam regions has been most serious. But other studies have argued that there isno regional antagonism (Kim, 1989 ; Kim, 1989). Even though it is true that Korean people exhibit a preference for people from the same region, they seem to be more neutral than negative or critical toward people from different regions. The claim that there is no exclusive regionalism has continued, but these kindsof arguments have usually been drawn out from studies on regional cleavage, which usually appear as promoted during election campaigns (Lee, 2002 ; Choi, and Cho, 2005 ; Choi, 2008).

8.3.3 Election and Regional Rivalry

It is undeniable that an important or even the most decisive factor in elections for the last few decades in South Korea has been regional consciousness or political regionalism. In particular, since 1987 when the authoritarian regime withdrew and presidential and congressional election winners were determined by direct election, regionalism has been mobilized by political parties to influence voting behavior. Election campaigns and competitions between parties have given priority to regional cronyism within candidates' native places over political ideology or government's policies.

Even though historical and cultural studies on the origin of regionalism in South Korea often trace back to the dynasty of Joseon or even Silla, it is generally understood that political regionalism began in the 1970s, was latent during the military dictatorship, and became more prominentafter the process of democracy in the mid-1980s. That is, political regionalism was mentioned for the first time whenPark Jung-Hee from Youngnam region defeated Kim Dae-Jung from Honam region, and Park's government seemed to create regional alienation or discrimination against Honam region with highly authoritarian policies (Table 8.13). Since then, the regional hegemonism of Youngnam region and the resistant Honam region have not only created but also continue to contribute to this kind of antagonism between two regions, which has become a typical pattern of political regionalism in South Korea (Hwang, 1997).

During the periods of the Yusin regime in the 1970s and of the new military regime in the

CHAPTER 8

Table 8.13 **Approval ratings for major candidates in presidential elections**

(unit : %)

Year	Candidate	Seoul	Gyeonggi-do	Gangwon-do	Chungcheongbuk-do	Chungcheongnam-do	Gyeongsangbuk-do	Gyeongsangnam-do	Jeollabuk-do	Jeollanam-do	Jeju Self-Governing Province	National
1971	Park JungHee	40.0	48.9	59.8	57.2	53.5	35.5	34.4	75.6	66.9	56.9	48.8
	Kim DaeJung	59.4	49.5	38.8	40.7	44.4	61.5	62.8	23.3	32.1	41.4	45.3
1987	Roh TaeWoo	29.9	41.0	59.3	46.9	26.2	14.1	7.3	68.1	36.6	49.8	36.6
	Kim YoungSam	29.1	28.1	26.1	28.2	16.1	1.5	1.0	26.5	53.7	26.8	28.0
	Kim DaeJung	32.6	22.1	8.8	11.0	12.4	83.5	91.3	2.5	6.9	18.6	27.0
1992	Kim YoungSam	36.4	36.6	41.5	38.3	36.3	5.7	3.5	62.5	72.8	40.0	42.0
	Kim DaeJung	37.7	31.9	15.5	26.0	28.6	89.1	93.4	8.8	10.9	32.9	33.8
1997	Kim DaeJung	44.9	39.1	23.8	37.4	46.7	92.3	95.9	13.1	13.7	40.6	40.3
	Lee HoiChang	40.9	35.7	43.3	30.8	26.4	4.5	2.5	67.3	54.2	36.6	38.7
2002	Roh MooHyun	51.3	50.5	41.5	50.4	53.4	91.6	94.1	20.2	29.4	56.1	48.9
	Lee HoiChang	44.3	44.3	52.5	42.9	40.1	6.2	4.1	75.5	65.3	39.9	46.6
2007	Lee MyungBak	53.2	51.2	52.0	41.6	34.0	9.0	8.9	70.6	55.9	38.7	48.7
	Jung DongYoung	24.5	23.5	18.9	23.8	22.0	81.6	78.6	6.4	13.0	32.7	26.1
	Lee HoiChang	11.8	13.7	17.6	23.4	31.2	3.6	3.5	15.7	20.0	15.0	15.1

(Source : National Election Commission, http://www.nec.go.kr/sinfo)

1980s, elections by direct popular vote were impossible. Political regionalism did not become a major contributing factor for political conflicts between regions until the 1987 democracy movement. In 1987, it cannot be denied that the political identity of people in the Honam region (Jeollanam-*do* and Jeollabuk-*do*) was formed, which might be framed as Honam vs. Youngnam antagonism (Jo, 2004). But the index of regional cleavage was relatively low in the 1985 Congressional Election before the 1987 democracy movement (Table 8.14). Political regionalism in the presidential election in 1987 was strongly revealed : candidate Roh TaeWoo had an approval rating of 68% in Gyeongsangbuk-*do*, while 7.3% in Jeollanam-*do* on the contrary, candidate Kim DaeJung had an approval rating of 91.3% in Jeollanam-*do*, while 2.5% in Gyeongsangbuk-*do*.

One of the major reasons for regionalistic elections prevailing may stem from the fact that the Unified Democratic Party, which was the biggest opposition party after the so-called 6.29 Declaration, could not find a single candidate (Seo, 2001). As the political conflict between 2 candidates, Kim DaeJung and Kim YoungSam, worsened, members of the National Assembly

Table 8.14 **Index of regional cleavage of major political parties in congressional elections**

The 12th Election (1985)		The 13th Election (1988)		The 14th Election (1992)		The 15th Election (1996)		The 16th Election (2000)		The 17th Election (2004)			
										candidate poll		party poll	
Democratic Justice Party	9.2	Democratic Justice Party	25.1	Democratic Liberal Party	20.3	New Korea Party	22.9	Democratic Party	38.0	Grand National Party	24.5	Grand National Party	26.3
New Korean Democratic Party	15.3	Unified Democratic Party	42.9	Democratic Party	46.9	National Congress for New Politics	54.9	Grand National Party	30.5	Uri Party	22.7	Uri Party	29.0
Democratic Korea Party	2.1	Peace and Democracy Party	78.5	United National Party	25.3	United Liberal Democrats	22.6	United Liberal Democrats	29.1	Millennium Democratic Party	30.5	Millennium Democratic Party	26.7
-		Democratic Republican Party	50.1	-	-	United Democratic Party	8.0	=	-	United Liberal Democrats	31.1	United Liberal Democrats	21.0

(Source : National Election Commission, http://www.nec.go.kr/sinfo)

Note : 1) The index of regional cleavage is calculated as the difference between the number of the most votes obtained among regions and the number of the average of votes obtained from other regions.

2) The Democratic Labor Party ranked 4th in candidate polls and 3rd in party polls, but it was excluded because of its low index of regional cleavage.

were divided on the basis of candidates' native regions. As a result, election campaigns of political parties suggested pledges for development of their own regions without any national validity for such development policies, and hence tried to appeal more to exclusive regionalism than political ideas.

This antagonistic structure with political conflicts between the Youngnam and Honam regions was reinforced through the process of the 13th Congressional Election, and the conflicts became more serious in the presidential election in 1992 with a confrontation between Kim DaeJung and Kim YoungSam. As the local municipality was implemented, the local election became another factor that promoted political regionalism. As seen from the constitution of local governments after the 6.27 Local Election in 1995, the Democratic Party won most of the provincial governorships and local administratorships in Seoul and Honam region, and this phenomenon was the same with the United Liberal Democrats in Chungcheong region, and the Democratic Liberal Party in Youngnam region. In essence, regional sectionalism, in which a single party dominates a specific region, became the norm. The 15th Congressional Election in 1996 was called "the struggle of three Kims" for political initiatives and for the next presidency. The presidential election that was held during the economic crisis in 1997 revealed regional competition for political power, which resulted in a victory for Kim DaeJung with a regional co-alliance with Kim JongPhil.

The congressional elections in 2000 were held under a new composition of parties after the horizontal change of regime between the ruling party and the oppositional party this election was characterized also as one in which civil movement groups intervened nationwide for the first time in Korean electoral history. As a result, though the walls of political regionalism were not torn down completely, there was an opportunity to decrease political regionalism with the arrival of the newly elected members from the so-called 386 generation to the National Assembly. Additionally, there also appeared to be a possibility of ideological and class-based cleavages that could rival the political influence of regionalism. That is, the Democratic Party showed the potential to be a progressive party for labor and the populace, while the Grand National Party became a conservative party for incumbents and middle-high classes.

One of the major issues of the 16th Presidential Election, which was held after the decline of the three Kims, was the cleavage between generations with the emergence of the so-called internet generation, though there was no big difference in regionalistic voting behavior (Ohn, 2004). Regional conflict became apparent immediately when a political crisis of impeachment and referendum erupted for President Roh Moo-Hyun, but this situation also revealed a cleavage along the lines of generation and ideology. This new kind of electoral cleavage continued to the 17th Congressional Election in 2004. Even though there was no fundamental transfor-mation of regional structure, The Uri Party, less than one year after its founding, became a national party, gaining parliamentary seats from all regions except Daegu and Gyeongsangbuk-*do*.

What is more, the generational cleavage revealed in the election was a result of specific ideological differences that were reflected in the vote choice (Tables 8.15 and 8.16) (Park, 2004). Morethan half of the conservative voters supported the Grand National Party, while a higher rate of moderate and progressive voters supported the Uri Party. In particular, the Democratic Labor Party with a socialist character, which gained 2 seats in local precincts and more than 10% of the proportional party vote on the national level, rose to be the 3rd party.

The presidential election in 2007 took on a character different from previous elections.

Table 8.15 **Ideological Orientation by Generation** *(unit : %)*

	Progressive	Moderate	Conservative
ages 20 - 29	41.6	48.3	10.1
ages 30 - 39	37.8	50.8	11.4
ages 40 - 49	26.1	49.5	24.4
ages 50 and over	17.1	52.2	30.7

(Source : Park, M-H. (2004)).

Table 8.16 **Voting Party by Ideological Orientation** *(unit : %)*

	The Grand National Party	The Uri Party	The Democratic Labor Party
Progressive	6.1	48.7	51.1
Moderate	22.6	32.4	41.5
Conservative	55.2	18.7	7.4

(Source : Park, M-H. (2004)).

Even though political regionalism remains a factor important to the outcome of elections, candidates seldom appealed to political regionalism during the campaign, and therefore the electoral power of regionalism was considerably weakened. This was partly because of voters' reluctance toward the Roh Moo Hyun Administration and partly because of the ideological cleavage between progressives and conservatives. In particular, voters in the capital region who previously considered candidates' native places and personal relations with a specific party as a highly important factor for voting escaped from such political regionalism and pursued their own economic interests : this can be called the "new regionalism of Seoul" (Park, 2008). This kind of phenomenon continued during the 18th Congressional Election in 2008, which resulted in the victory of conservative parties and the defeat of progressive-revolutionary parties, though political regionalism may not have disappeared completely.

In short, political regionalism, which emerged after the 1987 democratization process, was a decisive factor for all elections until recently. But this kind of regionalism has been combined with an ideological cleavage such that the Youngnam people tend to be conservative, while the Honam people tend to be progressive. This is not to say that political regionalism has disappeared. It seems that when a certain candidate or party again tries to appeal to political regionalism in order to realize a political purpose, regionalistic voting behavior could be revived. What is more, the capital region, which promoted a re-concentration of population and industry, has its share of the electorate, and hence there is concern that this region would stimulate a new regionalism that could be mobilized exclusively against all other local regions.

8.3.4 Local Consciousness and Urban Politics

In relation to regional consciousness or identity, there emerges a new local consciousness or identity that has been formed due to discrimination by those living in the capital region against those from the non-the capital region. Local consciousness is similar to regional consciousness in a sense that local people have developed their own historical and cultural consciousness on the basis of their own localities. Local consciousness in a traditional sense can be formulated on the basis of regional differences of weather, landscape, dialect, and other elements in modes of living. But recently, local consciousness is conceived within administrative units, resulting from the structure of relationships between the central and the local governments (Hong, 2005).

Indeed, local consciousness seems to be generated in the context of uneven regional development between the capital region and local cities and rural areas. In particular, the re-concentration of population and industries towards the capital region after the mid-1980s has made not only rural areas but also local cities experience a serious out-flow of population, resources, and local wealth, and hence enhanced local people's feelings of deprivation. What is more, the central government, which has ever strengthened its centralized power, has dominated local governments, requiring them to follow its one-way political and administrative directions.

Under this circumstance, the local municipality was introduced in 1995, which can be seen as a new impact upon local consciousness. The local municipality was expected not only to contribute to regional development and grassroots democracy (as it will allow local people's participation in local policies and encourage them to use local resources with efficiency and equity), but also to activate urban politics. As shown in a survey study (Choi, et al., 2004), there were more respondents who thought that the local municipality would activate urban politics than those who had a negative view of it. But in reality, the local municipality has hardly made any contribution to urban politics because local elections have been much more strongly influenced by the central power than local powers. And hence, in answer to the question, what is the biggest factor hindering development of urban politics, respondents pointed out the "centralization of power in the central government," the "structure of regional domination of central parties," and the "lack of quality of local politicians," in that order (Table 8.17).

354

Table 8.17 **Factors hindering development of urban politics**

	Centralization of power in the central government	Authoritative attitudes of local bureaucrats	Structure of regional domination of central parties	Lack of quality of local politicians	Deficiency of political conscious-ness of citizens	Inactivity of political participation of civic organizations	Insufficiency of local mass media to lead opinions	Dullness of local universities to develop local policies	Collusion between local politics and the economy	Undevelopment of linkage of Industry-university-government
Total	3.926	3.514	3.848	3.838	3.462	3.118	3.385	3.411	3.581	3.437
Seoul	3.606	3.557	3.667	3.790	3.495	3.174	3.335	3.318	3.683	3.417
Dejeon	4.093	3.537	3.907	3.832	3.474	3.083	3.279	3.326	3.483	3.363
Daegu	3.910	3.547	3.786	3.821	3.544	3.190	3.506	3.452	3.606	3.433
Gwangju	4.059	3.403	4.025	3.907	3.335	3.032	3.423	3.561	3.568	3.565

(Source : Choi, et al., 2004).

Note : Calculated on the basis of a five-point scale : 1=nil, 2=slight, 3=moderate, 4=high, 5=very high.

Other important momentums with which local consciousness could be developed were the campaign for decentralization of power initiated as a civil movement and the government policy for national balanced development. In spite of the implementation of the local municipality, political power was not properly decentralized, and hence a civil movement advocating for power devolution of the central government was launched in the early 2000s. Partly to meet this civic claim, the Roh Moo-Hyun Administration pursued strong policies for nationally balanced development, pointing out the disadvantages of overpopulation in the capital region. These policies included the construction of a multifunctional administrative city to bear some part of the Capital functions, the construction ofinnovation cities to relocate public sectors in the capital region to local areas, and other various urban and regional development projects.

As the local municipality has been implemented and nationally balanced development policies have been pursued actively, urban politics has changed its character. One of the major changes in urban politics is that heads of local governments are expected to have an entrepreneurial mind, which indeed has stemmed from neoliberalism. As shown in a survey on this issue, 70.7% of respondents to the question, "How important is an entrepreneurial mind for heads of local governments?", replied that it is "very important" or "important." The percent of such responses is higher in Gwangju than other cities. This value and recognition of

CHAPTER 8

entrepreneurial thinking for heads of local governmentshas been mainly generated ideologically through sweet pledges in election campaigns. Moreover, entrepreneurial urban politics has prevailed, emphasizing regional economic development in competition among regions for directly attracting international capital in the process of neoliberal globalization (Choi, 2007b).

On the other hand, the role of civil society also has been emphasized. In a question on the "influence of civil organizations on local politics," 46.2% of the total respondents replied that the influence has been "very high or considerable," while only 14.9% replied that these have had "little" or "no" influence. Even though the percent of positive responses is somewhat different in cities, various roles and the influence of civil organizations have encouraged introduction of local governance, which operates on the basis of mutual agreements and cooperation with networks of various subjects. The concept of local governance, which could be applied to local contexts, emphasizes members' partnerships and participation in policies planning and implementation in order to enhance their efficiency and equity.

The form of urban management with urban governance seems to be changing recently. Currently emerging are some examples of multi-level governance in which even transnational corporations as well as the central government participate, despite their local characteristics. Moreover, when such a regime of governance is applied to various types of projects to develop the urban economy, it tends to be mobilized as a means of pursuing interests of specific groups, though it appeals to democratic participation and fair distribution for all members of the local community. This tendency seems especially apparent in entrepreneurial strategies for urban regeneration.

Chapter 9.
REGIONAL DEVELOPMENT OF KOREA

THE EVOLUTION OF THE SETTLEMENT SYSTEM IN KOREA

9.1.1 The Urbanization Process and Settlement System

The urbanization process in Korea has accelerated since the 1960s when Korean society initially industrialized and the trend toward rapid urbanization continues today. In the year 2000, 39 million people, about 84.5% of the 46 million total Koreans, lived in cities, while 7 million people lived in rural farming or fishing villages.Along with the advancement of urbanization, the Korean urban settlement system has changed as well. First, cities with populations of less than 100,000 have declined continuously (Table 9.1). The proportion of cities with a population of 20,000-50,000 and 50,000-100,000 were 7.7% and 5.7%, respectively, in 1960, but by 2000, these cities had gradually declined to 4.3% and 5.0%,

Table 9.1 **Population distributions and Changes by City Sizes 1960-2000** *(unit : %)*

Section	1960	1970	1980	1990	2000
Over 5 million	-	17.6	22.3	24.4	21.4 (1)
1- 5 million	14.4	9.4	15.6	23.1	23.9 (5)
.5 - 1 million	2.7	2.1	3.7	7.0	14.3 (9)
.25 - .5 million	2.9	3.7	6.3	6.8	8.8(13)
.1 - . 25 million	2.8	5.2	8.5	7.8	6.8(19)
50,000 - .1 million	5.7	5.0	3.5	5.1	5.0(34)
20,000 - 50,000	7.3	6.8	6.7	5.3	4.3(63)
rural areas	64.2	50.2	33.4	20.5	15.5
Total (unit : 1,000 people)	100.0 (24,989)	100.0 (30,882)	100.0 (37,436)	100.0 (43,411)	100.0 (46,136)

note : number of cities
(Source : Statistics Korea, Kim, C. H. et al, 2003)

respectively. In contrast, the proportion of cities with a population of 100,000-250,000 and 250,000-500,000 were 2.8% and 2.9%, respectively, in 1960 and those cities drastically increased to 6.8% and 8.8%, respectively, in 2000. However, the largest growth took place in the cities with a population of half a million to a million residents, which grew from 2.7% in 1960 to 3.7% in 1980 and then exploded dramatically to 14.3% by the year 2000. The pattern indicates the urban sprawl progression around large metropolitan areas, as well as the megalopolitanization process of the greater the capital region, which resulted in many edge cities (suburbs) of over half a million people. At the same time, small- and medium-sized cities lost their competitive advantage and experienced a gradual decline.

This can be seen by examining the Seoul Metropolitan Area, which expanded to about a quarter of the nation's population (24.4%) in 1990however, in 2000 it declined to 21.4%. At the same time (in 2000), the largest proportion (23.9%) of the Korean population was absorbed by the group of cities ranging in size from 1 million to 5 million, represented by the 5 major cities of Korea.

9.1.2 Population Growth and Spatial Organization of Korea

As can be imagined from the statistics shown above, the urban settlement pattern in Korea reflects a rather uneven distribution of population. The long term out-migration of the population from rural areas to the capital region has brought a relative population loss, as well as a loss in absolute numbers. Table 9.2 indicates the population distribution of the capital region and 7 other regions of Korea, Gangwon-*do*, Chungcheongnam-*do*, Chungcheongbuk-*do*, Jeollabuk-*do*, Jeju special self-governing province and the metropolitan regions of Gwangju, Daegu and Busan.

Between 1970 and 2004, the population ratio of Gangwon-*do* declined from 5.9% to 3.1% of the total Korean population the Chungcheong region declined from 13.8% to 10.1%, Jeollabuk-*do* from 7.7% to 3.8%, Gwangju from 12.7 to 6.9%, Daegu from 14.5% to 10.9% and Jeju special self-governing province from 1.2% to 1.1%. The region that gained population was, as expected, the capital region, which includes Seoul, Incheon and Gyeonggi-*do*. The population of this area grew from 28.3% of the total population in 1970 to 47.9% in 2004, which indicates that about half of the country's population lived in the region by 2004. The other area that saw an increase was Busan, which grew from 15.9% in 1970 to 17.3% in 1980 ; however, it had declined to 16.2% by 2004.

Table 9.2 **Population Changes by Region (1970-2004)**

	Regions	1970	1980	1990	2000	2004
Korea Total	-	32,241 (100.0)	38,124 (100.0)	42,869 (100.0)	47,008 (100.0)	48,082 (100.0)
Capital Regions	Seoul, Incheon, Gyeonggi-*do*	9,126 (28.3)	13,544 (35.5)	18,342 (42.80	21,747 (46.3)	23,054 (47.9)
Gangwon Regions	Gangwon-*do*	1,914 (5.9)	1,824 (4.8)	1,562 (3.6)	1,516 (3.2)	1,487 (3.1)
Chungcheon	Daejeon, Chungcheong Nam & Buk-*do*	4,444 (13.8)	4,460 (11.7)	4,402 (10.3)	4,771 (10.1)	4,836 (10.1)
Jeonbuk Regions	Jeolla Buk-*do*	2,491 (7.7)	2,329 (6.1)	2,047 (4.8)	1,927 (4.1)	1,842 (3.8)
Gwangju Regions	Gwangju, Jeolla Nam-*do*	4,101 (12.7)	3,848 (10.1)	3,605 (8.4)	3,417 (7.3)	3,309 (6.9)
Daegu Regions	Daegu, Gyeongsang Buk-*do*	4,669 (14.5)	5,045 (13.2)	5,029 (11.7)	5,302 (11.3)	5,230 (10.9)
Busan Regions	Busan, Ulsan, Gyeongsang Nam-*do*	5,123 (15.9)	6,601 (17.3)	7,374 (17.2)	7,04 (16.6)	7,788 (16.2)
Jeju Regions	Jeju Special Self-Governing Province	374 (1.2)	472 (1.2)	509 (1.2)	524 (1.1)	537 (1.1)

(Source : Statistics Korea)

The regions of Gangwon-*do*, Jeollabuk-*do* and Gwangju experienced precipitous declines during the period from 1970 to 2004. The population of Gangwon-*do* in 2004 was 1.487 million, only 77.7% of its 1970 population ; that of Jeollabuk-*do* was 1.842 million, only 73.9% of its 1970 population and that of Gwangju was 3.309 million, only 80.7% of its 1970 population.

The changing patterns of spatial organization and settlements can be seen from the characteristics of the inter-regional population migration (Figure 9.1). All regions experienced an out-migration pattern to the capital region, with the leading out-migration coming from the southwestern Honam region. During the 1990s, however, the Homan region's out-migration to the capital region dropped to less than half and the Yeongnam region declined as well until leveling at about the same number of out-migrants originating from the area to the capital region. While out-migration to the capital region slowed in the 1990s, the increase of in-migration to the Chungcheong region is worth noting. The drastic decline of out-migration from the Chungcheong region to the capital region is most obvious. The Yeongnam region used to be the in-migration destination from all regions except the capital region, yet in the 1990s it experienced out-migration to other regions.

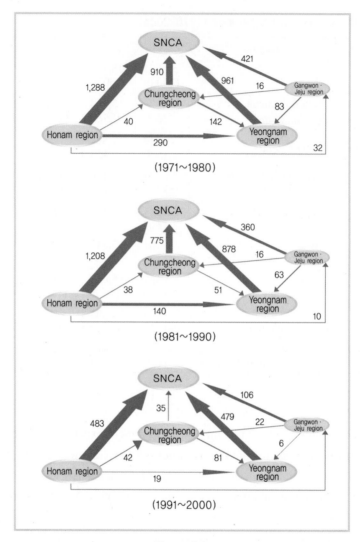

Figure 9.1
Note : net number of out-migration (unit : 1,000 population)
(Source : Statistics Korea, Kim, C. H. et al, 2003)

Chapter 9.2.

TERRITORIAL AXES AND SPATIAL ORGANIZATION

9.2.1 The Evolution of Territorial Axes

Territorial axes are represented by a series of central places and corridors of the daily urban system and along the axes all the major transportation networks and industrial sites are developed. These axes promote regional growth represented by the population and industrial migration into the region. When a city and the surrounding region become economically interconnected, a new development axis is established and nodal points along the axis and the hinterland accelerate the regional growth. Eventually the entire region becomes integrated into the national development system.

Table 9.3 indicates the territorial axes and spatial organization of Korea. In 1998, three-

Table 9.3 **Population changes by Territorial Axes (1970-1998)**

(unit : Sq. Km, 1,000 people, %)

Axis / Section	Area 1998	Population 1970	Population 1980	Population 1990	Population 1998
Korea Total	99.4	30,882	37,436	43,411	47,174
Gyeongbu	30.6 (30.8)	16,366 (53.0)	23,603 (63.0)	30,884 (71.1)	35,046 (74.3)
Hwan Hwanghae (Circum West Coast)	23.9 (24.1) (17.1)[*]	13,857 (44.9) (18.7)[*]	18,377 (49.1) (15.3)[*]	23,484 (54.1) (12.8)[*]	26,285 (55.7) (11.8)[*]
Hwan Namhae (Circum South Coast)	22.6 (22.7)	8,374 (27.1)	9,769 (26.1)	10,536 (24.3)	10,713 (22.7)
Hwan Donghae (Circum East Coast)	24.7 (24.9)	7,055 (22.8)	9,434 (25.2)	10,825 (24.9)	11,493 (24.4)
Central Interior	9.9 (10.0)	2,536 (8.2)	3,266 (8.7)	4,836 (11.1)	6,590 (14.0)
Southern Interior	15.4 (15.5)	4,560 (14.8)	5,134 (13.7)	5,429 (12.5)	5,575 (12.2)

(Source : Statistics Korea)

quarters of the Korean population (74.3%) were concentrated along the Gyeongbu (Seoul-Busan) Axis, while in 1970 the area had about half (53%) of the country's population. The Hwan Hwanghae Axis (or Circum West Coastal Axis) on the west coast accounted for 55.7% of the Korean population in 1998.

9.2.2 National Territorial Axes and Growth of Cities

The spatial accessibility of Korean cities has improved tremendously due to the growth of rail and highway transportation. In 2004, the opening of the new high speed railroad (KTX) brought a new era in express rail while new express highways, the Central Expressway, West Coast Expressway and Daejeon-Tongyeong Expressway, improved accessibility for the entire nation. Besides the high-speed transportation network, the communication information network has adopted high technology, which has helped integrate the national territory and brought structural changes to the network system.

The reinforcement of the national territorial axes resulting from the construction of major thoroughfare networks can be seen by the growth of major cities. Figure 9.2 indicates the time series representation of the spatial distribution of the top 30 cities in Korea. Shown are cities in 1942 and in 1966, before the construction of expressways all of the top 30 cities were related to traditional regional administrative centers as well as ports and some railroad junctions, such as Daejeon and Iksan. Most cities were evenly distributed throughout the country at that time. In 1985, cities along the expressways of Gyeongbu (Seoul-Busan) or Honam (Daejeon-Mokpo) continued to grow while the traditional cities with lower accessibility from the expressways were slowly declining. In 2000, 15 large cities from among the top 30 were all located in the capital region, which led to further spatial inequality. Not a single city from the top 30 was in Gangwon-*do* and most of the cities were along the axes of the Gyeongbu and Honam lines, indicating the close relationship between the growth of cities and the national territorial axes. Among the top 30 cities, 16 were along the axes in 1942 and the number increased to 28 in 2005.

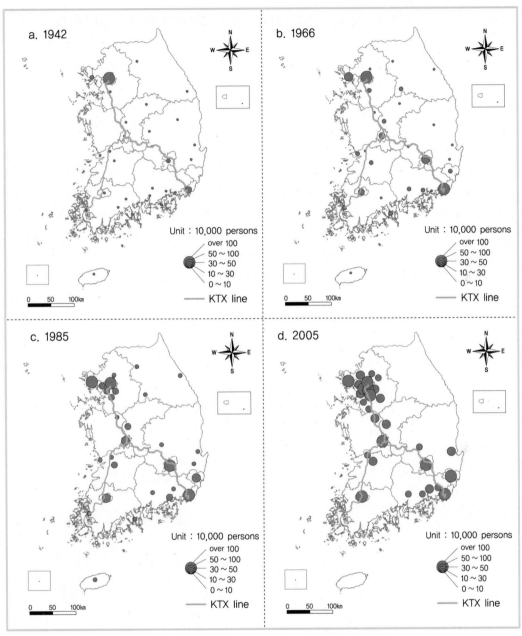

Figure 9.2 **Spatial changes of top 30 cities in Korea**
(Source : Lee, Y-W etc, (2006))

9.2.3 Megalopolitanization in the Settlement System

The time needed to travel in physical or virtual space has become surprisingly shortened by the expansion of expressways and the widespread use of high technology in communication networking. This trend has brought qualitative changes in urbanization, population migration patterns and the daily urban system of city residents. Economic and cultural exchanges have taken place regardless of the administrative boundaries and the daily urban systems of residents have rapidly expanded in the large urban areas. Figure 9.3 shows the urban sprawl and commuter zones of major cities for 1990 and 2000. In 1990, the commuter zone of the Seoul Metropolitan Area increased beyond Gyeonggi-*do* and moved to Asan, Cheonan and Cheongju in Chungcheongbuk-*do* and Chuncheon and Wonju in Gangwon-*do*. By 2000, the commuter zones of Seoul reached as far as Seosan, Eumsung and Jecheon. In addition to the distance, the volume of commuters overall has increased.

In other major cities around the country the territory of the commuter zone, with the exception of the Gwangju area, has expanded. First, the Daejeon metropolitan area gained a commuter zone as far as Jeonju in Jeollabuk-*do* by 2000. During the same time, the Daegu metropolitan area reached Andong in Gyeongsangbuk-*do* and Changnyeong in

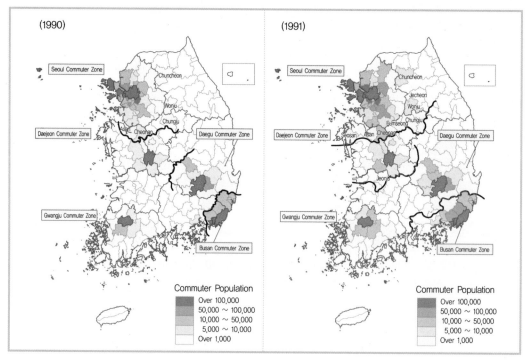

Figure 9.3 **Commuter Zone of Major cities in Korea in 1990 & 2000**
[Source : Statistics Korea ; Kim, C. H. et al, 2003]

Gyeongsangnam-*do*. The Busan metropolitan area, the largest city in the region, reached as far as Jinju and the volume of commuters to nearby Gimhae and Yangsan greatly increased during the same decade.

NATIONAL BALANCE DEVELOPMENT

9.3.1 Dominance of the capital region

One of the major concerns of Korean national planning has always been the uneven distribution of population and wealth between the capital region and the rest of the country. The trend has continued for the last 40 years and the result of this unbalanced development of the capital region has been a gap between the capital area and the provincial region that has deeply widened.

The population concentration around the capital region is due to the persistent in-migration of people to the Seoul metropolitan area for the last 4 decades. In 1960, the population of Seoul was 2.45 million and by 2000 it had reached over 10 million. Until the mid-1970s most of the increase was within the city administrative boundaries however, fast growth has occurred since then in the newly planned cities outside the Seoul city limits due to the

Table 9.4 **Population Concentration Trends in the capital region**

(1,000 people, annual increase rate %)

Section / Year	Seoul Commuter zone (A)		Capital Region (B)		contribution of commuter zone (A+B)		
	Population	annual growth rate	Population	annual growth rate	Population	annual growth rate	
1960	2,445.4	-	2,748.8	-	5194.2	-	-
1970	5,536.4	8.17	3,358.1	2.00	8894.5	5.38	16.5
1980	8,366.8	4.13	4,933.9	3.85	13298.2	4.02	18.8
1990	10,627.8	2.38	7,972.6	4.80	18600.4	3.36	57.3
1995	10,595.4	- 0.06	9,591.4	3.70	20186.8	1.64	102.0
2000	9,854.0	- 1.44	11,404.0	3.53	21258.0	1.04	169.2

(Source : Statistics Korea)

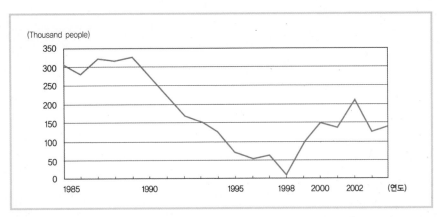

Figure 9.4 **Changes of Net number of In-migration for Seoul Metropolitan Area**
(Source : Statistics Korea)

Table 9.5 **Agglomeration of Activities in the capital region**

Section		Korea	Capital region	Seoul	Incheon	Gyeong gi-*do*	Degree of concentration (%)	
		(A)	(B)	(C)	-	-	B/A	C/A
Area (2007)	Sq. km	99,720	11,744	605	1,007	10,132	11.8	0.6
Population (2007)	1,000 persons	49,268	23,964	10,193	2,665	11,106	48.6	20.7
Population Density (2007)	persons/Sq. km	494	2,041	16,848	2,646	1,096	-	-
Industries (2006)	Employment (1,000 persons)	23,151	11,363	4,906	1,228	5,229	49.1	21.2
	Unemployment (persons)	827	483	232	57	194	58.4	28.1

improved accessibility of these areas (Table 9.4).

The net annual in-migration to the capital region reached its peak with slightly less than half a million (0.43 million) in 1983, but gradually slowed to the point of only 9,000 in 1998. However, the in-migration started to increase again in 1999, after the IMF crisis and by 2002 annual in-migration had reached 0.21 million, followed by 0.14 million in 2004,which was still 15 times higher than the figures for 1998 (Figure 9.4). The land area of the capital region is only 11.8% of the country. However, it has been the continuous center of population, industry, economy and education and the effect of agglomeration was a serious concern to policy makers. The population of the area in 2007 was 23.964 million, about half (48.6%) of the nation. the capital region had 49.4% of the total employment positions (2006), 51.9% of

CHAPTER 9

369

Section		Korea	Capital region	Seoul	Incheon	Gyeong gi-*do*	Degree of concentration (%)	
		(A)	(B)	(C)	-	-	B/A	C/A
Industries (2006)	Total Economic Activities participants (1,000 persons)	23,978	11,845	5,138	1,285	5,422	49.4	21.4
	Gross Regional Production (1 billion won)	856,192	408,592	193,776	40,607	174,209	47.7	22.6
Manufacturing (2006)	Establishments (units)	340,724	176,707	67,484	21,203	88,020	51.9	19.8
	Employees (1,000 persons)	3,435	1,669	445	228	996	48.6	13.0
	Total production (1 billion won)	215,566	80,581	10,100	11,238	59,243	37.4	4.7
Services (2006)	Establishments (units)	905,04	430,778	205,544	41,739	183,495	47.6	22.7
	Employees (1,000 persons)	4,729	2,552	1,442	195	915	54.0	30.5
Universities (2007)	Total schools	175	68	38	4	26	38.9	21.7
	Total students (1,000 students)	1,318	510	326	27	157	38.7	24.7
Medical Facilities (2005)	Total hospitals	49,566	25,488	13,344	2,312	9,832	51.4	26.9
Finance (2006)	Total Deposits (1 billion won)	592,721	407,361	299,425	20,899	87,037	68.7	50.5
	Total Loans (1 billion won)	699,430	469,374	291,319	33,705	144,350	67.1	41.7
Automobiles (2006)	Total vehicles (1,000 vehicles)	15,895	7,330	2,857	822	3,651	46.1	18.0
	Total cars (1,000 cars)	11,607	5,599	2,266	599	2,734	48.2	19.5

[Source : Statistics Korea]

all establishments (2006), 38.9% of all colleges (2007), 51.4% of all medical facilities (2005) and 68.7% of all savings and other financial institutions (2006) (Table 9.5).

9.3.2 Gaps between the capital Region and Provincial Regions

The dominance and concentration of the capital region is inseparable from the economic dependence and slower growth of the countryside. the capital region leads the country in economic, political, social, cultural and all other functions, which are concentrated in the capital region. This in turn creates further attractions for agglomeration. Consequently, the gapbetween the center and periphery becomes further amplified despite various government attempts to slow the process. Such inequality between the regions has brought conflict and even emotional discouragement and disparity to the population.

In contrast to the capital region situation, most of the regional centers have lost population and have experienced subsequent economic declines. In particular, Gangwon-*do*, Jeollabuk-*do* and Gwangju have consistently lost population and it has become difficult for these regions to find any stimulant for population or economic growth The economic comparison between the capital region and the rest of the county is shown in Table 9.6 and the trends of the changes between the regions are shown in Figure 9.5. The dominance of the capital region is overwhelming in all economic sectors (Table 9.6), while the gap between the 2 areas becomes widened and even shows the economic dependence on the capital region in some economic sectors. Consequently, some of the less developed regions suffer from economic difficulties, which weaken the economic competitiveness of Korea in the international market. There fore, it is a matter of the highest importance to adopt a strong decentralization policy from the

Table 9.6 **Comparison of Economic Power : Capital vs. Non-the capital region (2000)**

(unit : %)

Section	Population Proportion (A)	Total Economic Power								B/A
		Gross Regional Production	Manufacturing Employment	Retail wholesale Employment	Financial Activities	Tax Revenues	Total	Average(B)		
Korea	100.0	100.0	100.0	100.0	100.0	100.0	700.0	100.0	1.00
the capital region	46.3	46.3	45.3	47.5	66.8	70.9	368.2	52.6	1.14
Non-the capital region	53.7	53.7	54.7	52.5	33.2	29.1	331.8	47.4	0.88

(Source : The Korean Government, 2005, Development Strategies for the capital region.)

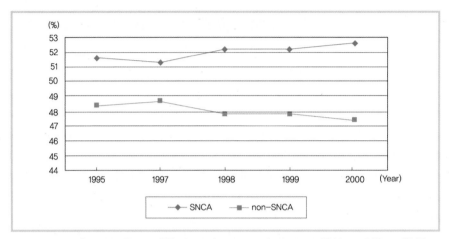

Figure 9.5 **Comparison of Economic output between SMA and Non-SMA**
(Source : Statistics Korea)

capital region to the peripheral areas. By doing so, the government can bring about balanced development for Korea by discouraging the population and industry from concentrating in the capital region.

Despite persistent efforts to balance development of the nation, the result has not been noteworthy. One of the main causes of slow changes has been that central administrative functions have all been concentrated in the capital region. These efforts include the head quartering of major companies, the locating of central governmental offices and the presence of prestigious universities, to name a few. These central administrative functions tend to concentrate in the capital region more than other functions (Park and Kim, 2001).

Table 9.7 indicates that the proportion of manufacturing employment situated in the capital region was about 46%, with 65% of prestigious universities and most of the central government offices located in the area. The headquarters of major companies were also heavily

Table 9.7 **Aggregation Rates of Central Nerve Functions in the capital region**

(unit : %)

Section			(%)
Population			46.0
Economic Opportunities for Manufacturing			46.0
Central Nerve functions	Political	Central government Offices	100.0
		Headquarters of public institutions	83.2
	Industrial	Headquarters of Top 100 companies	91.0
		Headquarters of Top 500 companies	82.6
		Headquarters of top 3,000 companies	71.9
	Academic	Top 20 Universities	65.0

(Source : Statistics Korea)

Table 9.8 **Public Administrative Functions of the capital region**   (unit : %)

	Section	Capital region	Non-capital region	Total	Ratio of Capital region
Central government offices	Central government offices	50	8	58	86.2
	Subsidiary offices	109	25	134	81.3
	total	159	33	192	82.8
Institutions administered by Government	Government invested companies	23	3	26	88.5
	Government direct investment companies	14	1	15	93.3
	Government participating companies	80	24	104	76.9
	Private-public partnership	70	3	73	95.9
	total	187	31	218	85.8
Total		346	64	410	84.4

[Source : Kim, 2005]

concentrated in the capital region. More precisely, 83% of the headquarters of publicly-owned companies and 83% of the Fortune 500 companies' headquarters, are located in the capital region. The region boasts 82.8% of the central government offices and 85.8% of the institutions administered by the government. As shown in Table 9.8, central government offices are heavily concentrated in Seoul, since it is the capital region and the nerve center of Korea.

Table 9.9 **Location Changes in Headquarters of Top 3,000 Businesses (1990-2000)**

Section	Regional Distribution (Unit, Thousand person)				Distribution Proportion (%)				Population and Distribution Ratio (%)			
	Establishment		Employment		Establishment		Employment		Establishment		Employment	
	1990	2000	1990	2000	1990	2000	1990	2000	1990	2000	1990	2000
Korea	3,000	3,000	2,350	1,855	100.0	100.0	100.0	100.0	100.0	100.0	100.0	100.0
The capital region	2,062	2,158	1,826	1,512	68.9	71.9	77.7	81.5	160.9	155.4	181.5	176.2
Chungcheong region	120	180	60	58	4.0	6.0	2.5	3.1	39.1	59.1	24.8	30.8
Honam region	87	102	30	37	2.9	3.4	1.3	2.0	22.1	29.9	9.7	17.8
Yongnam region	694	533	422	239	23.2	17.8	18.0	12.9	80.1	63.7	62.1	46.2
Gangwon, Jeju region	30	27	12	8	1.0	0.9	0.5	0.5	20.8	20.8	10.2	10.4
Non-the capital region	931	842	524	343	31.1	28.1	22.3	18.5	54.4	52.3	39.0	34.4

[Source : Park and Kim, 2001.]

CHAPTER 9

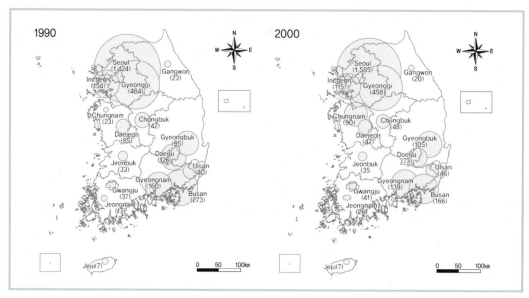

Figure 9.6 **Spatial distribution of top 3000 corporations for 1990 & 2000.**
(Source : Park and Kim, 2001.)

Among the top 100 businesses in Korea based on their sales volume, 91 businesses were located in Seoul and 9 were in the rest of the country in 2000 : of the 9 not located in Seoul, 5 were located in the Yeongnam (Southeast) region and 4 in the Chungcheong (central) region. According to Table 9.9, out of the top 3,000 companies based on their sales in 1990, 931 companies (31.1% of total) were in the non-the capital region, but in 2000 the number declined to 842 companies (28.1%). Considering the population decline in the non-the capital region, the business decline in the area was expected. By regions, the Chungcheong and Honam regions increased slightly while the Yeongnam region, Gangwon-*do* and Jeju special self-governing province experienced some decline. In other words, the regional disparity grewlarger during the decade of 1990-2000 between the capital region and the rest of the country (Figure 9.6).

In terms of manufacturing companies, the capital region has maintained dominance for the last 30 years. In 1970, the capital region had 32.8% of manufacturing firms and in 2005 the area had 57.2% of the total national manufacturing firms concentrated in the capital region (Table 9.10 and Figure 9.7). The number of manufacturing employees represented over 45% of the total population in the capital region. More importantly, the newly growing high technology companies, information communication companies and venture capital businesses had over 70% of their facilities located in the capital region.

Table 9.10 **Concentration of Manufacturing firms and employees in SMA**

(Unit : a unit, %)

Section	Year	1970	1975	1980	1985	1990	1995	2000	2005
firms employees	Capital region	7,916 (32.8)	8,305 (36.4)	13,512 (43.8)	24,142 (54.8)	40,005 (58.1)	53,492 (55.6)	55,874 (57.0)	67,079 (57.2)
	Seoul	5,708 (72.1)	5,542 (66.7)	7,652 (56.6)	13,627 (56.4)	17,520 (43.8)	20,288 (37.9)	18,401 (32.9)	19,787 (29.5)
	Incheon	0 (0.0)	0 (0.0)	0 (0.0)	1,989 (8.2)	4,381 (11.0)	7,680 (14.4)	8,525 (15.3)	9,465 (14.1)
	Gyeonggi-*do*	2,208 (27.9)	2,763 (33.3)	5,860 (43.4)	8,526 (35.3)	18,104 (45.3)	25,524 (47.7)	28,948 (51.8)	37,827 (56.4)
	non-Capital region	16,198 (67.2)	14,482 (63.6)	17,311 (56.2)	19,895 (45.2)	28,867 (41.9)	42,710 (44.4)	42,236 (43.0)	50,126 (42.8)
	Total	24,114 (100.0)	22,787 (100.0)	30,823 (100.0)	44,037 (100.0)	68,872 (100.0)	96,202 (100.0)	98,110 (100.0)	117,205 (100.0)
firms employees	Capital region	396,014 (46.0)	685,714 (48.3)	923,920 (45.9)	1,153,255 (47.3)	1,443,365 (47.8)	1,380,313 (46.8)	1,234,960 (46.6)	1,346,360 (47.0)
	Seoul	291,679 (73.7)	433,313 (63.2)	445,242 (48.2)	482,690 (41.9)	470,565 (32.6)	369,607 (26.8)	279,314 (22.6)	261,102 (19.4)
	Incheon	0 (0.0)	0 (0.0)	0 (0.0)	174,705 (15.1)	236,424 (16.4)	245,790 (17.8)	208,096 (16.9)	198,962 (14.8)
	Gyeonggi-*do*	104,335 (26.3)	252,401 (36.8)	478,678 (51.8)	495,860 (43.0)	736,376 (51.0)	764,916 (55.4)	747,550 (60.5)	886,296 (65.8)
	nin-Capital region	465,027 (54.0)	734,430 (51.7)	1,090,831 (54.1)	1,284,742 (52.7)	1,576,451 (52.2)	1,571,572 (53.2)	1,417,630 (53.4)	1,519,189 (53.0)
	Total	861,041 (100.0)	1,420,144 (100.0)	2,014,751 (100.0)	2,437,997 (100.0)	3,019,816 (100.0)	2,951,885 (100.0)	2,652,590 (100.0)	2,865,549 (100.0)

(Source : Statistics Korea)

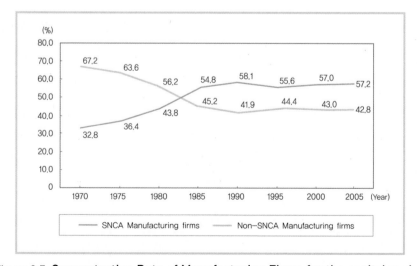

Figure 9.7 **Concentration Rate of Manufacturing Firms for the capital region**
(Source : Statistics Korea)

Table 9.11 indicates that information-based industries are also concentrated in the capital region, while the non-the capital region have a lower proportion of these industries and a higher proportion of the conventional industries as of 2005. the capital region has 52.9% of Korea's overall information-based industries, mainly information-based manufacturing, at 64.8% and information-based services at 51.9%.

In the future, if the non-the capital region loses traditional manufacturing firms to overseas competitors without the growth of high technology industries in the area, the inequality and regional disparity between the capital and the rest of the country will only increase and the peripheral areas will repeat the vicious cycle. The establishment of information-based high technology industries in the peripheral regions is more important than ever in Korea to revitalize regional economic development in the areas that are currently under represented.

The economic disparity between the regions is well represented in the income level. There was a big gap between the capital region and the rest of the country in terms of per capita

Table 9.11 **Distribution of Information Based Industries by Region**

(Unit : a unit, %)

Section		2000			2005		
		Korea	Capital region	Non-Capital region	Korea	Capital region	Non-Capital region
Farming, Lumbering, Fishery		3,061 (0.1)	280 (9.1)	2,781 (90.9)	2,309 (0.1)	223 (9.7)	2,086 (90.3)
Mining		2,066 (0.1)	210 (10.2)	1,856 (89.8)	1,858 (0.1)	210 (11.3)	1,648 (88.7)
Manufacturing	Information based	21,882 (0.7)	14,153 (64.7)	7,729 (35.3)	26,821 (0.8)	17,390 (64.8)	9,431 (35.2)
	Other manufacturing	291,364 (9.7)	144,813 (49.7)	146,551 (50.3)	313,362 (9.8)	159,512 (50.9)	153,850 (49.1)
	Total	313,246 (10.4)	158,966 (50.7)	154,280 (49.3)	340,183 (10.6)	176,902 (52.0)	163,281 (48.0)
Services	Information based	227,558 (7.6)	111,835 (49.1)	115,723 (50.9)	300,981 (9.4)	156,085 (51.9)	144,490 (48.0)
	Other manufacturing	2,467,486 (81.9)	1,078,798 (43.7)	1,388,688 (56.3)	2,559,478 (79.9)	1,158,679 (45.3)	1,401,205 (54.7)
	Total	2,695,044 (89.4)	1,190,633 (44.2)	1,504,411 (55.8)	2,860,459 (89.3)	1,314,764 (46.0)	1,545,695 (54.0)
Total Information based industries		249,440 (8.3)	125,988 (50.5)	123,452 (49.5)	327,802 (10.2)	173,475 (52.9)	153,921 (47.0)
Total Other industries		2,763,977 (91.7)	1,224,101 (44.3)	1,539,876 (55.7)	2,877,007 (89.8)	1,318,624 (45.8)	1,558,789 (54.2)
Total Industries		3,013,417 (100.0)	1,350,089 (44.8)	1,663,328 (55.2)	3,204,809 (100.0)	1,492,099 (46.6)	1,712,710 (53.4)

(Source : Statistics Korea)

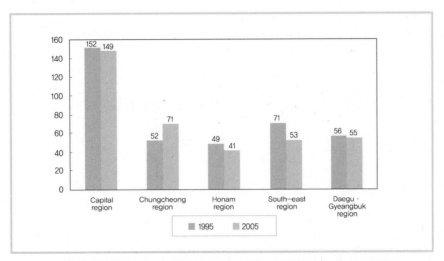

Figure 9.8. **Inland Tax per capita by Regions in 1995 & 2005.**
(Source : Statistics Korea)

income tax (Figure 9.8). When the national average was considered using the index of 100, the capital region had a value of 145 in 2005 and the non-the capital region ranged from 40-70. Between the regions the disparity was still large. For instance, the index for the Honam region was 41, about one-third of the capital region's. In individual regions, all regions indicated lower indices in 2005 than 1995, with the exception of the Chungcheong region. The Yeongnam region showed a major decline, reflecting the weakening of its economy.

Regional finances also reflect this same regional disparity. According to the Finance Independence Ratio, which represents the health of regional finances, the capital region had a ratio of 83% in 2005, while regions outside the capital region were about 40% on average. For individual areas, the Yeongnam region was the highest, but the Honam region was shown as just around 20%, indicating the major disparity between the regions. A low finance index is a major indicator of the weakening independence of the local economy.

POLICIES FOR DEPRESSED AREAS

9.4.1 Problems Concerning Farming, Lumbering and Fishing Villages

The primary concern of farming villages has been the decline of rural economic power. The advent of free trade of agricultural products in Korea resulted in the lowering of domestic agricultural production to the extent that a threat to local agriculture was created. The lack of non-agricultural job opportunities in farming communities has worsened the overall rural economy. The proportion of agriculture and lumbering in the Gross Domestic Production in 1992 was 16.7%, but it declined to 3.7% in 2002. The income level of farming villages declined radically as well. In 1990 the average farm household income was 97.4%of the average urban household and in 1995 it declined to 95.1%. However, in 2000 it declined precipitously to 80.6% and even further to 73% in 2002. There has been some effort to build rural industrial centers, but the effect has been minimal.

The second major concern in farming or fishing villages is the decline of the population and the aging of rural residents (Table 9.12). Over a 20-year period (1980-2000) the urban population increased at an annual rate of 1.4%, while the rural areas (*myeon*) declined at an annual rate of 3.4%. In the meantime, the number of *myeon* with less than 3,000 people that weretoo small to self-sustain in terms of local education or retail business increased from 152 in 1990 to 447 in 2000. This increase to about 3 times as many below-*myeon* level units may force the merging of some of the smaller *myeon* in order to better serve the rural residents. The higher proportion of seniors in the rural population also predicts the decline of the absolute number of rural residents in the near future. The population cohorts of people over 65 in rural areas were 2 times higher, 15.5% compared to 6.2%, than among their urban counterparts.

Table 9-12. *Gun* (county) and *Si* (City) Population distribution by Age Groups

Section	*Gun* (persons) (A)	Ratio (%) (A)	*Si* (persons)	Ratio (%)	Difference (A - B)
Total	5,511,526	100.0	40,624,575	100.0	0.0
0 - 14	1,029,450	18.7	8,760,118	21.6	- 2.9
15 - 24	733,979	13.3	6,805,791	16.8	- 3.4
25 - 44	1,542,828	28.0	14,830,667	36.5	- 8.5
45 - 64	1,348,621	24.5	7,710,973	19.0	5.5
65 이상	856,541	15.5	2,515,265	6.2	9.3
미상	107	0.0	1,761	0.0	0.0

(Source : Statistics Korea)

The third concern is the lagging quality of life in rural areas. There has been continuous investment in the infrastructure in rural areas however, the overall quality of life is still behind that of the urban areas. Among the items that indicated this were the tap water provision statistics, which showed 97.3% of the urban areas had access to tap water, while the percentage for rural areas remained at 46.3%. The urban areas had centrally treated waste water systems in 83.4% of their areas, while the percentage for rural areas was only 18.6%. Better medical services and public transportation, especially for the senior rural population, were keenly needed.

9.4.2 Policies for the Depressed Areas

Since 1970, the government has promoted policies to help the depressed areas of Korea. Until 1980 the emphasis was on basic sustenance of the rural residents. The typical policy of the 1970s was the "New Village Movement," and the 1980s heralded the Comprehensive Island Development Plan, the Remote Area Development Plan and the Rural Settlement Development Plan. Since the 1990s, the emphasis of development has been on the improvement of the living environment, tourism and industrial development based on regionally specific characteristics. Since 2000, local and regional development plans have been based on self-sufficient local development plans and regional revitalization. There has been a growing interest in the depressed regions and their development, the DMZ border regions, small villages, spatial economic zones for revitalization and the beautification of villages. The policy for depressed areas has been to invest in them continuously to provide services for the basic needs of the residents, such as infrastructure, health care and housing.

CHAPTER 9

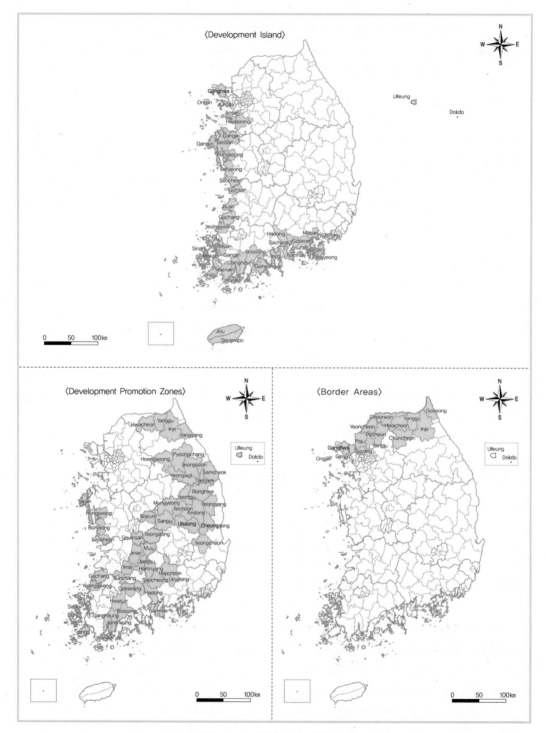

Figure 9.9 **Spatial Distributioon of Depressed Area**
(Source : Presidential Committee on Balanced National Development, 2004, Revitalization Program for Depressed Areas.)

Since there has been no agreed upon definition of depressed areas, it is difficult to estimate how large or how many such areas there might be. Typically, depressed areas would include remote areas, islands, the DMZ border regions, development promotion areas and 780 rural and remote areas (Figure 9-9). The possibilities will become even more numerous if the 70 newly designated development promotion areas are included. "Remote areas" mean the areas that are far from any urban areas, with poor accessibility, low household incomes and poor standards of living. The 399 *myeon* are designated as "remote areas." "Islands" selected as candidates for development are the 225 islands that are not connected to the Korean Peninsula by dykes or bridges. "The DMZ border regions"represents the areas within 20 kilometers of the DMZ that have a low level of development. Designated for this category are 98 *myeon*, eup and dong. During the last 5 planning stages, 31 "development promotion areas" have been selected as development areas. Lastly, 70 new spatial economic zones have been designated for revitalization based on population, finances and economic foundation. They are either mountainous interior areas or islands along the west or south coast, or the DMZ adjacent areas. Six areas are *si* (city) and 64 areas are *gun* (county). The economic gap between these areas is clearly noticeable. Their average population density is 73 persons/km², compared to other areas' 895 persons/km², which is only one-tenth of the depressed area. Per capita income tax is only 3% of that of other areas, indicating that the spatial economic zones for revitalization are rather depressed socially and economically. The population of these areas declined from 8.1 million to 3.6 million duringthe time period of 1970-2003. In terms of their population percentages, they have gone from 26.4% to only 7.7%, a radical decline (Table 9.13).

Table 9.13 **Major Economic Indicators of Depressed Areas**

Grade	Area	Population (2003)	Population change	Population Density	Economic Power Index	Income Tax	Per capita income tax
Unit	km²	Thousand person	%	Person/km²	%	Million won	Won
Korea	99,913.0 (100.0)	48,387 (100.0)	1.62 (100.0)	484 (100.0)	37.7 (100.0)	3,859,503 (100.0)	83,655 (100.0)
Non-Designated areas	49,982.0 (50.0)	44,745 (92.3)	2.90 (179.0)	895 (183.5)	47.6 (127.6)	3,744,138 (97.0)	87,919 (105.1)
Depressed areas	49,931.0 (50.0)	3,642 (7.7)	-1.90 (-117.6)	73 (16.0)	13.6 (36.2)	115,365 (3.0)	32,500 (38.8)

[Source : Chung, 1989a, Korea Geography]

CHAPTER 9

9.4.3 National and Regional Development Policy

1) Background of Korean national planning

Korea has transformed from an agrarian society to a developed country in only the last 50 years. It has accomplished in that time period what most countries in the developed world today have reached after several hundred years. This process of rapid industrialization and urbanization has also changed the spatial organization of Korea accordingly. After World War II, the Korean economy was paralyzed due to the division of the country into South and North Korea. Until then, the northern half of the country had more heavy manufacturing industries, while the southern half of the Korean Peninsula was mainly for light manufacturing and agriculture. As a result of the Korean War, most of the industrial facilities and 60% of farm lands were devastated. The main purposes of the Korean government's policies were to establish the infrastructure, encourage manufacturing, enforce national security and increase consumer confidence. Accordingly, the main emphasis of national development in the 1950s was establishing roads, bridges and the construction of homes that were destroyed during the Korean War, along with promoting the growth of domestic industries that provided goods for the domestic market.

2) National Territorial Development Plan in the 1960s-the initial stage of national physical planning

In terms of stages of economic growth in Korea, one can label the 1960s as the take-off stage of Korean economic development. President Park's military administration, after the successful military coup of May 16, 1961, made a sincere effort to correct the vicious cycle of poverty from the aftermath of the Korean War and established new economic policies in order to build the foundation of a self- sufficient Korean economy. Hence, the first of a series of 5-year economic development plans, FY1962-1966, was established for aphysical development plan for Korea.

The goals of physical plans in the 1960s were economic growth and regional development from resource exploration and nurturing of key industries. At this initial stage, development was selected in the growth pole areas. Although the development plans at this time were limited to specific parts of the country, it was an important turning point. For the first time in Korean economic history, a national physical plan was adopted.

3) National Territorial Development Plan in the 1970s-The main stage of national physical planning

After the adaptation of the National Territorial Development Plan, Korean national physical planning approached full swing in the 1970s. Economic development policies in the 1960s were mainly fragmented and scattered development around the country by designations of industrial complexes or physical development based on resource exploration. In the 1970s the development was a more systematic overall national physical development. The first long-range National Territorial Development Plan (1972-1981) was established and various supporting programs and policies were adopted.

There were 4 major goals in the first National Territorial development Plan. These included the following : 1) efficient land use and management 2) a strong physical development framework to support the economic growth 3) development of natural resources as well as protection of the environment from large-scale industrial complexes and 4), improvement of urban environmental issues and overall quality of life.

The major characteristic of the 1970s National Territorial Development Plan was the acceleration of industrialization, in order to support efficient industrialization, establish industrial complexes, intensify development around the growth pole and provide social indirect capital to supply energy, water and transportation. The success of the economic development policy of the 1970s was in its emphasis on the growth pole and unequalled development of the country. However, the policy became the basis of the concentration of wealth and growth in the capital and the southeast region. The industrialization process also started around the growth poles and the urban centers. The subsequent results were a population concentration shift to the major urban centers, growth of the gap between the cities and the agricultural regions and a loss of farm land. With the strong decentralization policy, Seoul and Busan actually lowered the population in the cities themselves. However, population in the surrounding areas gained most rapidly (KRIHS, 1996).

4) National Territorial Development Plan in the 1980s-balanced national development policy

Rapid urbanization and industrialization brought fundamental changes to Korea during the 1960s and 1970s. An unprecedented economic surge and regional development resulted in an unbalanced grow than all the subsequent urban ills-the extreme gap between the urban and rural areas, chaotic land use, real estate speculation, urban sprawl and the loss of natural

CHAPTER 9

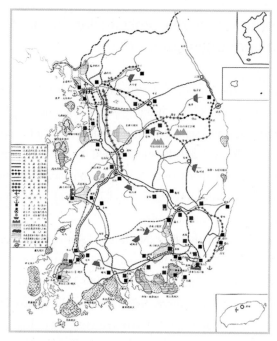

Figure 9.10 **The Second National Territorial Development Plan (1982~1991)**
(Source : The Korean Government, 1982)

resources, etc. It also brought a new era of globalization in politics, economics, society and culture, as well as the democratization of Korean society and politics. The government policy changed from one of economic efficiency to one of balanced growth and welfare. In addition, there was a greater emphasis on more systematic land use and growth management policies during the last 20 years.

To satisfy the new balanced development notion and the demands of the time, the second National Territorial Development Plan (1982-1991) was established and adopted. The main policy goal was to eliminate the regional imbalance created by the over-emphasis on growth poles and to establish a well-balanced national development (Figure 9.10). The modes of regional development shifted from the previous economic infrastructure to a more balanced social infrastructure, such as housing, medical care, education and social welfare.

Population concentrations in the major metropolitan areas, especially in the capital region, became the major focus in the 1980s. A new law, the Seoul Metropolitan Area Readjustment Planning Act, was established in 1982 in order to encourage the equalization of the population through movement from the capital region and to discourage further concentration in the capital region. It also sought to induce more balanced national development. Yet the policy was not successful, mainly because most of the capital investment for the development took place around the metropolitan region. The population decentralization policy for the capital region also failed because the implementation of this policy in the capital region occurred during the time of the Asian Games in 1986 and the Olympic Games in 1988. Subsequently, in 1987, the revised second national physical plan had to be established to help decentralize the capital region and encourage rural development, as well as focus on a more balanced national development. The major change was establishing multiple growth nuclei in areas such as Daejeon, Gwangju, Daegu and the Busan metropolitan cities to counteract the growth of the capital region.

5) National Territorial Development Plan in the 1990s- decentralization policy and establishing integrated territorial axes

The National Territorial Development Plan became more stabilized in the 1990s. Yet, the problems associated with the unbalanced growth that started in the 1980s continued to be the main policy concerns of the time. Economic investments were more concentrated along the Seoul-Busan axis and the uneven territorial development worsened as the population and economic activities were persistently concentrated in the capital region. Internationally, this marked the period during which Korea adopted the policy of opening international trade with the Uruguay Round Agreement. Domestically, local governments enjoyed a newly gained local autonomy. The globalization of Korea accelerated in all areas of society including economic, political and social aspects.

The goal of the National Territorial Development Plan of Korea in the 1990s was to continue the basic policies of the 1980s-a balanced national development policy in all regions of Korea, while keeping up international competitiveness in high technology industries and working toward the globalization of the national economy. The main emphasis of the policy was to secure raw materials, utilize efficient spatial organization to proceed with globalization, allow local autonomy and encourage self-sufficiency. This new policy gave more freedom to local governments to encourage creativity from local autonomous organizations and private individuals. Consequently, more government authority was shared between the central government and local governments. Such a shift welcomed increased capital investment from private individuals.

The main purpose of the third National Territorial Development Plan (1991-2001) was to solve the problems created by rapid national economic development : population concentrations mainly in the capital region, regional disparity, sky-rocketing real estate values, environmental pollution, etc. To resolve these issues, the third National Territorial

CHAPTER 9

Development Plan focused mainly on establishing territorial axes to disperse population, encouraging productive land use, improving the welfare of people, protecting the environment and preparing for the unification of Korea.

6) National Territorial Development Plan in the 2000s-continuation of a balanced national development policy

The National Territorial Development Policy has been a more complex attempt to deal with the coming of new mega trends in the 21st century. These include the worldwide freeing of trade, the explosion of high-technology industries and information services, the separation of political power and government administration, the globalization of environmental issues, etc. In addition to the new mega trends, Korea is still faced with the previously-mentioned continuing problems of rapid economic growth : the concentrated development in the capital region, the regional disparity, the lack of social overhead capital, the environmental pollution due to an economic, efficiency-oriented developmental policy and conflict between regions based on the discrimination between classes, to name a few. To overcome these socioeconomic and physical land use problems, a more delicate, well-balanced national development plan was introduced.

The long-range fourth National Territorial Development Plan was introduced to satisfy all these needs. First, it was designed to establish harmonized growth with the environment in all areas of physical planning, such as urban development, industrial location, tourism development and social overhead capital. Second, the fourth development plan included all levels of participants : national, local government and community groups. This bottom-up planning approach collected opinions from all parties involved and reflected those in the final plan. Third, the range of planning for this program was 20 years instead of the previously utilized 10 years, so as to include a well-thought-out, long-range plan for the country (2000-2020). It was assumed that the major infrastructure needed for the long-range plans, such as the network of expressways, an international hub airport and a nodal port for international traffic, would all take at least 20 years to be completed.

7) Accomplishments and the future tasks for the National Territorial Development Plan

For the last 50 years Korean economic development has established various goals and strategies depending on the tasks ahead. In the 1950s, the plans focused on how to normalize the country after the scars of the Korean War and reconstruct the infrastructure that was abused under Japanese occupation. It was also the time to secure social overhead capital with the assistance of the United States Agency for International Development (USAID). The 1960s saw the initial stage of Korean national development from the first and second 5-year economic development plans. This stage sought to establish more systematic national development strategies. The policies were to designate special development areas through resource development and establishment of industrial complexes. In 1963, the first National Land Development and Planning Act was established, the first such law to legalize the framework of national development planning.

The decade of the 1970s was a time of major construction development. The first National Comprehensive Development Plan established in 1972 was the first such comprehensive national plan to accomplish efficient national land use management, establish a land development foundation to protect the natural environment and develop natural resources and to improve the quality of life for Korean citizens. The projects were national programs in support of major economic growth, namely, construction of large-scale industrial complexes, network development of transportation and communication and water and energy resource development.

The period of the 1980s was the maturing stage of Korean national development. The main policy had been to suppress the growth of the Seoul-Busan corridor and induce development in other depressed areas by developing the regional developmental nodes and the regional commuter zones. Policy shifted from an economic, growth-centered approach to the protection of the natural environment. The national development policy arrived at a stabilized stage in the 1990s. Such problems as regional disparity in growth, rising land values and speculation and environmental pollution allowed the new policy to discourage concentrations of population in the capital region, while encouraging growth in rural areas, as well as growth of high-technology industries. The national policy shifted in many ways in 2000. It focused on the integration of Korea through globalization, specialization and diversification of the national development policy in order to be prepared for extreme global competition and the new era of a future unified Korea.

During the process of national development over the last 50 years, Korea has experienced exponential growth, as shown in Table 9.14. Per capita GNP has grown over 26 times the figures shown in 1971 industrial areas have increased 7 times over past figures, from 101.7 square kilometers in 1971 to 720.9 square kilometers in 2001.

The main artery of the country, the expressways, have increased 4 times in total length, from 655 kilometers to 2,637 kilometers in 2001. Port facilities have also grown by 25 times, providing the gateway for import and export of goods. Water resources have increased in volume due to the improvement of drainage basins and the construction of many multi-purpose dams. The output of water has increased from 10 billion cubic meters in 1970 to 33.6 cubic meters in 2001 to provide water resources for fast-growing industrial development. Subways and electrified railroads have also grown 15.9 times and 1.5 times, respectively, since 1981 and have provided major improvements for the daily commute of many citizens, as well as for their overall quality of life.

Despite all these improvements and accomplishments, the National Territorial Development Plan in Korea still has problems. First and foremost, the uneven development of the country along with regional disparity, disproportionate growth of the capital region, the metropolitan and rural gap in economic growth and the cost resulting from the inefficiency of this regional disparity have become major concerns of the country. Second, construction of water and sewer lines, parks and open spaces and other urban services to improve the quality of life for people are lagging behind the fast growth of housing development. Third, fast economic growth has created instability in supply and demand of land and a subsequent rise in the real estate market

Table 9.14 **Major Infrastructure Constructions in Korea (1971-2001)**

Section	Unit	1971(A)	1981(B)	1991	2001	C/A
Per capita GNP (1985 price constant)	$	391	791	6,265	10,179	26.0
Industrial areas	km²	101.7	332.3	474.7	720.9	7.1
Electricity Production (1,000KW)	1,000KW	2,628	9,835	21,021	50,858	19.4
Total Length of Expressway	km	655	1,245	1,597	2,637	4.0
Percent of Paved Road	%	31.4	55.3	92.0	96.5	3.1
Total Length of Subways	km	-	25.3	148.9	401.4	15.9(B/C)
Total Length of Electric Railways	km	-	442.5	524.5	667.5	1.5(B/C)
Port Loading Facilities (1,000Ton)	1,000 ton	18,781	87,423	248,365	469,585	25.0
Total households (1,000 households)	1,000 households	4,418	5,582	7853.0	10,959	11.0
Per capita Drinking Water supply (liters/day)	l/day	175	256	372.0	374	2.1
Total water resource supply (million cubic meters)	Million m³	10,039	18,175	30,900	33,622	3.4

(Source : Statistics Korea)

along with land speculation. Policies to suppress land speculation and regulate development around major development areas created a distorted real estate market, while relaxation of land use regulations around the traditional greenbelt brought chaotic development to the suburban areas, which developed without the benefit of urban services. Fourth, investments of social overhead capital were often decided politically and were ill-suited ventures. In transportation planning, short-term quick remedies frequently overrode the long-term perspectives concerning the inter connectivity between the modes of transportation and the entire network plan. Finally, there were problems between the national development policy makers and the program delivery. In the process of creating a national development plan, there was a tremendous lack of communication and even the presence of conflicting policies between the central government and the regional development offices. This has resulted in the limited accomplishment of goals and a lack of integration in the overall planning.

Chapter 10
PROSPECTS FOR THE FUTURE

Chapter 10.1

POTENTIAL OF NATIONAL TERRITORY

10.1.1 Prospects of Territorial Development

1) Scientific and technological innovations and socio-economic paradigm changes

The development of accelerated technological advances during past decades will continue in the future, resulting insignificant changes in economic and social spectrums. Following the development of information and telecommunication technologies, innovations in bio, nano, and new and renewable energy technologies will accelerate the fusion of science, technology, and industry well as the creative destruction of existing industries (Figure 10.1). Future development in these areas will be led by the so-called NBIC fusion technologies-nano

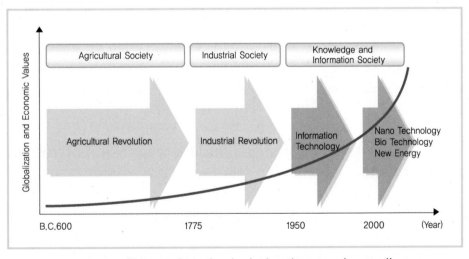

Figure 10.1 **Changes in technological and economic paradigm**
(Source : Woo et al., 2007)

technology (NT), biotechnology (BT), information technology (IT), and cognitive technology (CT). These technologies will have enormous impacts, comparable to the Industrial Revolution it is impossible to estimate the magnitude of the value added. These fusion technologies are brain-ware technologies, vastly different from existing group of technologies such as those of labor-intensive, hardware, and software, and will replace existing industries, especially those based on hardware technologies. It is expected that the fusion of NT, BT, IT and CT will integrate scientific technologies and the pharmaceutical industry within the next 25 years (Woo et al., 2007).

The world is being transformed to an age of the second digital revolution. The first revolution, from analog to digital, focused on the establishment of the physical structure that is necessary for processing, storing, and transmitting information. As a result of the first digital revolution, the creation and diffusion of applied information became the core of national competitiveness. The second digital revolution is expected to result in drastic changes in politics, economies, society, culture, regulation, and the environment through the divergence and integration of IT technologies, the fusion of different technologies and industries, and the realization of ubiquitous ages (Lee et al, 2007).

In the meantime, the social structure of the 21st century is expected to transform to a public participation society based on a decentralized and horizontal division of labor. Deep changes resulting from new means of production and trades, cultural and communication methods, responses to environmental issues, and political and social participation will increasingly require the reform of regulations formed during the past ages of mass production and consumption, a vertical control system. Therefore, a uni-directional and hierarchical division of role systems and corresponding power relationships will be changed to a new governance system based on a multi-lateral and horizontal role-sharing system and mass participation. In addition, changes in family structure, represented by the increase in nuclear and single families, the expansion of cultural individualism, and the increase in international human exchanges, will diversify the values of society and the way of life of people (Woo et al., 2007).

2) The rise of Asian economies and the expansion of free trade agreements

The center of the world economy is expected to move to Asia in the future. According to a Goldman Sachs report (2003), the size of the gross domestic product in 2050 will be led by China, followed by the United States, India, Japan, Brazil, and Russia. Asian economies, owing to the rapid rise of China, will grow to the same size as North America and Europe by around 2020, from two-thirds currently. China has set a goal, through its Grand Development Plan of the West Region (2000-2050), of increasing its national per capita income to $3,000 from 2010 to 2020, and to $10,000 from 2020 to 2050. As the economies of Brazil, Russia, India, and China grow rapidly, Korea will face numerous challenges, including a more active response to these emerging markets, securing advantages responding to strong international competition, and improving the competitiveness of major industries (Woo et al., 2007).

One of the biggest changes in global trade since the 1980s is a rapid increase in free trade agreements (FTAs) among countries. Korea, like many other countries, recognizes FTAs as important tools of trade policy and is working to reach agreements with important trade partners, including the U.S. and the EU. In the long run, Korea needs agreements with emerging economies represented by the BRICs to secure a sustained economic growth engine. Since the establishment of the FTA Roadmap in 2003, Korea has actively engaged in FTA negotiations with over 50 countries. As of early 2010, FTAs with Chile, Singapore, EFTA, ASEAN and India have entered into force. Korea and the US signed FTA in April 2007 and currently await approval for ratification. In addition, Korea and the EU finished the negotiation in 2009 and agreed to work toward putting the agreement into effect in 2010 (Ministry of Foreign Affairs and Trade).

3) Lower birth rates and the accelerated aging of the population

One of the most important factors that will determine future society is the aging of the population. Although the population structure of Korea is at an earlier stage of aging, no other country has experienced aging as rapidly as Korea. The primary reason for this aging is the dramatic decrease infertility, induced by several factors such as national economic growth, higher education, increasing economic activity and the marriage age of women, and increasing costs related to the nurturing and education of children. The total fertility rate of Korea has decreased to 1.08 in 2005 from 4.5 in 1970 and 2.83 in 1980. Korea's fertility rate is well below that of advanced countries such as the U.S. (2.04), the UK (1.74), Germany (1.37), and Japan (1.29) (Joint Task Force of the Government and Non-Government, 2006).

The share of aged people (65+) in Korea reached 7.2 percent in 2000, labeling the country as an aging society, and increased to 9.9 percent in 2007 (Figure 10.2). By 2018, this is expected to increase to 14.3 percent. By 2026, Korea will become a hyper-aged society, with the share of older population at 20.8 percent. Furthermore, by 2016, the aging index will be 100.7 the number of people age 65+ will surpass the number of those age 0-14 years

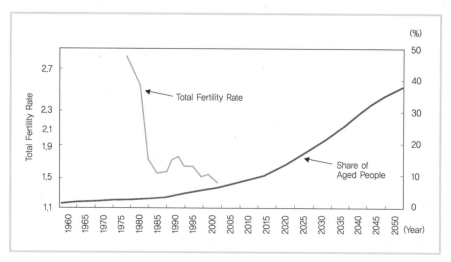

Figure 10.2 **Trend and forecast of total fertility rate and share of aged people**
(Source : Woo et al., 2007)

(Statistics Korea, 2007 ; Moon et al., 2006).

This rapid increase in the aged population will affect various sectors of the national economy, including macroeconomies, the labor market, the financial market, and government finances. Ten years from now, a decline in the productive population and the saving rate will lead to a decrease in the potential for economic growth. Aging of the population will increase not only the share of older people but also the average age of the productive population, resulting in the aging of the labor force (Moon et al., 2006).

4) Increasing importance of energy and global environment issues

The rising prices of energy centered on crude oil will threaten the sustainable growth of the global economy. The increasing demand for fossil fuels that are essential for sustained economic growth will push up prices and generate environmental problems. This, in turn, will spawn efforts to develop alternative energy sources such as solar, biomass, wind, tidal, small-scale hydroelectric, and earth heat. A key goal for dealing with global warming will be the reduction of carbon dioxide generated from the use of fossil fuels. Technological innovation for more efficient use of resources, smaller sizing of products, and the development of energy-saving methods will continue. In addition, the use of hydrogen energy as an alternative to fossil fuels will increase.

Environmental industries that produce environmentally-friendly goods and reduce environmental pollution will increase their share in national economies rapidly with support from governments and technological innovation. In social realms, a tendency for environmentally-friendly living patterns such as well-being and LOHAS (Lifestyle of Health and Sustainability) will be increased further.

In government policy, linkages and integration between the environment and economic policies that are closely related, including finance, industry, energy, land, agriculture, and tourism, will be strengthened. Stronger responses to international agreements related to global warming, bio-diversity, and toxic wastes will be required (Lee et al., 2007).

10.1.2 Future Images of National Development

1) Long-term vision of national development

Long-range plans formulated by the government present future images for territorial development in Korea. These government plans do not simply forecast the future but have strong intentions and measures to realize desirable future images. The future images of territorial development presented in this chapter are based on the Korean government's two long-range plans : The Vision 2030 and the Revised Fourth Comprehensive National Territorial Plan (2006-2020).

The Vision 2030 attempts to develop Korea into a country of innovation, energy, safety, opportunity, stability, and high class. The most important objective of The Vision 2030 is to make Korea a first-class country of the world. The process to fulfill this objective includes three stages : (1) to complete a renovation of major socio-economic institutions that are the bases for national development until 2010 (2) to move into an early stage of advanced country during the 2010s through sustained economic growth and secured social safety networks and (3) to upgrade to a first-class country with mature politics, economies, and culture and social networks during the 2020s, and to advance further in each area to the world top-10 level after 2030 (Joint Task Force of the Government and Non-Government, 2006).

2) Indicators of territorial development in the future

Major indicators of development in the future (Table 10.1) show that per capita GDP (constant price of 2005) of Korea will rise from $16,000 in 2005 to $49,000 in 2030, reaching the level of today's Switzerland. The share of welfare spending in the government budget will

Table 10.1 **Forecast of Korea's position in the world**

	2005	2020	2030	Comparable Countries (as of 2005)
GDP (billion $)	788 (788)	1,824 (2,567)	2,406 (4,145)	US 12,486, Japan 4,571, UK 2,201, Italy 1,766
Per Capita GDP (thousand $)	16 (16)	37 (51)	49 (84)	Switzerland 50, US 42, Japan 36, France 34
National Competitiveness (ranking)	29	15	10	US 1, Singapore 3, Switzerland 8, Japan 21
Quality of Life (ranking)	41	20	10	Australia 1, Switzerland 4, US 14, Japan 35

Note : GDP figures are 2005 constant prices, with current prices in parentheses.
(Source : Joint Task Force of the Government and Non-Government, 2006)

Table 10.2 **Major indices of territorial development**

	1998	2003	2020
Urbanization Rate (%)	86.4	89.0	95.0
Population Share of the Capital Region (%)	45.6	57.6	47.5
Per Capita Urban Park Area (m²)	6.4	7.0	12.5
Share of Logistics Costs against GDP (%)	16.5	12.5	10.0
Number of Houses Per Thousand (Unit)	-	270	370
Per Capita Housing Area (m²)	-	20.2 (in 2000)	35.0
Tap Water Supply Ratio (%)	85.2	89.4	97.0

(Source : Government of the Republic of Korea, 2006)

increase from 8.6 percent in 2005 to 15 percent in 2019 (2001 U.S. level), 17 percent in 2024 (2001 Japan level), and 21 percent in 2030 (2001 OECD average level). Quality of life will reach 10th in the world, surpassing today's U.S. level. The IMD ranking of comprehensive national competitiveness, with the combination of deregulation and enhanced growth potentials, will rise from 29th in 2005 to 15th in 2020 to 10th in 2030 (Joint Task Force of the Government and Non-government, 2006).

As the Korean economy moves forward to a global top-10 power, territorial development will increase to a comparable level. The Vision 2030 also presents major territorial indicators. In the area of the environment, the reduction of air pollution and the expansion of green space in urban areas will ensure a pleasant and healthy life. The level of air pollution in the Seoul capital region is expected to improve to $35\mu g/\text{m}^3$ in 2030 from $58\mu g/\text{m}^3$ in 2005. In the area of housing welfare, the residential stability of the weaker classes, such as the elderly and those with low incomes, will be improved through the sustained supply of public housing and housing assistance programs. In rural areas, living conditions will be improved with the supply of road, housing, tap water, and the internet.

The Revised Fourth Comprehensive National Territorial Plan (2006-2020) forecasts territorial development indicators (Table 10.2). According to the plan, spatial disparities will be reduced, and both efficiencies and competitiveness of the national territory will be enhanced, while progress also will be made in people's quality of life. The share of urban population will increase to 95 percent in 2020, from 89 percent in 2003. Government policy efforts for balanced development is expected to continue in the future, as evidenced by the share of population of the Seoul capital region, which will be stabilized to 47.5 percent in 2020, the same level as in 2003. An expansion of the interregional road network and intra-urban transportation system will reduce the share of logistic costs against GDP, an indicator of territorial competitiveness, to 10 percent in 2020, from 12.5 percent in 2003. In terms of quality of life, improvements are expected in the per capita supply of urban parks, housing, and tap water.

ANALYSIS OF CONDITIONS OF TERRITORIAL DEVELOPMENT

10.2.1 Disparities of Territorial Development

1) Over-concentration of the capital region and deepening spatial disparities

Over-concentration of the Seoul capital region and deepening spatial disparities are among the most significant problems of territorial development in Korea. In spite of various government efforts to control the over-growth of the capital region, concentration into the region has been strengthened over the past three decades. The result is deepening territorial disparities represented by the over-concentration of population, industries, central government agencies, and key functions of the private sector in the capital region, in contrast to a decrease of population and economic vitality in the provincial regions. With population as an indicator, the share of the capital region has increased from 28.3 percent in 1970 to 48.2 percent in 2005 and is expected to surpass 50 percent in the near future (Table 10.3).

The economic concentration of the capital region induces more new economic activities and job opportunities for the region. For example, the capital region surpasses provincial regions in changes in the total number of business establishments and employment. During 2000-2005, the capital region accounted for 74 percent of the increase in the number of business establishments and 63 percent of the increase in employment. Gyeonggi-*do* in the capital region includes the seven fastest-growing areas in business establishment and the eight fastest-growing areas in employment for the period (Lee and Park 2007) (Figure 10.3).

Spatial concentration is an important factor in the disparities of wealth between the capital and provincial regions. For example, the share of total value of land of the capital region has increased to 63.9 percent in 2006, from 59.3 percent in 2003, far exceeding the share of population (48.7 percent in 2006).

Table 10.3 **Population concentration of the capital region (thousand people)**

	1970	1980	1990	2000	2005
Nation (A)	30,882	37,436	43,411	46,136	47,279
Capital Region (B)	8,730	13,298	18,587	21,354	22,767
Seoul	5,433	8,364	10,613	9,895	9,820
Incheon	634	1,084	1,818	2,475	2,531
Gyeonggi	2,663	3,850	6,156	8,984	10,415
B/A(%)	28.3	35.5	42.8	46.3	48.2

(Source : Statistics Korea, Population Census)

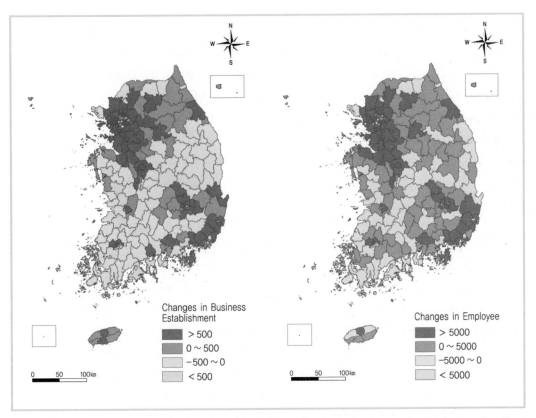

Figure 10.3 **Changes in business establishment and employees at city and county levels (2000-2005)**

(Source : Lee and Park, 2007)

Table 10.4 **Trends of the gross regional domestic production (billion won)**

	GRDP1 (2005)	Share (2005)	Annual Average Rate of Increase (%)		
			1998 - 2005	1998 - 2001	2001 - 2005
Nation	729,240	100.0	6.0	7.3	5.0
Capital Region	349,766	48.0	6.3	8.2	5.0
Seoul	159,588	21.9	4.0	5.6	2.8
Incheon	33,007	4.5	5.8	7.3	4.7
Gyeonggi	157,171	21.6	9.4	11.9	7.5
Provincial Regions	379,474	52.0	5.6	6.5	5.0

Note : 1) Numbers are the Constant Prices of 2000
(Source : Statistics Korea, Korean Statistical Information Service)

2) Stagnant economies of provincial regions

Compared to the capital region, economies of the provincial regions are depressed and growing slowly. Table 10.4 indicates that the capital region accounts for 48 percent of the country's GRDP. Seoul's share of GRDP decreased 3.1 percent during 1998-2005, and Gyeonggi-do led the growth of the capital region with a 4.3 percent increase in the share.

The provincial regions witnessed a decrease of 1.2 percent in the share of GRDP during 1998-2005. The annual average growth rate of GRDP of the provincial regions was 5.6 percent, lower than that of the capital region's 6.3 percent. In the sub-periods of 1998-2001 and 2001-2005, the capital region showed a larger decrease in growth rates of GRDP compared to the provincial regions, which, however, did not help to increase the share of the provincial regions.

3) Problems of depressed areas

Many rural counties and some cities are depressed, losing economic and social vitality. According to the definition of the special law on balanced national development, as many as 780 areas that include county towns, rural towns, and urban districts were designated as depressed regions as of 2003. In addition, 70 counties and cities were newly-designated as revitalization areas in 2004 (Figure 10.4). These areas have common features such as low accessibility due to longer distance from urban areas, low income levels, and poor living conditions.

Comparing depressed regions to more advanced regions, disparities are clear between the two groups. The 70 revitalization areas occupy 48.8 percent of the nation's land area but the share of population is only 7.4 percent. The population density of the revitalization areas is 73 per square kilometer, a stark comparison to 876 per square kilometer of other areas. Due to the stagnation of socio-economic conditions, the population of the revitalization areas has decreased from 8.1 million in 1970 to 3.5 million in 2003.

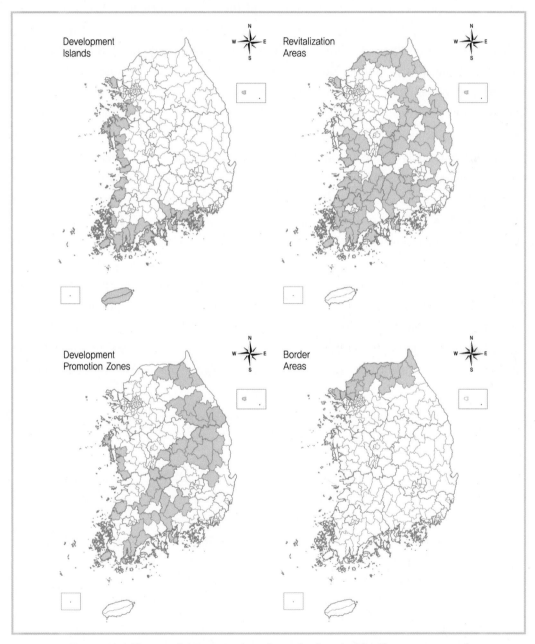

Figure 10.4 **Types of depressed regions designated by the government**
[Source : Lee, 2006]

10.2.2 Insufficient Quality of Living Environment

Amenities and the attractiveness of urban areas in Korea are considerably weak compared to those of advanced countries. In general, Korean cities lack high-quality urban infrastructure for living, leisure, entertainment, culture, and the urban landscape. According to an international survey on the quality of life of 215 cities throughout the world, Seoul ranked 86th. This is far lower than competing cities in Asia, including Tokyo (35th), Singapore (32nd), and Hong Kong (70th) (Mercer Korea 2008). In addition, urban planning and the land management system are not fully organized, causing disorder of land use and uncontrolled expansion of urban areas as well as inefficiencies in the urban structure, rising social costs, and a deteriorating natural environment.

The housing supply has increased steadily for past decades, but large urban areas including the Seoul capital region still have housing problems due to supply shortages and skyrocketing prices. Comparing housing welfare indices to advanced countries, Korea's per capita housing area is less than half that of the U.S. and Japan. The share of public housing is only 5.1 percent of the total housing supply in Korea, significantly lower than 20 percent in major advanced countries. In addition, housing prices measured against income level are the highest in the world. For example, PIR (Price to Income Ratio) is much higher in Seoul (7.7) than in New York (2.7), London (4.7), or Tokyo (5.6), indicating that housing prices of Seoul are higher compared to purchasing power.

Recurrent fluctuation of the real estate market has had negative effects on business activities as well as residential stability. Housing prices in Korea have risen 220 percent

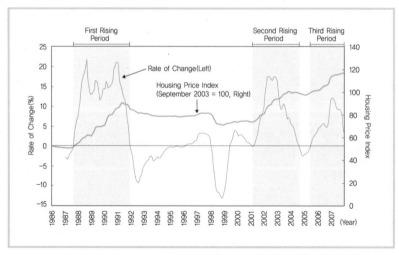

Figure 10.5 **Trend of housing price changes (1986-2007)**
(Source : Choi et al., 2008)

between 1986 and 2007 (Figure 10.5), accelerating the difficulties of those with low incomes to buy homes (Choi et al., 2008). The real estate market boom in the 2000s is a result of excessive money inflow from financial markets to the real estate market due to low interest rates. Real estate market policy lacked preemptive measures against unpredictable changes in market conditions, and short-sighted policies also caused periodic instability in prices and reduced creditability of policies.

10.2.3 Reckless Land Development and Decreasing Sustainability

In spite of the increased investment for improvement of the environment, pollution has been aggravated due to the destruction of nature from reckless land development and increases in urbanization and industrial activities. Urban expansion requires changes in zoning from conservation to development purposes, and rapid urbanization has resulted in an increase in new urban land for residence and public facilities. During 1994-2001, a total of 1,405.4km^2 was converted to urban areas from agricultural areas.

Environmental issues are especially notable in the capital region, where an over-concentrated population and industries generate external diseconomies and environmental pollution in air, water, and wastes. For example, in 2002, the capital region accounted for 32.1 percent of NOx emissions, 24.6 percent of fine particles, 38.6 percent of VOC, 44.3 percent of CO, and 13.8 percent of SO_2 of the country. In addition, the air quality of the capital region, measured by the densities of fine particles ($71\mu g/m^3$) and NO_2 (37ppb) was the poorest among major OECD countries' metropolitan areas in 2004.

A systematic national land management plan that takes into account environmental capacity has not been established yet. Whereas spatial and physical allocations have been made for land development plans, environmental conservation and management plans have not fully considered the spatial dimension ; specific development indices were presented, but environment indices were not presented in detail. Due to the disconnection between environmental plans and territorial plans, damage to the natural environment could not have been controlled during the planning stages. Furthermore, national territorial plans do not have practical tools that link environmental sectoral plans and other sectoral plans.

CHAPTER 10

FUTURE PROSPECTS OF TERRITORIAL DEVELOPMENT

10.3.1 Vision and Objectives of Territorial Development

1) Objectives of the comprehensive national territorial plan

The Revised Fourth Comprehensive National Territorial Plan (2006-2020) presents a long-term vision and objectives of spatial development of Korea (Figure 10.6). The plan presents a "Dynamic and Integrated National Territory" as the vision and contains two elements. First, it presents a vision of a dynamic national territory inducing a national leap forward and regional innovation. Second, it aims at balanced regional development and mutually-beneficial integrated spatial development. Reflecting the new vision for territorial development, five primary objectives have been established : balanced territory, open territory, welfare territory,

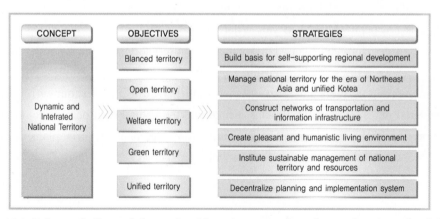

Figure 10.6 **Schematic flow of the revised fourth comprehensive national territorial plan**
(Source : Government of the Republic of Korea, 2006)

green territory, and unified territory. The five objectives are to achieve balanced development and increased competitiveness, with emphasis on the welfare of people. Six strategies were presented to realize the vision and objectives of the plan : building the basis for self-supporting regional development, managing the national territory for the era of Northeast Asia and a unified Korea, constructing networks of transportation and information infrastructure, creating a pleasant and humanistic living environment, instituting sustainable management of the national territory and resources, and decentralizing the planning and implementation system.

2) Directions for a national territorial structure

The Revised Fourth Comprehensive National Territorial Plan presents a new territorial structure that is open to the world and networked as an integratedeconomic region (Figure

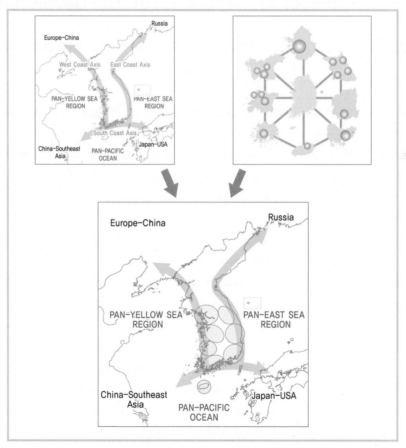

Figure 10.7 **Configuration of national territorial structure**
(Source : Government of the Republic of Korea, 2006)

10.7). The concept of three axes and 7+1 economic regions were introduced. First, the π shape open territorial axis consists of the south coast axis, the west coast axis, and the east coast axis, extending toward the Pan Pacific Ocean, the Pan Yellow Sea Region, and the Pan East Sea Region. This globally-open territorial axis refers to the "coastal territorial axis" and forms the basis for the creation of a national growth engine for the future. It attempts to take advantage of the geographic location of the Korean peninsula in Northeast Asia. The 7+1 economic regions will build a networked territorial structure through self-supporting localization, specialized industries, and the mutually-beneficial development of regions. The economic regions are composed of a network of large cities connected to their neighboring areas and are designed to overcome inefficiencies from a single-core (Seoul capital region) territorial structure by nurturing a multi-centered territorial structure.

10.3.2 Strategies for the Future Territorial Development

1) Establishing a decentralized territorial structure and growth management in the capital region

Macroeconomic and long-term efforts are needed to reconfigure the national territorial structure. Medium to long-range projects should be implemented to transform the current single-core territorial structure to a multi-dimensional structure (Figure 10.8). Strategies such as relocating national public agencies away from the capital region and constructing innovation cities and enterprise cities are examples that attempt to enhance the competitiveness of provincial regions.

Despite spatial decentralization, the Seoul capital region should not lose its competitiveness. The capital region needs to reposition itself as a global city region and focus on improving quality. As Korea's representative region toward the global stage, the capital region should upgrade its basic living conditions and build a higher economic infrastructure as well as establish systematic growth management measures to ensure sustainable development for the future.

Provincial regions should focus on building self-supporting regional economies. To improve the competitiveness of regional industries, advanced clusters of strategic industries need to be nurtured. A strengthened network of enterprise-research institutes-colleges-industry should be established together with supporting organizations. Existing industrial complexes should be transformed to innovation clusters with strengthened research and

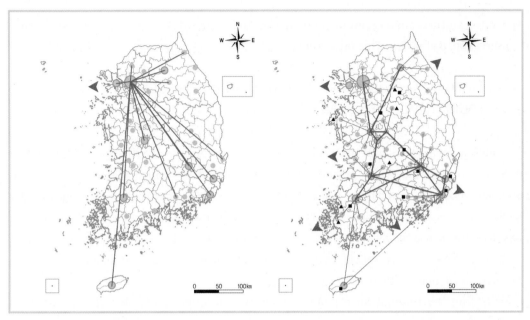

Figure 10.8 Reorganization of spatial structure toward multi-cored decentralization
(Source : Presidential Committee on Balanced National Development, 2007)

development, distribution, design, and marketing functions. In addition, the development of various regional growth poles as well as global open poles such as free economic zones should be continued.

Differentiated culture and tourism facilities fitting regional characteristics contribute to improving regional competitiveness. Cultural tourism should be promoted to enhance the competitiveness of the tourism industry, responding to the increasing demand for recreation and leisure. Building tourism belts along the south coast, the west coast, the east coast, and bordering are as and cultural regions including the Baekje culture, the Confucian culture, and the Jirisan Mountains can make the Korean peninsula a tourism center in Northeast Asia.

The capital region needs a new growth management system aimed at enhancing qualitative development in accordance with the decentralization policies. Impending policy issues for the capital region include an efficient management of the spatial structure, enhanced economic competitiveness, improved quality of life, and sustainable development. Ideas for a new growth management policy for the capital region can be summarized as follows : The basis of the new policy is systematic growth management with new approaches to future socio-economic changes. Systematic growth management means planned management of the capital region with objectives and implementation measures, which is supported by a region-wide governance system. The growth management plan of the capital region should include a spatial structure, management of land use and urban development, environmental conservation, and region-wide infrastructure.

2) Building the bases for the age of Northeast Asia and reunification of Korea

Future-oriented territorial management demands perspectives on the issues of the world and Northeast Asia. An important task is to develop strategies that enhance global competitiveness of the territory and promote international cooperation. Various open poles such as free economic zones, free trade zones, and international free cities need to be developed to accommodate global activities. World-class logistics and IT infrastructure as well as conditions for investment, living, and natural amenities need to be supplied in the open poles to invite global capital.

Building the foundation for the Northeast Asia community through multilateral cooperation and economic integration among Northeast Asian countries also is needed. Establishment of international highway networks linking South and North Korea and China will contribute to reducing the gap in development in Northeast Asia as well as to integrating

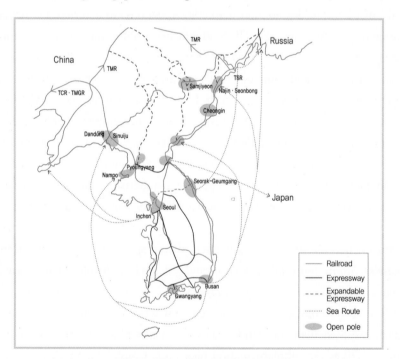

Figure 10.9 **Conceptual map of international open poles and infrastructure development of Korean peninsula**

(Source : Government of the Republic of Korea, 2006)

a transportation and logistics system for the region. In addition, establishing an energy network can be a symbolic as well as practical project for international cooperation among Northeast Asian countries, including South and North Korea, Russia, China, and Japan.

South-North Korea cooperation should be expanded to promote the settlement of peace and co-prosperity on the Korean peninsula. Establishing the Peace Belt on the border region will help strengthen the base for exchanges and cooperation between the two Koreas. Flood control measures for major river valleys and manage water resources can be jointly set up along the border region. In addition, special economic zones can be developed in selected areas of North Korea to facilitate cooperation. Transportation networks and infrastructure linking the special zones and the rest of Korea should be built in the long run (Figure 10.9). South and North Korea also can jointly develop mineral resources in North Korea and manage the Grand Baekdu Mountains, major rivers, and coastal regions.

3) Constructing networks of transportation infrastructure

To strengthen territorial competitiveness and improve the quality of life, an integrated transportation system and effective modal sharing should be built among road, railway, airline, and sea transportation. The arterial road network consists of seven south-north axes and nine east-west axes, constituting a lattice-type network (Figure 10.10).

For railways, the second phase of the Gyeongbu Express Railway will be completed, and the Honam Express Railway will be built to meet the increased transportation demands following development of the west coast region. The express railways will be linked to existing railway networks, serving gateway roles to Asian and European railways, including Trans-Siberian Railway and Trans-China Railway.

For airports, the Incheon International Airport will be expanded in stages to make it a hub airport of Northeast Asia. In addition, key regional airports will be expanded or newly built to accommodate increasing demand for international transportation services.

For ports, concentrated investments will be made in the new ports in Busan and Gwangyang to make them hub ports of Northeast Asia. Additionally, there will be new port construction and regional port expansion to establish a hierarchical national port system. An integrated network linking ports and the hinterland and a logistics complex and information system will be constructed, establishing a multi-modal transportation system.

A safe and environmentally-friendly transportation system should be built so the transportation sector can contribute to saving energy and lead to sustainable territorial development. Examples include an advanced public transit system and a human-oriented

CHAPTER 10

411

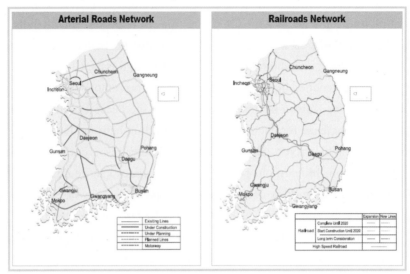

Figure 10.10 **Arterial road and railroad network plan**
(Source : Government of the Republic of Korea, 2006)

transportation network as well as an increased investment in the prevention of transportation-related accidents. A readjustment of investment priorities should be made as an attempt to enhance efficiencies of the transportation system while placing importance on the use of existing facilities and demand management.

4) Creating a pleasant and humanistic residential environment

Whereas past urban development placed emphasis on expanding urban space to keep up with industrialization and urbanization, future urban development should create a pleasant and humanistic urban environment. A livable city is a healthy urban community that offers basic services in residence, welfare, and transportation ; a workable and dynamic city with strong economies and job opportunities ; and a pleasant cultural city with distinctive characteristics and a beautiful landscape (Figure 10.11). For this, improvement in the basic urban facilities that will ensure a high quality of life is a necessity. Particular attention should be given to improving public facilities and basic services that ensure a barrier-free life for the less privileged. Emphasis also should be given to the development of historical and cultural resources, expansion of parks and green space, restoration of the ecosystem, and creation of a harmonious and beautiful landscape.

An important policy agenda in urban areas is social integration through improvement of housing welfare for low-income people. To improve housing welfare, an important objective

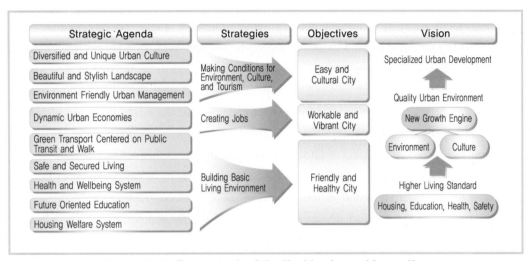

Figure 10.11 **Framework of the livable city making policy**
(Source : Ministry of Construction and Transportation, 2006)

is to reorganize the existing policies to be consumer-oriented. For this, regular surveys on housing conditions are needed, including consumer demand, regional housing conditions, and the development of a regional housing welfare index. Housing welfare programs should support those who are low-income, the elderly, and persons with disabilities. A comprehensive housing management system needs to be established to improve housing conditions and consumer protection.

The projected new housing supply during the first half of the plan (2006-2010) is 500,000 units annually. The housing supply rate will reach 117 percent by the year 2020 and 120 percent thereafter, eradicating problems arising from supply shortages. The ratio of long-term public housing will be increased to 15 percent of the total housing stock in 2012, and 20 percent in 2017, from 5.1 percent in 2005. In addition, none of the housing will be below the minimum level of residential welfare after 2030, compared to 13 percent in 2005 and 9 percent in 2020 (National Economic Advisory Council, 2007).

5) Sustainable territory and natural resources management

Sustainable territorial management requires not only conservation of the natural environment but also management of water resources and creating bases for disaster prevention. To create a healthy and pleasant green territory, an environmentally-friendly regional and city management system should be built, including sustainability indices, strategic environment assessment, and regional environmental governance system with public participation. A national ecosystem linking major mountain ranges, coastal regions, river basins, and the Grand Baekdu Mountains should be strengthened. In addition, regional and urban plans should encourage the use of recycled energy and reshuffle spatial structure to enhance efficiencies of land use. As for climatic changes and global warming, special attention will be given to territorial development, inducing the decreased emission of carbon dioxide and strengthened international cooperation for ecological restoration and prevention of environmental pollution from sand dust and acid rain in the Northeast Asian region.

A stable supply of clean water requires efficient management of water resources through the expansion of waterworks and various means of supply that consider characteristics of the regions. To correct the regional disparities in the water supply, the waterworks supply rate, which stood at 89.3 percent in 2003, will be increased to 97 percent (85 percent in rural villages) by 2020. In regions that water supply facilities cannot reach, alternative water resources such as filtered river water, well water, rain water, and recycled water will be used in addition to an increase in the capacity of supply from existing dams. As a key measure to secure clean water, a total pollution load management system will be introduced in major river basins along with nature-friendly river bank improvement works.

To form a disaster-resistant territorial base against climatic changes and abnormal meteorological phenomena, an integrated national disaster prevention system should be built through a comprehensive river flood control system and increased safety supervision of facilities. To minimize flood damages, new prevention facilities should be built combined with strengthened linkages among existing facilities. In addition, the disaster policy paradigm needs to be changed from short-term palliative measures to mid- to long-term proactive measures. The central government, local governments, and other related organizations should work together for prevention and for recovering damages from disasters.

REFERENCES

Agricultural Cooperation Cooperative, 2008, National Commodity Center Status.

Agricultural Sciences Institute, 1992, Korean Soil Survey and Classification, ASI/RDA, Suwon, Korea.

Bae, Mi-Ae, 2007, Social geography of poverty and social welfare services, Journal of the Korean Geographical Society, 42(2), 177-195.

Baek, Hyeon, 2007, A Study on the Korea Tourism Policy, Korea Tourism Policy, vol.30, 16-22, Korea Culture and Tourism Institute.

Berry, B.J.L., 1961, City Size Distributions and Economic Development, Economic Development and Cultural Change, 9, 573-588.

Berry, B.J.L., 1964, Cities as Systems within Systems of Cities, Proceedings of the Regional Science Association, 12, 147-163.

Berry, B.J.L., 1991, Long-wave Rhythms in Economic Development and Political Behavior, Baltimore: Johns Hopkins University Press.

Bourne and Simmons, 1978, Systems of Cities: Readings on Structure, Growth and Policy, NY: Oxford University Press.

Bryson, John R., Daniels, Peter W. & Warf, Barney, 2004, Service Worlds: People, Organisations, Technologies, Routledge, London and New York.

Cable Television Broadcasting Society, 2008, Subscriber Status of Cable Television (http://www.kcta.or.kr).

Chang, H., 1977, A Geomorphic Study of the Low-level Erosion Surfaces in Gangneung Area, Chirihak Yeongu, 3, 153-175.

Chang, J. H., 1984, A geomorphic study on piedmont gentle-slopes in Korea, Ph.D. thesis, Kyunghee University.

Chang, Se-Hoon, 2002, Urbanization, in Kim, Doo-Sub and Cheong-Seok Kim (eds.), The Population of Korea, Daejeon: Korea National Statistical Office, 495-524. (in Korean)

Cheil Communications Inc., 2003, The Lifestyle and Characteristics of the P-generation.

Child, V.G., 1950, The Urban Revolution, Town Planning Review, 21, 3-17.

Cho, Kwang Ick, 2005, Leisure and Tourism as Apparatuses of Power: An Approach from the

Foucault's Genealogy of Power, Journal of Tourism and Leisure Research, vol.17, no.2, 97-116.

Choi, Byung-Doo, 2000, Spatial characterization of the quality of life and community, Journal of the Korean Geographical Society, 35(2), 321-340.

Choi, Byung-Doo, 2007, Logics of strategies of urban entrepreneurialism and its limitations, Economy and Society, 75, 106-138.

Choi, Byung-Doo, 2007, Shift from developmentalism to neoliberalism and changes in spatial policy in South Korea, Journal of The Korean Association of Regional Geographers, 13(1), 82-103.

Choi, Byung-Doo, Lee, Kyung-Ja, and Choi, Gum-Ae, 2004, Citizens` consciousness on urban changes in large cities in the 1990s(1): A comparative study on urban social sectors, Journal of The Korean Association of Regional Geographers, 19(2), 428-446.

Choi, J.H. and Chang, Se-Hoon, 2004, Population Distribution, Internal Migration and Urbanization, in Kim, Doo-Sub and Cheong-Seok Kim (eds.), The Population of Korea, Daejeon: Korea National Statistical Office, 225-251.(in Korean)

Choi, J.H., 1997, Changing Patterns of Internal Migration of Korea, 1960-90 in the Population Association of Korea (ed.), Population Change and Quality of Life, Seoul: Il Shin Sa. (in Korean)

Choi, Jae Heon, 2000, Economy, Financial Cities' Globalization, Darakbang.

Choi, Jun-Young and Cho, Jin-Man, 2005, Is regional cleavage in Korea disappearing-: empirical analysis of the ideological and generational effects on the outcomes of the 17th congressional election, Korean Political Science Review, 39(3), 375-394.

Choi, Jun-Young, 2008, Does regional prejudice exist- : a study on regional prejudice through an unobtrusive measurement, Study of Contemporary Politics, 1(1), 199-222.

Choi, S. G., 1996, Chronological Study of Late Pleistocene Marine Terraces around Pohang Area, Southeastern Coast of Korea, Journal of the Korean Geographical Society, 3(1), 29-44.

Choi, Y. J., et al., 2008, An Analysis of the Trend of Housing Price and Its Regional Impacts, Seoul: Bank of Korea.

Choi, Yoonhee, Lee, H., Park, J., Yu, H., Oh, H., Ahn, K., 2005, Competitiveness and Market Strategy of the Next Generation Growth-Engine Industry, KIET Research Report, KIET, Seoul.

Choo, Sungjae, 2006, "Development of the Korean film industry and its spatial characteristics: Gangnam region of Seoul as a new cluster in a new renaissance-" Journal of the Korean Geographical Society, 41(3): 245-266 (in Korean with English summary).

Chung, C. H., 1989a, Geography of Korea, Woosungmunhwasa.

Chung, C. H., 1989b, Introduction to Geology, Pakyoungsa.

Chung, Ki-Seon, 2005, Changes in regionalism and social cognition of regional conflicts between 1988 and 2003 in Korea, Korean Journal of Sociology, 39(2), 66-98.

DACO D & S, 2007, Korea Broadcasting Yearbook, Seoul.

Dating on the Terrace Deposits in Yangnam and Yangbuk Area of the Gyeongju City, South Korea, Journal of the Geomorphological Association of Korea, 14(3), 1-14.

Davies, W.K.D., 1967, Centrality and the Central Place Hierarchy, Urban Studies, 4, 61-79.

F.A.O., 1976, Forest Resources in the Asia and Far East, FAO, Rome.

Formations Covering Basalt Plateau in Chungok area, The Korean Journal of Quaternary Research, 8(1): 43-68.

Goldman Sachs, 2003, Dreaming with BRICs: The Path to 2050, Global Economics Paper No 99.

Government of the Republic of Korea, 2006, The Revised Fourth Comprehensive National Territorial Plan (2006-2020).

Hagman, M., L. Freiberg, T. Lagerstr-m, & J.E. Sanda, 1978, The Nordic Arboretum Expedition to South Korea 1976, Helsinki.

Han, Ju-Seong, 2001, "Spatial Characteristics by Physical Distribution System and Sales Activities of Agricultural Co-operation Chain Stores in Korea,"Journal of the Korean Geographical Society, 36, 258-277.

Han, Ju-Seong, 2003, Geography of Distribution, Hanul Academy, Seoul.

Honda, S., 1922, Forest Zones of Japan, Tokyo (In Japanese).

Hong, Ilyoung, 2008, "The spatial change of agglomerated location and the characteristics of firm movement in Korean software industry"Journal of Economic Geographical Society of Korea 11(2): 175-191 (in Korean with English summary).

Hong, Kyung Hee, 1982, Functional Classification of Korean Cities, Jirihak, 26, 1-14.

Hong, Seok-Joon, 2005, Central-local structure in Korean society and regional identity, Trends and Prospects, 62, 13-47.

Hwang, Joo Sung, 2000, "Location of software industry and industrial district"Journal of the Korean Geographical Society 35(1): 121-139 (in Korean with English summary).

Hwang, Tae Yeon, 1997, The Country of Regional hegemony, Moodang Media.

Im, C. J., 1989, A geomorphological study on river terraces along the upper course of the Namhan-Gang, Ph.D. Thesis, Dongguk University.

Im, S.U., 1996, Soil Science, Munwundang, Seoul, Korea, p.383

Jeong, J.H., Kim, C.S., Goo, K.S., Lee, C.W., Won, H.G., and Byun, J.G., 2003,

Jo Seon Kwangmunhoe (朝鮮光文會), 1915, Jung Kyung Ji (Geography of Central Capital of Gae Seong (開城), Minsokwon.

Jo, Soon-Jhe, 2004, The east-west conflict and alternatives to overcome, Korean Journal of Political Science, 12(1), 191-213.

Jo, W. R, 1987, Alluvial plains of Korea, Kyohakyeongusa.

Joint Task Force of the Government and Non-Government, 2006, Wishful Korea Going All Together.

Joo, Kyung Sik, 1983, Urbanization and the Urban System of Korea (Ⅱ, Journal of Kora Planners Association, 18, 134-156.)

Joo, Kyung Sik, 1998, Which Urbanization Process-: Development of Edge Cities in Korea and the U.S., Journal of the Korean Urban Geographical Society, 1, 61-83.

Jung, Byeong-Eun, 2005, Voter's. social capital and regionalism in Korea, Korean Journal of Sociology, 39(5), 83-118

Kang, Dae Hyeon, 1981, Urban Geography, Kyo Hak Sa Publisher.

Kang, Seong-Kwan, Lim, Ho, Lee Jeong-Phil, Kim, Heong-Bin, 2004, Recognition and Prospect on Busan as a global city, Busan Development Institute.

Kang, Y.P., 1978, The characteristics of weathering processes of red soils in South Korea, Journal of The Korean Geographical Society, 18: 1-12.

Kim, Chang-Hyun et al, 2003 Characteristics and policy implications of territorial structure changes in Korea. KRIHS

Kim, Doo-Sub and Kim, Cheong-Seok (eds.), 2004, The Population of Korea, Daejeon: Korea National Statistical Office. (in Korean)

Kim, Hae-Sook, 1989, Reality of stereotype and prejudice between regions, Korean Psychological Association (ed.), Regionalism seen from Psychology, Seonwhasa.

Kim, Hyang Ja, Yoon, So Young, 2007, The Leisure Policy of the Participation Government and the Way and the Subject to the Next, Korea Culture and Tourism Institute.

Kim, In, 1981, Recent Development of Korean Urban System and Perspectives, Urban Problem, 6, 10-42.

Kim, In, 2005, Theories in World Cities, Bup Mun Sa.

Kim, J. W., 1983, The form and morphogenesis of the western piedmont surface of Mt. Waryoun, Journal of Geography(Jirihak Nonchong), 10, 359-369.

Kim, J. W., Chang, H. W., Choi, J. H., Choi, K. H., and Byun, J. M., 2007, Landform Characteristics of Coastal Terraces and Optically Stimulated Luminescence

Kim, J.M., 1976, Ecology of Korean Plants, Jeonpakwahaksa, Seoul (In Korean).

Kim, Jin-Gook, Political cleavage, party politics, and regionalism, Korean Journal of Political Science, 28(2), 215-237.

Kim, Kyeong Chu, Size Distribution of Korean Cities and Analysis of Zipf's Model Geography and Geography Education, 10, 18-36.

Kim, Me-Gon, 2006, Current situations of poverty in Korean society and improvement measures, Study on Democracy Society and Policy, 9, 71-95.

Kim, S. H., 1973, Geomorphic studies of the erosion surfaces in central Korea, Seoul University Journal (A), 21, 85-114.

Kim, Seung Taek, 1998, Development Vision and Directions for Fostering of New Industry, KIET Research Report, KIET, Seoul.

Kim, Seung-Kwon, 2004, Change in Fertility Rates in Korea: Causes and Future Prospects, Journal of Korean Population Association, 27(2), 1-34.

Kim, T., 2007, Spatial dispersion policy for the multi-core distribution reform of the national territorial structure, in Presidential Committee on Balanced National Development, 2007, Balanced National Development Policy in Korea: Theory and Practice.

Kim, Y. 1987 History of Korea national Territorial Development., University Press.

Kim, Young-Soo, 2003, Regional Development Trend and Policy Issues of Knowledge-based Industry, KIET Research Report, KIET, Seoul

Kim, Youngwoong, 1999, Regional Development Theories, Bubmoonsa.

Kim, Yu-Seon, 2005, Strategies to resolve polarization: policy tasks to improve distribution structure of labor wage, Labor Society, 96, 4-19.

King and Robins¡

Knox. P. and McCarthy. L., 2005, Urbanization, 2nd ed, NJ: Pearson Prentice Hall.

Ko, Jeong Min, 2004, Emerging of the Film Induced Tourism and the Conditions of Success, CEO Information, No.439, Samsung Economic Research Institute.

Ko, Jeong Min, 2006, Leisure Trend, Samsung Economic Research Institute.

Ko, Jun Ho, 2007, An Investigation of the Fear of Crime in the Neighborhood, Journal of the Korean Geographical Society, 42, 243-257.

Kong, W.S., 1989, The biogeographic divisions of Korea and their species composition, Geography (Korean Geographical Society), 40, 43-54 (In Korean with English abstract).

Kong, W.S., 2000, Vegetational history of the Korean Peninsula, Global Ecology & Biogeography, 9(5), 391-401.

Kong, W.S., 2002, Species composition and distribution of Korean alpine plants, Journal of Korean Geographical Society, 37(4), 357-370 (In Korean with English abstract).

Kong, W.S., 2004, Species composition and distribution of native Korean conifers, Journal of Korean Geographical Society, 39(4), 528-543 (In Korean with English abstract).

Kong, W.S., 2005, Selection of vulnerable plants by global warming, Journal of Korean Meteorological Society, 41(2-1), 263-273 (In Korean with English abstract).

Kong, W.S., 2007, Biogeography of Korean Plants, Geobook, Seoul (In Korean).

Kong, W.S., 2007, Biogeography of Korean Plants, Geobook, Seoul, Korea.

Korea Agro-Aquatic Trade Corporation, 2008, Statistical Yearbook of Agro-Aquatics Wholesale Market (http://www.kamis.co.kr).

Korea Culture and Tourism Institute, 2007, 2007 White Paper of Leisure.

Korea Culture and Tourism Policy Institute, 2006, Research and Evaluation of Korea Regional Festival.

Korea Energy Economics Institute, 2008, Statistics Data Base.

Korea Energy Economics Institute, 2009, Statistics Data Base.

Korea Forest Research Institute, 2005, Forest Soil Profiles, KFRI Research Monograph Vol 6, Seoul, Korea, p.143

Korea National Statistical Office, 1980-2008, National Statistical Portal (www.kosis.kr).

Korea National Statistical Office, 2004, Statistical Yearbook of Korea.

Korea National Statistical Office, 2007, Korean Statistical Information Service (http://kosis.kr).

Korea National Statistical Office, 2007, Statistical Yearbook of Korea.

Korea National Statistical Office, 2008, Korean Statistical Information Service (http://kosis.kr).

Korea National Statistical Office, e-National Indicators (http://www.index.go.kr)

Korea Petroleum Association, 2008, Yearbook of Korean Petroleum Industry (http://www.petroleum.or.kr).

Korea Planners' Association (ed.), 2004, National Territory and Regional Planning,

Bosunggak.

Korea Rail Network Authority, 2005, Centennial History about Korean Railroad Construction, Seoul.

Korea Railroad, 1994, History for Korean Rail, 5, Seoul.

Korea Tourism Organization, 2007, Korea Statistics of Tourism.

Korean Culture and Information Service, Korea.net: The Official Website of the Republic of Korea (http://www.korea.net)

Kresl, P.K., Ni Penfei, 2006, Global Urban Competitiveness Report (2005-2006), Social Science Academic Press: Cjian.

Kwon Yong Woo and 2005, Hwan Jong, Ryu, Changes in Korean Urban System and Directiond of Urban Management, Research of Geography, 39(1), 149-159.

Kwon, D.H., 2007, Results of the research on Korea' granite weathering landforms and tasks, Journal of the Korean Geomorphological Association, 14(2): 21-31.

Kwon, H. J., 1973, A geomorphic study of the Naktong Delta, Geogrpahy, 8, 8-23.

Kwon, H.J., 2005, The Geography of Korea (Overview), Bupmunsa, Seoul, Korea, p.579

Kwon, Tai-Hwan, 2002, Understanding Population (2nd ed.), Seoul: Seoul National University Press.

Kwon, Yong Woo, 1998, Rank-size Rule in Korean Cities, Research of Geography, 32(1), 57-70.

Kyoyukdoseochulpansa, 1963, Biogeography for Collegeof Education, Educational Publishing House, Pyongyang, DPRK (In Korean).

Lautensach, H., 1945, Korea, Koehler Verlag, Leipzig.

Lee Hee Yeon, 2003, Population: Geographical Perspectives of Population, Seoul: BubMoon-Sa.

Lee, J. W., et al., 2007, Science and Technology in the Future Economy and Society, Seoul: Science and Technology Policy Institute.

Lee, Joung-Woo and Lee, Seong-Lim, 2001, Economic Crisis and Income Disparity: income distribution and poverty before and after the 1997 crisis, Study on International Economy, 7(2), 79-109.

Lee, Kap-Yun, 2002, Political orientations and attitudes of regionalism in Korea, Korea and International Politics, 18(2), 155-178.

Lee, Ki Suk, 1999, Bangri (Grid) System and Urban Structure in the Korean Ancient Cities, Journal of the Korean Urban Geographical Society, 2, 1-16.

Lee, W. S., 2006, A Study on the Establishment of the Regional Development Corporation in Depressed Regions in Korea, Anyang: Korea Research Institute for Human Settlements.

Lee, W. S., and Park, K. H., 2007, Spatial Impact and Policy Agenda of the Balanced National Development Policy, Anyang: Korea Research Institute for Human Settlements.

Lee, W., 2006 Study on the establishment of the regional development corporation in depressed regions in Korea. KRIHS.

Lee, W.T. and Y.J. Yim, 1978, Distribution of Korean vascular plants, Journal of Korean Taxonomical Society, 8(Appendix), 1-33 (In Korean with English abstract).

Lee, Y.N., 1976, Flora of Korean Flowering Plants, Ministry of Education, Seoul (In Korean).

Lee, Yong-Jae, 2007, A study of the factors and the regional difference of medical aid program recipient`s medical utilization, Social Welfare Policy, 28, 233-251.

Lee, Y-W., J-K. Chung, Y-S. Yun and S-Y Lim, 2006, High speed Rail and the Changes of Spatial Structure(II). KRIHS

Lee. M. B., Lee. G. R., and Kim, N. S., 2004, Drainage Derangement and Revision by the Formation of Cheolwon-Pyeonggang Lava Plateau in Chugaryeong Rift Valley, Central Korea, Journal of the Korean Geographical Society, 39(6), 833-844.

Linsky, A.S., 1965, Some Generalizations Concerning Primate Cities, A.A.A.G, 55, 506-513.

Mercer Human Resource Consulting, 2004, Cost of Living Survey.

Mercer Human Resource Consulting, 2005, World-wide quality of life Survey.

Mercer Human Resource Consulting. 2004. 7. Cost of Living Survey.

Mercer Human Resource Consulting. 2005.3.. World-wide quality of life Survey.

Mercer Korea, 2008, Quality of Living Survey 2008.

Ministry of Commerce, Industry and Energy and Korea Institute for Electronic Commerce; Korea National Statistical Office, 2007, Statistical Yearbook of Korea.

Ministry of Commerce-Industry and Energy, Korean Institute for Electronic Commerce, 2006, e-business white paper, Seoul.

Ministry of Construction and Transport, 2007, Annual Statistics for Construction and Transport (momaf.go.kr).

Ministry of Construction and Transport, 2007, Statistical Yearbook of Ministry of Construction and Transportation (National Statistical Portal: www.kosis.kr).

Ministry of Construction and Transportation, 2006, Implementation Plan for the Livable City Making.

Ministry of Culture and Tourism, 2007, The Changes and Outcomes of Cultural Tourism

Festival: 1996-2005.

Ministry of Culture, Sports and Tourism, 2007, 2006 Cultural Industry Annual Report, Seoul.

Ministry of Culture, Sports and Tourism, 2007, White Book of Cultural Industry.

Ministry of Culture, Sports and Tourism, 2008, Material Ground (http://mcst.go.kr).

Ministry of Environment, 1997, A White Paper on Environment, Ministry of Environment, p.686

Ministry of Environment, 2002, Ecological Strategy for the Construction of Ecological Community of the Korean Peninsula, Ministry of Environment, R.O.K., Seoul (In Korean).

Ministry of Environment, 2005, Conservation Plan of Island and Coastal Ecocorridors, Ministry of Environment, R.O.K., Seoul (In Korean).

Ministry of Environment, 2007, The Distribution of Soil Monitoring Network and Results of Soil Analysis, Ministry of Environment.

Ministry of Knowledge Economy, 2007, Mineral Resources Reserves, Seoul. Ministry of Land, Transport and Maritime Affairs, 2008, Maritime and Fishery Statistics (http://momaf.go.kr/matrix/momaf/main/index.jsp).

Ministry of Maritime Affairs and Fisheries, 1996, 1998, Survey on the Integrated Management System of the Coast, Ministry of Maritime Affairs and Fisheries, ROK, Seoul (In Korean).

Ministry of Maritime Affairs and Fisheries, 1999, Tidal Flats of Korea, Ministry of Maritime Affairs and Fisheries, ROK, Seoul (In Korean).

Ministry of Public Administration and Security, 2008, Local Government Boundary and Population.

Moon, H. P., et al., 2006, Socio-economic Impacts of Population Aging and Policy Issues, Seoul: Korea Development Institute.

Mun, B.G. and J.W. Hah, 2007, An Analysis of the Effects of the Aged Population on the Structure of the Local Public Spending, Journal of the Korean Association for Local Finance, 12(3), 1-28.

Murphy, R.E. and Vance, J.E., 1954, Delimiting the CBD, Economic Geography, 30, 189-222.

Na, Khan-Chae, 1991, Social distances between regions, Kim, Jeong-Chul and Choi, Jang-Jip (eds.), Study on Regionalism, Hakminsa.

Nakai, T., 1935, East Asian Plants, Iwanami Publishing, Tokyo (In Japanese).

Nam, Young Woo, 2006, Theories of World Cities in the Global Era, Bup Mun Sa.

National Agricultural Cooperative Federation, 2008, Status of National Physical Distribution Center of Commodities of Life.

National Economic Advisory Council, 2007, New Visions and Strategies for Collaborative Growth.

National Geographic Information Institute, 1980, Regional Geography of Korea: Introduction, 143-196.

National Geographic Information Institute, 2007, National Atlas of Korea, NGII, Suwon, Korea, p.298

National Geographic Information Institute, 2007, The National Atlas of Korea (http:// atlas.ngii.go.kr)

National Geographic Information Institute, 2007, The National Atlas of Korea,

National Geographic Information Institute, 2008, Regional Geography of Korea: Introduction, 101-135.

National Geographic Information Institute, ROK.

National Institute of Agricultural Science and Technology (NIAST), 2000, Taxonomical Classification of Korean Soils, NIAST/RDA, Suwon, Korea.

National Internet Development Agency of Korea, 2008, Internet Statistics Information Check System (http://isis.nida.or.kr).

National Statistical Office, 2006, Population Projects for Korea, Daejeon: Korea National Statistical Office.

National Statistical Office, 2007, 2007 Statistics on the Aged People.

National Statistical Office, 2007, Population Projects by Provinces: 2005-2030, Daejeon: Korea National Statistical Office.

National Statistical Office, each year, Statistics of Employment, Seoul

Noh, Sa Shin and Yang, Seong Ji, et al, Eds. (Jung Jong 25 Yr.), Sin Jeung Dong Kuk Yeo Ji Seung Ram (New and Replenished Geography of Korea).

Noyelle, T.J. and Stanback, T.M. Jr., 1984, The Economic Transformation of American Cities, NJ: Rowman & Allanheld Publishers.

OECD, 2004, Aging Societies and the Looming Pension Crisis, Paris: OECD.

Oh, K.S. and Kim, N.S., 1994, Originand Post-depositional Deformation of the Superficial

Oh, S.Y., 1977, Distribution and phytogeography of Korean vascular plants, Thesis Collection of Andong Teachers College, 7, 13-39 (In Korean with English abstract).

Ohn, Mahn-Geum, 2004, Region and generation in the 2002 presidential election,

Social Research, 2, 79-96.

Pacione, 2005, Urban Geography: A Global Perspective, 2nd ed., London: Routledge.

Park, D.W., 1985, A Study on the loessial red yellow soil of Hwangsan, Kimje county and Gamgok, Chungeup county of the south western coastal area of Korea-with special reference to the possibility of loess deposition, Journal of The Korean Geographical Society, 32: 1-10.

Park, Dong-Hyun, 2008, Regionalism in the presidential election in 2007, weakened or evolved, The Spirit of the Times, Spring.

Park, Myoung-Ho, 2004, The 17th congress election and changes in party politics, The Journal of Political Science and Communication, 7(1), 1-26.

Park, S. J. and Son, I., 2005, Discussions on the distribution and genesis of mountain ranges in the Korean Peninsular (I) : The identification mountain ranges using a DEM and reconsideration of current issues on mountain range maps, Journal of the Korean Geographical Society, 40(1), 126-152.

Park, S.J., 1993, Hydrogeochemical research on the characteristic of chemical weathering in a granitic catchment, Journal of the Korean Geographical Society, 28(1): 1-15.

Park, Sam Ock and Nahm, Kee-Bom, 2000, "Development of regional innovation system sand industrial district for the promotion of small and medium enter Prises", The journal of Korea Planners Association 35(3): 121-140 (in Korean with English summary).

Park, Sam Ock and Wheeler, James O., 1983, "Industrial location policies and manufacturing employment change: the case of the Republic of Korea"Regional Development Dialogue 4(2): 45-64.

Park, Sam Ock, 1993a, "Structural changes in manufacturing and directions of structural adjustments of industries in the Capital Region,"Journal of Geography, 21: 1-16 (in Korean with English summary).

Park, Sam Ock, 1993b, Industrial Restructuring and the Spatial Division of Labor: The Case of the Seoul Metro polation Region, the Republic of Korea, Environment and Planning AVol.25(1): 81-93.

Park, Sam Ock, 1999, Modern Economic Geography, Arche, Seoul (in Korean).

Park, Sam Ock, 2009, "A history of the Republic of Korea's industrial structural transformation and spatial development", In Huang, Yukon and Bocchi, Alessandro Magnoli, eds., Reshaping Economic Geography in East Asia, The World Bank, Washington, D. C.:319-337

Park, Yang-Ho and Chang-Hyun Kim, 2001, Integrated Territorial Axes for Balanced National Development Strategies. KRIHS.

Park, Young Han, 1973, A Study on Delimiting the CBD and Internal Structure, Jirihak (Geography), 8, 51-62.

Park, Young-Cheol, Kim, S.W., Kim, K. I., Jang, C. S., Park, S. H., 2003, Research on the Locational Policy of Knowledge-based Industry, KRIHS research Report, KRIHS

Personal Communication, 2008, Interviews Survey of Each Physical Distribution Center.

Peters, G.L. and R.P. Larkin, 2002, Population Geography: Problem, Concepts and Prospects (7th ed.), Dubuque, Iowa: Kendall/Hunt.

Physico-chemical properties of Korean forest soils by parent rocks, Journal of Korean Forest Society, 92(3): 254-262.

Presidential Committee on Balanced National Development, 2007, Balanced National Development Policy in Korea: Theory and Practice.

Presidential Committee on Balanced National Development, 2007, Theories and Practice on the Balanced National Development Policy.

References In Korea

Rhu, S.H., 2000, Dictionary of Soils, Seoul National University Press, Seoul, Korea.

Ryu, Yeon-Taek, 2002, Housing Markets and Geographical Scale : Korean Cities in the 1980s and 1990s, Univ. of Minnesota. Ph.D. Thesis.

Seo Min Cheol and Joo, Kyung Sik, 1998, Boundary, Function and Internal Structure of CBD in Seoul, Journal of the Korean Geographical Society, 33, 41-56.

Seo, Kee-Jun, 2001, A study on structure of political conflicts between regions in Korea, The Journal of Korea Northeast Association, 19, 219-242.

Seong, Jun Yong, 1992, Urban System of Korea, Kyo Hak Sa.

Shim, J.H. and J. H. Chai, 2004, Analysis of Effects of Aging on Local Public Finance, Journal of the Northeast Asia Association of Korea, 31, 261-284.

Shin, J.S., 1997, Soil properties of agricultural lands and management, Proceedings of International Seminar on Reclamation Technologies on Polluted Soils, Korean Society of Soil and Environment, p. 23-30.

Sjoberg.G., 1960, The Pre-industrial City: Past and Present, NewYork: Free Press.

Small and Medium Business Administration and Federation of Small and Medium Enterprises, 2007, Technology Survey of Small and Medium Enterprises, Seoul

Sohn, H.S., 2005, A Study on the Necessary Family Support Services Required to Solve the Low Birth Rate, Korean Journal of Family Welfare, 10(1), 43-63.

Sohn, Jungyul and Oh, Soo-Kyung, 2007, Measuring accessibility of day care centers for the elderly in Seoul using GIS spatial analysis techniques, Journal of The Korean Association of Regional Geographers, 13(5), 576-594.

Soja, 2000, Postmetropolis: Critical Studies of Cities and Regions, MA: Blackwell.

Son Y.G., 2007, The classification of standard catchments according to soil catenary soil sequences, NIAST Symposium Data available from http://asis.rda.go.kr/

Son, Seung Ho and Nam, Young Woo, 2006, Change in Urban Structure of Seoul, Darakbang.

The Korea Institute for Health and Social Affairs, 2000, 2005, Survey on the Disabled.

The Korea Institute for Health and Social Affairs, 2006, Survey on the Near Poor.

The Korean Government and Public-Private Task Force, 2006, Vision 2030.

The Korean Government, 1972, National Territorial Development Plan

The Korean Government, 1982, The Second National Territorial Development Plan.

The Korean Government, 1992, The Third National Territorial Development Plan.

The Korean Government, 2000, The Fourth National Territorial Development Plan (2000-2020).

The National Railroad Administration, 2004, Annual Statistics for the National Railroad Administration.

The Presidential Commission on Policy Planning, 2006, Visions and Strategies for Advanced Welfare of Korea, Dongdowon.

Thomas, D.S., 1963, Agriculture in Wales during the Napoleonic Wars, Univ. of Wales Press, Cardiff, 79-95.

Udvardy, M.D.F., 1975, A Classification of the Biogeographical Provinces of the World, IUCN Occasional Paper No. 18, Morges, Switzerland.

Uyeki, H., 1933, On the forest zones of Korea, Acta Phytotax. Geobot., 2, 73-85 (In Japanese with English abstract).

Vance. J., 1971, Land assignment in pre-capitalist, capitalist and post-capitalist cities, Economic Geography, 47, 101-120.

Wang, C.W., 1961, The Forests of China with a Survey of Grassland and Desert Vegetation, Maria Moors Cabot Foundation Publ. Ser. No. 5, Harvard University Press, Cambridge, Mass.

Weeks, J.R., 2002, Population: An Introduction to Concept and Issues (8th ed.), Belmont: WadsworthPub.

Wilson, E.H., 1919, A phytogeographical sketch of the ligneous flora of Korea, J. Arnold Arboretum, 1, 32-43.

Won, C. K,. Lee, H. Y., Chi, J. M., Park, Y. A., Kim, J. H., and Kim, H. S., 1989, Principles of Geology, Woosungmunhwasa.

Woo, C. S., et al., 2007, Policy Directions and Agenda for Advanced Korea: Focusing on Six Major Areas, Seoul: Korea Development Institute.

Yim, K.B., 1970, Principles of Forest Science, Hwangmunsa, Seoul (In Korean). Yonhap News, 2003. June, 01 (In Korean).

Yoon, S. O. and Hwang, S. I., 2004, The geomorphic development of alluvial fans in the Gyeongju city and Cheonbuk area, southeastern Korea, Journal of the Korean Geographical Society, 39(1), 56-69.

Yoon, So Young, 2007, Study of the Finding and Broad Plan for Social Leisure, Korea Culture and Tourism Institute.

Yoon, Yang Su, Kim, Eui Sik, 2002, Leisure Activity Changes and Outdoor Recreation Resources Development in the Capital Region, Korea Research Institute for Human Settlements.

Zipf, 1949, Human Behavior and the Principle of Least Effort, MA: Addison-Wesley.

Data from Internet Sites:
http://alienplant.nier.go.kr
http://ecosystem.nier.go.kr
http://nre.me.go.kr
http://www.forest.go.kr
http://www.konetic.or.kr
http://www.kosis.kr(Korean Statistical Information Service)
http://www.me.go.kr
Mercer Korea, http://www.mercer.co.kr
Ministry of Land, Transport and Maritime Affairs, http://www.mltm.go.kr
Ministry of Public Administration and Security, http://www.mopas.go.kr
National Statistical Office, http://www.kosis.kr.
Presidential Committee on Balanced National Development, http://www.balance.go.kr

INDEX